THE HISTORY OF THE
ROYAL ARMY VETERINARY CORPS
1919-1961

The History of The
Royal Army Veterinary Corps
1919-1961

by

BRIGADIER J. CLABBY, O.B.E., M.R.C.V.S.

With a Foreword by

GENERAL SIR CECIL S. SUGDEN, G.B.E., K.C.B.

J. A. ALLEN & CO.

I LOWER GROSVENOR PLACE, LONDON, SWI

First published 1963

© Copyright 1963 J. A. Allen & Co. Ltd.

Printed in Great Britain by

Brown Knight & Truscott Ltd., London & Tonbridge

Contents

Illustrations

6

Acknowledgments

DURING the war years much of our historical background was associated with the exploits of the pack-transport companies of the Royal Army Service Corps and the Royal Indian Army Service Corps. I am indebted to the authors of *The Story of the Royal Army Service Corps* for a great deal of information concerning these units.

The main bulk of the narrative has been derived from writings of administrative veterinary and remount officers, personal communications from retired officers and articles published in the *Journal of the Royal Army Veterinary Corps* and the *Veterinary Record*. I am indebted to the Wellcome Foundation for information concerning their collaboration with the R.A.V.C. during the war.

Colonel G. Barnett, O.B.E., M.C., M.R.C.V.S., Colonel Commandant, Royal Army Veterinary Corps, contributed to the chapters dealing with India in collaboration with Brigadier J. J. Kane, O.B.E., M.R.C.V.S., who also wrote the chapter on the Burma campaign.

The account of the veterinary and remount services in the campaigns in Sicily and Italy was produced by Colonel D. F. G. Smith, O.B.E., M.R.C.V.S.

The chapter concerning war dogs was contributed by Lieutenant-Colonel G. D. Young, M.B.E., M.R.C.V.S., and Major Denys Danby, M.R.C.V.S. was kind enough to add a section describing his work at the dog training school during 1942-1945.

Lieutenant-Colonel J. H. Wilkins, B.SC., M.R.C.V.S., furnished the chapter on research.

Major W. P. Moss, M.C., T.D., M.R.C.V.S., provided the prints of the Yeomanry horses of the 1st Cavalry Division. I am indebted to the Imperial War Museum for permission to publish certain of the photographs and I have to thank Lionel Edwards, R.I., for permission to make use of some original drawings made when he was a remount officer at Romsey Depot during World War I.

I am grateful to Major A. V. Franklin, O.B.E., T.D., M.R.C.V.S., for reading the type-script and for his helpful comments and suggestions.

The problem of finding sufficient funds with which to undertake the work was overcome by the generosity of The Wellcome Trust and by donations received from the Royal College of Veterinary Surgeons, Pfizer Ltd., Messrs. May and Baker Ltd., Burroughs, Wellcome and Co., Glaxo Laboratories Ltd., Cooper, McDougal and Robertson Ltd., Allen and Hanbury's Ltd., Radiol Chemicals Ltd., Imperial Chemical Industries Ltd. and many retired officers and other friends of the Corps.

J. C.

Droitwich
November 1961

Foreword

As Quartermaster-General to the Forces, I was responsible for the Army Veterinary and Remount Services from 1958 to 1961 and I naturally take a deep personal interest in the past and present achievements of the Royal Army Veterinary Corps which has given such distinguished service in two World Wars and in many minor campaigns.

I am sure that this book will have a very wide appeal. The Service reader will be interested in the way a very small technical Corps, designed originally to support the mounted Arms, evolved to meet the needs of a modern Army. Some perhaps will be surprised to hear for the first time of the vital part played in some of the campaigns in World War II by what has always been a small Corps of dedicated specialists.

Past and present members of the Royal Army Veterinary Corps, of course, will find this book of fascinating interest. Seldom can a history have contained so much detail or mentioned so many soldiers by name, which is only right and proper in a Corps whose contribution to victory was out of all proportion to the numbers involved.

The Veterinary Surgeon may read with pride of the achievements of his Army colleagues and for him this book is a fund of information of the practical application of his profession under war conditions.

I especially commend this book to the general public, particularly to all animal lovers. This is more than just a regimental history—it is a text-book on the care of animals in all parts of the world, ranging from horses, dogs and chickens to camels and bullocks; within its covers there is much that you will find of absorbing interest.

Ashgden.

General.

CHAPTER I

Introduction

IN *A History of the Royal Army Veterinary Corps* 1796/1919 by Major-General Sir Frederick Smith is described the evolution of the Royal Army Veterinary Corps from the genesis of the Army Veterinary Service in 1796 to its elevation to the status of a "Royal" Corps in 1918.

Until the end of the eighteenth century the responsibility for the treatment of sick animals in the Army rested upon the farrier who held a contract with the State for shoeing and medicine. The losses in animals due to disease, neglect and ignorance were startling and glanders was endemic amongst the horses of both the cavalry and the artillery.

In 1795, as an experimental measure, a young graduate from the newly founded London Veterinary College, William Stockley, was attached to the 1st Fencible Cavalry. He quickly proved the value of veterinary skill to a mounted unit. The following year Professor Edward Coleman, the head of the Veterinary College, was appointed Principal Veterinary Surgeon to the Cavalry and Veterinary Surgeon to the Board of Ordnance (Artillery) and charged with the creation of the Army Veterinary Service.

Under professional care the health of army horses improved beyond recognition. By a better understanding of glanders this disease was brought under control, and by great improvements in the hygiene of stables and the application of the principles of animal dietetics vast and permanent reforms were effected throughout the Service which many times covered the cost of the veterinary department.

Further improvements in animal management were facilitated by discoveries concerning the nature of various equine diseases which had resulted from the research work of individual veterinary officers. For example there was James Turner of the Royal Wagon Train, who first recognized navicular disease; Thomas Peall of the Royal Artillery who proved that glanders and farcy were identical and James White of the Royal Dragoons who, by carefully planned experiments, showed that glanders could not be produced by a miasma of the stable but was readily conveyed by inoculation or through the digestive canal. It was largely due to the achievements of such men as these that the Army Veterinary Service grew in efficiency and importance for there was at this time no administrative officer other than Coleman; and no veterinary units. Everything was on a regimental basis and veterinary officers seldom saw each other. On the line of march or in war the sick and lame animals were either left on the wayside, or, if they could move, marched with the baggage in the rear of the regiment. No provision existed for veterinary hospitals though in the Peninsular campaign "sick-horse depots" were formed, but without trained staff, and casualties were left in them to get along as best they could.

At the start of the Crimean campaign there was still neither co-ordination of veterinary duties nor a systemized method of dealing with the sick. The losses during the winter of 1854 on the heights of Balaclava were a scandal but it was not until a year later that a Principal Veterinary Surgeon was appointed and some effort made to organize the care of animal casualties.

The Crimean War was barely over before the Indian Mutiny broke out and 70,000 troops, including eleven cavalry regiments, were dispatched from England. All the cavalry regiments had to be remounted in India with horses drawn from Australia and South Africa. The operations were long and arduous but the veterinary organization remained entirely on a regimental basis.

An Indian Army Veterinary Service had been in existence since 1826. Its organization was similar to the British one, and its officers came from England, but it was without a single administrative officer and there was no liaison between the two services. After the Mutiny the Indian and Imperial Armies were amalgamated. Seven veterinary officers of the East India Company's service transferred to the British establishment while twenty-four others elected to remain on the local list in India. The post of Principal Veterinary Surgeon in India was created in 1866.

In 1867 a British expeditionary force became engaged in a small war in Abyssinia. The country was rough and mountainous, and everything depended on transport animals. For the first time an effort was made to deal with casualties amongst animals by the immediate formation of hospitals, or "sick depots", on the lines of communication. They were necessarily crude improvised establishments but they were in the charge of veterinary officers and the results were so superior to anything previously achieved that the Commander-in-Chief made a special point of introducing the subject into his Despatch.

The Franco-Prussian War of 1870 opened the eyes of the nation to the helplessness of an unorganized army in a struggle with an organized and powerful adversary. In the ensuing years a number of military reforms were instituted and the Army Veterinary Service benefited together with the other Corps. The regimental system was abolished, all veterinary officers excepting those of the Household Cavalry being transferred to one list, and wearing the same uniform. The Veterinary Service was renamed the Army Veterinary Department. The Principal Veterinary Surgeon became a member of the War Office Staff, moving his office from the Royal Horse Infirmary, Woolwich to Pall Mall. In 1891 the appointment was redesignated as Director-General, Army Veterinary Department and regulations were published which provided for the establishment of field veterinary hospitals and store depots. However, no provision was made for trained subordinate staff, the equipment was largely obsolete, and only one hospital sufficient for 300 animals was allotted to a force expected to have about 36,000 animals on its strength. But it was a basis for a workable system and could have been improved upon had it not been that in 1898, a year before the South African War, a new edition of war establishments was published which omitted provision of any kind for the care of sick animals in the field. The outbreak of that war found the veterinary service without the shadow of an organization and it was

Training remounts for artillery. Romsey Remount Depot, 1916.
From the original drawing by Lionel Edwards, R.I.

left to the authorities in the operational area to devise a system to meet the deficiency. These authorities, having little veterinary knowledge, produced an archaic organization opposed to all common sense and experience. The army was riddled by contagious diseases and deprived of the means of dealing with them. It has been said that never in the history of any British war has there been such a deliberate sacrifice of animal life and of public money.

The Director-General, Army Veterinary Department attempted to alleviate the situation by borrowing field veterinary hospitals from India where long experience with frontier wars had compelled the authorities to recognize the need to maintain veterinary hospitals for both peace and war. Throughout the first year of the campaign these were the only semblances of veterinary organization available. The total losses during this war were estimated at horses 326,073 (67 per cent.) and mules 51,399 (35 per cent.). Glanders and epizootic lymphangitis were widespread and mange cases existed by thousands. Casualties due to enemy action were not in general a major source of loss. It is recorded by the veterinary officer of the Inniskilling Dragoons, a regiment which saw a good deal of fighting, that out of the 4,170 cases of sickness occurring in his unit during the two and a half years of war, only 163 were due to bullet wounds, and three to shell fire.

When the war ended 140,000 horses and 74,000 mules were declared surplus to army requirements and hurriedly disposed of without adequate veterinary control, spreading glanders and epizootic lymphangitis throughout South Africa. Returning army units introduced epizootic lymphangitis to England and started an epidemic which was not eliminated for several years.

The reports in the national newspapers of the sickening waste of animal life in the South African War aroused public opinion. The Council of the Royal College of Veterinary Surgeons, headed by J. F. Simpson, F.R.C.V.S., made numerous representations to the Secretary of State for War that there should be an effective reorganization of the Army Veterinary Department. Finally, in 1902, a parliamentary committee was assembled to consider the matter and to make recommendations.

On 5th October 1903 King Edward VII signed a warrant which provided for the creation of an *Army Veterinary Corps*. Under the same warrant the Director-General remained a Colonel but was "to rank as Major-General".

For the first time it was possible to have veterinary units staffed entirely with veterinary personnel.

Hospitals were established at Woolwich, Aldershot, Bulford and the Curragh. The Corps Depot and Stores were at Woolwich. Six sections of the A.V.C. were kept complete with veterinary stores in readiness for active service if required.

In 1907 Major-General Frederick Smith became Director-General. He was a man of outstanding ability, devoted to his profession and the Army Veterinary Corps. He spared no effort to bring the Corps up to the highest standard of technical efficiency and was determined that it should be able to keep animal suffering and wastage to a minimum under any conditions in peace or war. He considered that the South African War had been prolonged for two unnecessary years by the immobility the British Army brought upon itself through its neglect of the most elementary principles of animal management and veterinary science. He started to build up a veterinary organization which could effectively support a large mounted field force, and keep it mobile.

Amongst Smith's chief tasks were the reorganization of the veterinary service of the Territorial Force on modern lines; the creation of a special reserve of officers for the A.V.C.; arrangements for the holding of a mobilization stock of veterinary stores and equipment for the Field Army and the Territorial Force and the improvement and modernization of field veterinary equipment.

"A bad 'un to shoe." Romsey Remount Depot, 1916.
From the original drawing by Lionel Edwards, R.I.

The surgical and medical appliances issued to veterinary officers and to hospitals were the subject of his unremitting attention. Modern instruments and dressings, modern drugs and appliances were the key notes throughout his directorship; and officers were encouraged to adopt the latest methods of treatment.

Smith retired in 1910 but as he was re-employed in the Army during World War I he had the satisfaction of witnessing the fruition of his labours to advance the status and efficiency of the Corps. In 1918 he was created a Knight Commander of the Order of St. Michael and St. George. Seldom has the honour been so richly deserved.

In 1912 an A.V.C. Records Office was formed at Woolwich. The same year also saw a change in the official designation of administrative officers of Commands, the title of Assistant Director of Veterinary Services being substituted for that of Principal Veterinary Officer.

In 1913 sanction was given for the creation of Mobile Veterinary Sections, one to each cavalry brigade and infantry division, tc serve as connecting links for sick and lame animals evacuated from field units to veterinary hospitals on the lines of communication. Experience during the South African War had shown that some means of collecting sick and injured animals shed by a force during its advance was absolutely necessary.

About the same time the Veterinary Directorate was freed from the Remount Directorate and made an independent department responsible only to the Quartermaster-General. Its office was, however, moved from the main War Office building to Victoria Street, S.W. in order to make way for the newly formed Military Aeronautics Directorate.

The outbreak of war in August, 1914 found the A.V.C. ready to mobilize and carry out its wartime rôle. Its establishment was 164 officers and 208 other ranks; by 1918 it had expanded to 1,356 officers and 23,146 other ranks.

A full account of the war years is given in the *Official History of the War, Veterinary Services*.

The British Expeditionary Force in France and Belgium in 1914 included an animal strength of 53,000; as veterinary support it had six veterinary hospitals, each for 250 patients, eleven mobile veterinary sections and two base depots of veterinary stores. Subsequently the animal establishment rose to approximately 450,000 and the veterinary organization increased to eighteen hospitals, each for 2,000 patients; four convalescent depots, each for 1,200 patients; sixteen veterinary evacuating stations; and fifty mobile veterinary sections.

In the varying circumstances of war changes in organization were inevitable but in the main the system which evolved from the chaos of the South African War worked well. Hospital accommodation had to be markedly increased and an additional unit, the Veterinary Evacuating Station, was found necessary at Headquarters of Army Corps to enable the mobile veterinary sections of divisions and cavalry brigades to function more effectively. Horse-drawn ambulances were used by the mobile sections and there were several motor-driven horse ambulances attached to the evacuating stations.

In 1917 the strength of British Army animals on all fronts totalled over one million. The average daily number sick at that period was 110,000. The total admissions to hospital 1914–1918 were 2,562,549 patients of which 78 per cent. or approximately two million were returned to duty.

The causes of animal wastage varied considerably with the climate, terrain and type of warfare. The chief causes of mortality in horses and mules were: battle casualties and injuries; debility and exhaustion; contagious disease; intestinal diseases.

The Director of Veterinary Services, British Expeditionary Force, Major-General Sir John Moore, states in his treatise *The Army Veterinary Service in War* that "The greatest wastage in France was in the light draught horses of the artillery. The work of getting ammunition up to gun emplacements, over shell-pitted ground and through seas of mud at dead of night was of the severest possible description, and the situation was further complicated by lack of fit remounts of that class to keep pace with the wastage. Bad rainy weather was always succeeded by an aftermath of debility evacuations, in artillery units particularly. The churned-up mud of Flanders, the shell holes filled with liquid mud every few steps into which animals under load dropped exhausted —probably to drown, was a picture which required to be seen to be realized to its full degree of awfulness."

Battle casualties showed some new features. The employment of chemical warfare led to the issue of anti-gas respirators for horses but equine losses due to chlorine gas were few and, when mustard gas superseded chlorine, respirators were withdrawn as useless. Mustard gas casualties were largely avoidable by skirting ground which had been recently subjected to gas shelling. On the Western Front for the period July 1916 to November 1918 the equine casualties due to gas were 211 dead and 2,220 wounded. In the same period gunshot wounds accounted for 58,090 killed and 77,410 wounded. By the summer of 1918 a considerable proportion of the wounds were being caused by bombs dropped from aircraft.

In East Africa the German Commander-in-Chief, harassed by strong Imperial mounted forces, found a valuable tactical rôle for his veterinary services. He employed them in making tsetse fly-belt surveys of the country in his rear and based his line of retirement on areas containing the most acute and malignant type of trypanosomiasis; the route reported to be most deadly to animal life being invariably chosen. The British and South African veterinary services countered as best they could with the preventive measures then known, including daily prophylactic doses of five to ten grains of arsenic to each animal. It is estimated that by these tactics alone, in the period August-October 1916, the German inflicted a loss of 12,000 horses and mules on the British and secured immunity from mounted pursuit at a most critical period.

In previous wars, those animal casualties which could not be treated under regimental arrangements were usually destroyed or abandoned, and so became a total loss to the Army. Now for the first time in our military history provision was made at the Front for the effective control and prevention of contagious diseases; sick and wounded animals were promptly evacuated; adequate hospital accommodation was provided and patients were discharged in good condition ready for duty.

The Corps had the benefit of the services of many eminent members of the profession who volunteered for war service; including Major (later Professor Sir Frederick) Hobday who was appointed consultant surgeon to the veterinary hospitals in France and who introduced a number of improvements in surgical technique.

It is significant of the great work achieved by the Corps that on 27th November 1918 King George V conferred upon it the title of "Royal".

The Quartermaster-General to the Forces in congratulating the Director-General and all ranks of the Royal Army Veterinary Corps on this proud distinction, wrote "On the occasion of His Majesty the King being graciously pleased to raise the Army Veterinary Corps to the status of a 'Royal' Corps the Quartermaster-General to the Forces wishes to convey to all ranks his congratulations and appreciation of the good work which they have performed during the present war. The Corps by its initiative and scientific methods has placed Military Veterinary Organization on a higher plane. The high standard which it has maintained at Home and throughout all theatres has resulted in a reduction of animal wastage, an increased mobility of Mounted Units and a mitigation of animal suffering, unapproached in any previous Military Operation."

The Veterinary Service had made a notable contribution towards winning the war. The Commander-in-Chief, Field Marshal Sir Douglas Haig recorded "If in March 1918 the equine force of Germany had been on the same scale, and as efficient as the British equine force, the Germans would unquestionably have succeeded in breaking through between the French and British armies, and inflicted a defeat so great that recovery might have been impossible."

In contrast and to understand what might have occurred if an Army Veterinary Corps had not been formed one can read in the *Veterinary Military History of the United States* of the arrival in Europe in 1917 of the American Expeditionary Force. It had no veterinary organization and the resulting gross wastage of valuable animals so alarmed the Allies that both the French and the British insisted that an American Veterinary Corps should be organized on European lines. The French were particularly concerned at the probability of disease spreading to civilian animals and also doubted the ability of the American units to retain their mobility in battle. The British Quartermaster-General in a personal letter to General Pershing, General Officer Commanding-in-Chief A.E.F. France, wrote, offering the assistance of the Army Veterinary Corps: "In making this offer I venture to think it would be to our mutual advantage, for we are naturally anxious, not only to place our experience of war at your disposal, but to safeguard our own animals, which we feel run a grave risk of contracting contagious diseases." The real failure was that animal casualties became total losses. It is estimated that the American Expeditionary Force lost 23,000 animals due to the lack of an adequate system of casualty clearance and hospital facilities, and this at a time when the world supply of animals was proving too small for the needs of the Allied Armies. It was a repetition of the experience of the British Army in the South African War.

After the Armistice in 1918 came the problem of the demobilization of the Veterinary Service. For the first three months the rate of demobilization was necessarily slow as the Royal Army Veterinary Corps assumed additional responsibilities. These included the disposal of the great majority of the army animals now surplus; measures to ensure the freedom from contagious disease of the 62,000 animals to be returned to England from overseas; and a quarantine scheme for the dogs of repatriated servicemen.

The Director-General, Sir Layton Blenkinsop, had had personal experience of the epidemics which followed the haphazard dispersal of army animals after the South

African War and he was determined that there should be no repetition. The Directors of Veterinary Services in the various theatres of war submitted their proposals based on a knowledge of local conditions, and from these a well-considered scheme was drawn up whereby, step by step, animals were tested with mallein, examined for epizootic lymphangitis and either sold or passed as fit for return to England, a corresponding proportion of men of the R.A.V.C. being simultaneously released. No disease was left behind in the various countries, and no disease was introduced into Britain.

By 31st March 1920 only 334 officers and 1,280 other ranks remained on the establishment.

Despite its recent splendid services it seemed that the R.A.V.C. was doomed to disappear as the Army turned more and more to the use of the lorry and the armoured fighting vehicle. Until 1939 a gradual shrinkage of the Corps took place. This trend was then reversed by the pressure of war.

During the period 1920-1930 many units were mechanized, and, as a major war seemed unlikely, drastic economies were made in the establishment and upkeep of the Forces. The chief rôle of the Army was that of imperial policing in numerous trouble spots including Ireland, Turkey, China, Palestine and the Indian frontiers, and with its mounted and animal transport units went detachments of the R.A.V.C. In addition, reinforcements had to be found for normal duties in the Sudan, Egypt and India, and plans made for the formation of the Indian Army Veterinary Corps.

In India at this time the veterinary hospitals of British units were run largely on a regimental basis and Indian cavalry regiments were often without skilled veterinary supervision. The advantages of a self-contained Army Veterinary Corps having been proved in World War I, it was recommended to the Government of India that an Indian Army Veterinary Corps should be formed, responsible for providing veterinary services to both the Indian Army and the British Army units in India. This scheme was sanctioned in December 1920. It was further developed a few years later by the grant of commissions to Indians who had qualified as Members of the Royal College of Veterinary Surgeons.

By 1931 it was evident that the British Army must be equipped and trained to fight if necessary on the continent of Europe. The mechanization programme was accelerated but it was appreciated that the fully mobilized army, with its units operating in widely differing terrain in all parts of the world, would still need a considerable establishment of horses and mules. The Army Veterinary Services therefore made plans for mobilization and in 1936 started research into the problem of the protection of animals in chemical warfare. The German Army was showing considerable interest in this subject and the Italians were reported to have used mustard gas in their Abyssinian campaign of 1935. Improved methods of disseminating chemical agents had been developed since World War I.

During the nineteen-thirties there were a number of minor campaigns on the North-West Frontier which gave the R.A.V.C. opportunities to test out its organization under operational conditions and to learn to use mechanized transport both for the clearance of casualties and for the rapid large scale movement of fit animals by road.

A flare-up of the Arab-Jewish trouble led in 1938 to the dispatch to Palestine of the last two horsed cavalry regiments of the line of the British Army (The Royal Scots Greys and the Royal Dragoons) with No. 1 Cavalry Mobile Veterinary Section R.A.V.C. in support.

In 1939 mobilization of the R.A.V.C. took place as planned. An account is given in the chapters which follow of the Veterinary Services in World War II and the adaptation of the Royal Army Veterinary Corps to the requirements of the modern army.

In the Burma and Italian campaigns of World War II pack transport was used on a considerable scale. For many years there is likely to be a continuing need for the employment of mules and ponies in mountain or jungle warfare when conditions limit the use of mechanized transport, helicopters and aircraft for the carriage of men, arms and supplies. The number of animals required for such operations is comparatively small, and the field hospital and casualty clearance system, which was so valuable in World War I, is obsolete. In its place is a combined veterinary and remount organization which must purchase pack animals when called upon to do so; deliver them wherever they are required in a fit condition for immediate service; provide for their veterinary care in the operational area; and arrange for the clearance and replacement of casualties.

In addition to this variation of its traditional rôle, the range of services entrusted to the Corps has been broadened to include fresh meat and milk inspection, animal husbandry, the veterinary aspects of nuclear, biological and chemical warfare, and the training of war dogs and their handlers.

The war dog has an established place in the British Army. One well-trained guard dog and its handler can, in suitable circumstances, replace up to eight ordinary sentries. Tracker dogs have proved invaluable on security operations; and many an infantry patrol has escaped ambush thanks to the alert senses of a dog. The training and care of these animals constitute the main duties of the Corps at present.

Finally reference must be made to the Depot and the School and Stores providing as they do the training and equipment upon which depends the whole efficiency of the Army Veterinary and Remount Services. The School, with its laboratory, has for many years been a centre of research. Some of its achievements are recorded in the chapter concerning the contributions of the Corps to veterinary science.

CHAPTER II

The Years Between 1919-1939

THE first post-war report on the Army Veterinary Services was published in 1921. At this period the main equine establishments of the Army were deployed as follows:—

United Kingdom	16,101
British Army of the Rhine	1,950
British Troops in Egypt and Palestine	4,724
British Army of the Black Sea	1,660

There were also extensive animal establishments of the Indian Army in India, Iraq and Persia.

The strength and distribution of the Royal Army Veterinary Corps were:—

	Officers	Other Ranks
Home	69	331
Rhine	7	60
Constantinople	8	42
Egypt and Palestine ..	20	48
Iraq and Persia	38	30
India	85	6
Colonies	3	2
Egyptian Army	16	7
	246	526

The Army had recently been engaged in Russia, the Third Afghan War, the Arab Revolt and in the Irish troubles. Small-scale military operations were in progress in Somaliland, Waziristan and Malabar. At home as a result of the Coal Strike, the Army Reserve had been called out and a Special Defence Force formed. In consequence many war-worn horses and mules had been retained.

Sand colic was a cause of much inefficiency in the Middle East amongst horses which had been living in the open desert; and periodic ophthalmia, with its sequelae of impaired vision and cataract was prevalent amongst the animals of the Black Sea Force. But the structure of the equine establishment and the pattern of diseases were changing as more orderly conditions developed.

In war-time large numbers of animals, many of them immature, have to be hurriedly purchased and shipped overseas where only a minimum period is possible for acclimatization, conditioning and training before they are subjected to the rigours of war—exposure, overwork, inadequate feeding, shortage of water, inexperienced handling and enemy action. Under these circumstances at least 10 per cent. of the animal establishment is constantly in hospital under veterinary care.

In peace the need for haste and improvisation is reduced. There is time to select, mature and train horses before issue. Animals are adequately fed and housed. Their work is reasonable and they are cared for by experienced people. Horses and mules are purchased when four or five years old and disposed of as too old for military duties at the ages of fifteen years and eighteen years respectively. A typical population of army horses has an average age of eleven years and about 12 per cent. are young remounts. Such was the position during the nineteen-twenties: sickness and wastage rates were steady and predictable and infectious diseases were mostly confined to the remounts.

Despite the mediation of the British Forces in the Turco-Greek war in 1922, and the dispatch of units to form the Shanghai Defence Force in 1927, this was a period of comparative calm in which the Corps had time both to attend to its military duties and to develop its corporate life.

In 1921 approval was given for the appointment of a Colonel Commandant, Royal Army Veterinary Corps. The first officer to receive this distinction was Major-General Sir Layton Blenkinsop. Soon after assuming his appointment he delivered an address on behalf of the Corps to commemorate the unveiling of a memorial tablet erected by the Royal College of Veterinary Surgeons in honour of those of its members who had fallen in the recent war. The Council of the College also established a war memorial library.

Two years later the Colonel Commandant unveiled the Corps war memorial in St. George's Garrison Church, Woolwich. It commemorates the officers, warrant-officers, non-commissioned officers and men of the Royal Army Veterinary Corps who gave their lives during the Great War 1914-1918. The memorial, which is of mosaic with marble panels bearing both the old A.V.C. badge and the new badge of the Royal Army Veterinary Corps, was transferred to the Depot at Melton Mowbray in 1961.

The present-day design of cap badge, collar badge and button was adopted in 1921. The official description of the crest being "within a laurel wreath surmounted by a crown the figure of Chiron."

The Old Comrades' Association held its first reunion and dinner that year. The Association had been inaugurated in 1920 prompted by a feeling held by all ranks that the many friendships made during the war should be maintained. Briefly its objects are to provide opportunities to meet old friends again and to help members who have struck hard times. It has succeeded magnificently in its purpose: the annual dinners today are as well attended as they were from the very start, and hundreds of less fortunate members and their families have been helped in times of unemployment and illness by the Old Comrades' Association working in close co-operation with the Corps Benevolent Fund.

Similar motives led at the same period to the formation of the Royal Army Veterinary Corps Officers' Club. In fact, a dining-club had been in existence since 1880 but it was not until 1920 that a general fund was formed with objectives which were partly charitable and partly to provide the machinery and financial backing for the social life of the Corps. The Corps dinner is held on the Friday before Royal Ascot week and is preceded by the Annual General Meeting and a tea party when the wife of the Director is At Home to members and their families.

In 1924 the Club formed the Corps Golfing Society, and in 1925 a Point-to-Point Association was started, the first race being held at the Hambledon Hunt meeting at Liss in 1926. In 1927 it undertook to publish the manuscript of Major-General Sir Frederick Smith's *History of the Royal Army Veterinary Corps*, and, two years later, financed the production of the newly-created *Journal of the Royal Army Veterinary Corps*.

The Veterinary Service had needed a periodical in which the experience and observations of its members might be recorded because, since 1890, the *Quarterly Journal of Veterinary Science in India and Army Animal Management*, founded by veterinary surgeons J. H. Steel and F. Smith in 1882, had ceased publication, due to Steel's death.

Sir Frederick Smith took a keen interest in the inception of the new journal. He was then seventy-two years old and in failing health. The first number contained the last of his many contributions to veterinary literature—"A Critical Examination of so-called Dislocation of the Patella". The script was received with a request that the printer's proof be prepared with all possible speed, since he felt his end was near, and he desired particularly to see his article in the Journal in printed form before, as he expressed it, "the old gentleman with the scythe, whose advent I shall welcome, bids me come." Sir Frederick died as he had lived—an enthusiast in everything concerning the profession.

Major-General Sir Frederick Smith, K.C.M.G., C.B., formerly Director-General Army Veterinary Service, Fellow and Honorary Associate of the Royal College of Veterinary Surgeons, Fellow of the Institute of Chemistry, died in July 1929. He was probably the greatest veterinarian produced by the Army of this or any other country.

His death marked the end of an era for the Corps. The process of mechanizing the Army combined with the "Geddes Axe" measures for the reduction of the Armed

Forces were cutting down the number of veterinary units needed for the Regular and Territorial Armies at home; whilst abroad where the scope for mechanization was more limited than in Europe, greater use was to be made of locally-enlisted personnel.

At this period the chief overseas stations for the British Army were India, Egypt and the Sudan. In addition, a number of officers were seconded for permanent duty with the Indian and Egyptian Armies.

In 1924 the Corps handed over to the Sudan Government a flourishing veterinary department which, since 1898, had played a major part in developing the livestock industry. Quarantine stations had been placed along the trade routes; civilian veterinary hospitals established in suitable localities; and everything possible done to encourage good animal husbandry. The resulting control of contagious diseases coupled with the improved conditions of agriculture led to a great expansion of the sheep and cattle population, and turned the Sudan into an animal-exporting country. In 1918 no fewer than 30,000 cattle and 250,000 sheep were exported to Egypt and elsewhere.

Five R.A.V.C. officers remained with the Sudan Defence Force until 1931 when the veterinary services of the country were completely under the control of the civil authority. The plate and trophies from the R.A.V.C. Officers' Mess, Khartoum are now at the Headquarters Mess, Melton Mowbray.

In addition to pioneering the way for the civil veterinary service, the Corps dealt with its routine tasks—the prevention and treatment of disease in military animals in Egypt and the Sudan.

For many years the Army had owed its continuing freedom from glanders to the systematic application of the mallein test combined with the speedy destruction of all reactors. In 1927 a series of misconceptions led to the destruction of 380 animals, many of which were probably unaffected by glanders. One positive reaction to mallein had led to the testing of all army horses and mules in Egypt and 660 animals giving positive or doubtful results were condemned. An investigating officer sent out by War Office showed that the mallein reactions were not typical; that the pulmonary nodules found on post-mortem resembled glanders lesions macroscopically but were, in fact, worm cysts; and that none of the surviving cases showed either loss of condition or other clinical symptoms of glanders. These findings saved 280 animals but no explanation was forthcoming for the unfamiliar mallein reactions; nor for the reports of three out of the four pathologists to whom material was submitted that they had isolated an organism which resembled *Pfeifferella mallei* but which did not produce the characteristic orchitis when injected into guinea-pigs.

By far the largest commitment of the Corps was the supply of officers to India either on a five-year tour or for continuous service in the Indian Cadre. Despite the fact that an Indian Army Veterinary Corps had existed since 1921 it included no officers and this deficiency had to be made good right up to 1935 when the first three Indian Commissioned Officers were gazetted. Indeed, until well into World War II, every

Major-General Sir Frederick Smith, K.C.M.G., C.B., 1857-1929.

CHAPTER I. Preliminary veterinary inspection of horses at night, Romsey Remount Depot, 1916. From the drawing by Lionel Edwards.

CHAPTER I. Pack horses taking ammunition up to the guns, Western Front 1916. *Imperial War Museum photo.*

CHAPTER II. Type of trailer used for the evacuation of casualties on North-West Frontier, 1934.

CHAPTER II. Loading a sick camel into an ambulance, North-West Frontier, 1935.

CHAPTER II. Paddock of V.H. Hong-Kong, 1933. Batch of remount mules after arrival from Tientsin. Operating theatre with thatched roof in background.

CHAPTER III. Training horses for pack work, Melton Mowbray, 1942.

CHAPTER III. Pack training, Melton Mowbray, 1942.

CHAPTER III.   Yeomanry camp in the rain. From the etching by Major W. P. Moss.

CHAPTER IV. "Meat safe" treatment of wounds to combat the fly menace. No. 1 V.H. Ramle, 1940.

CHAPTER IV. Another "meat safe" for fistulous withers. No. 1 V.H. Ramle, 1940.

CHAPTER IV. No. 1 V.H. Ramle. View of No. 2 Section from the bathing pool, with C.O.'s government car in foreground.

CHAPTER IV. Remount Depot, Alexandria, 1941. Note continuous trough.

CHAPTER IV. No. 1 Field Remount Depot at Tel-Mond, Palestine, 1941.

CHAPTER IV.   Training of Cavalry Division riders for draught work at No. 3 Base Remount Depot, 1941.

CHAPTER IV.   No. 2 Livestock Depot in Syria. Inspecting the animals.

CHAPTER IV.   *Left* Mule purchase in Mosul, P.A.I.C., 1943, and, *right*, one of the very many starving horses taken over from the Vichy French, Syria, 1941.

CHAPTER IV. North Africa, 1943. Pack mules waiting to take supplies up the mountains. *Imperial War Museum photo.*

CHAPTER IV. Method of transporting feeds in receptacles made of unserviceable motor tyre. Veterinary Hospital, Ramle, 1940.

administrative and senior executive appointment was held by a R.A.V.C. officer. The Army Veterinary Service in India, therefore, figures to no small extent in the history of the Corps. There was a Directorate at Army Headquarters under the Quartermaster-General consisting, up to the outbreak of the 1939 War, of a Director (Brigadier), Assistant Director (Major) and (from 1937 only) an attached officer (Captain). An administrative veterinary officer (Colonel or Lt. Colonel) was at each Command; a D.A.D.V.S. was on the staff of each major District, combining this appointment with that of O.C. Military Veterinary Hospital Class I and the related Section I.A.V.C., while executive veterinary officers were posted to various stations throughout India (according to the strength of animals located there) and to the Army Remount Department.

The Secretary of State sanctioned, in 1926, the grant of King's commissions in the I.A.V.C. to Indian gentlemen who had been educated at the Prince of Wales' Royal Indian Military College, Dehra Dun, or at a British public school and who had subsequently obtained the diploma of M.R.C.V.S. It was not, however, until March 1935 that the first three I.C.Os. were gazetted into His Majesty's Indian Land Force; these were followed by eight more in the course of the next year and by 1938 there were fifteen against an establishment of sixteen. Brigadier H. S. Mosley, D.V.S. India 1932-36, met with prejudice and criticism from his colleagues when he effected this policy. But there is no doubt now that he was right. These officers rendered valuable service during World War II and after it, when the time came to hand over India, they took charge of the Remount, Veterinary and Farms Corps of India and Pakistan in a most competent manner.

Veterinary assistant surgeons played an important part in the Army Veterinary Service; they were graduates of the Veterinary Colleges of Lahore, Bombay, Madras and Calcutta. The course was normally of three or four years' duration. Many of these men, with practical experience and careful training by R.A.V.C. officers, became very valuable members of the Service, skilled in their profession, conscientious, and reliable. In the days when many Indian units which had a significant animal establishment had their own V.A.Ss. the total number of 306 was employed. In 1920 sanction was accorded to the formation of an Indian Army Veterinary Corps into which were absorbed all the technical personnel of such units as silladar cavalry, Indian pack batteries, and Indian Army Service Corps. This measure enabled a reduction of no less than 131 V.A.Ss. to be made giving an establishment in 1921 of 175, and so successful did this policy of unity of control prove that the following year the number was still further reduced to 153. The cadre was reorganized in 1923 into four grades—risaldar-majors, risaldars, jemadars, and warrant officers, the last named being eligible for promotion to jemadar after five years' service. The first three grades were granted Viceroy's commissions, as opposed to the King's commissions given to the I.C.Os.

British other ranks I.A.V.C. in 1930 were transferred to the departmental section of the Indian Unattached List on the lower time-scale of promotion and revised rates of pay as sanctioned for the I.U.L. in 1927. These men served as quartermasters.

Indian other ranks I.A.V.C. were reorganized in 1922 on an establishment of 600 for all India. There were eventually thirteen Sections I.A.V.C. to which these men were posted. Eight of these were Mussalman and five Hindu and they were located at important stations such as Rawalpindi, Peshawar, Quetta, Lahore, Meerut, Razmak and Mhow.

Military veterinary hospitals in India were divided into three grades—Class I, Class II and Branch. Needless to say the numbers and grading varied considerably. In 1937 there were twenty Class I, twenty-four Class II and twenty-three Branch hospitals.

The Army Veterinary Schools at Poona and Ambala carried out courses of instruction in animal management from 1920 onwards, save for a period of three years from 1930 when they were suspended for economic reasons. These courses were very greatly appreciated particularly by units, such as infantry battalions, which had no I.A.V.C. staff on their establishment.

The I.A.V.C. Depot and Record Office continued to function throughout the period between the wars. The temporary depot, formed at Kirkee to deal with recruitment to the newly-formed I.A.V.C. in 1920, was closed in 1922, as was a temporary Record Office which had been established in Poona.

The Military Veterinary Laboratory was formed at Lahore during 1936 and did excellent work thereafter, in close collaboration with the Imperial Veterinary Research Institute, Mukteswar; including the examination of thousands of morbid specimens, the study of diseases of army animals, and the investigation of outbreaks of contagious disease occurring among them and among horses in the army remount breeding areas.

The animal strength naturally varied from time to time; for purposes of comparison the statistics of three years are given:—

	1921/22	1937/38	1939/40
Horses and ponies	39,096	31,540	24,522
Mules	31,272	28,219	26,194
Camels	7,260	3,781	5,825
Bullocks	4,290	—	—
Cattle	—	12,758	13,512
Donkeys	306	172	—
	82,224	76,470	70,053

The totals do not include horses in the breeding areas of the Army Remount Department. In 1937–38 these totalled 432 stallions and 14,877 mares and young stock.

The bullocks shown in 1921–22 were those of the Bullock Transport Companies I.A.S.C. which were subsequently disbanded. The cattle shown in 1937–38 and 1939–40 belonged to the Military Dairy Farms for which the A.V.S. was not responsible until 1925 except in so far as outbreaks of contagious disease were concerned.

The main responsibilities of the Army Veterinary Service were twofold. The first was the regular inspection—every month whenever possible—of all military animals to ensure their fitness for the purpose for which they would be required in peace and war. The second was the prevention and control of contagious disease. The extent to which the A.V.S. succeeded in both these tasks has never been disputed. Few animals were fitter than those of the Indian Army and contagious disease was kept under remarkable control in a country in which it abounded among civilian animals often located only a few yards from military.

The main contagious diseases encountered were anthrax, biliary fever (piroplasmosis), camel pox, contagious abortion, epizootic lymphangitis, foot-and-mouth disease, glanders, haemorrhagic septicaemia, influenza, jhooling, Johne's disease, rabies, rinderpest, strangles, surra (trypanosomiasis), tetanus and tuberculosis. Restrictions of space preclude more than a passing reference to some of the more important of these.

Anthrax was generally sporadic, about fifteen to twenty-five cases being recorded every year. Owing to its widespread distribution in Burma the policy was adopted, in 1936, of protecting all military animals arriving there from India by spore vaccine from the Civil Veterinary Institute, Insein, Rangoon. In that year, too, all animals (1,721) in the Zhob Area were similarly immunized with the result that no case occurred despite the prevalence of the disease among local civilian animals. A serious outbreak occurred at a small camp, Ali-Khel, during the Waziristan operations of 1937. Its source was a consignment of green fodder. It was indeed fortunate that expert control was available as there were over 1,100 horses and mules confined in a very small area and the number of deaths could easily have exceeded the nineteen which occurred.

Encephalomyelitis was first recorded in 1933 when seventy-one cases occurred, with twenty-four deaths, in a cavalry regiment marching from Loralai to Jullundur (about 540 miles). The mere statistics of this outbreak convey no impression of the consternation which it caused. Firstly, no previous cases of this disease had ever been recognized in India. Secondly, the regiment was on the march, out "in the blue", moving every day. When a veterinary officer arrived on the scene, alarmed by curious reports from the veterinary assistant surgeon accompanying the regiment, he found a number of cases exhibiting varying degrees of paraplegia, some unable to rise, some discernible only by a slight "wobble" when an affected horse turned after trotting. There were no facilities for diagnosis or post-mortem examination, and to make matters still more difficult several animals exhibited quite definite symptoms of piroplasmosis which was later proved to be co-existent. The assistance of the pathological department of the Punjab Veterinary College was sought immediately, the regiment was diverted to Multan to avoid infecting other animals at Jullundur, and eventually the diagnosis of encephalomyelitis was established. In later years other cases were detected but there were no outbreaks on a similar scale.

Epizootic lymphangitis was liable to be encountered anywhere in India and constant vigilance was necessary but the Army was free of it during the nineteen-thirties. This point is of some interest in view of the problem created by this disease at the end of World War II.

Foot-and-mouth disease was of frequent occurrence on military farms. The methods of control were not nearly so drastic and expensive as in Britain but outbreaks had an economic importance owing to the reduction in milk supply while affected cases were under treatment, and a certain number of deaths in highly-bred and imported stock owing to pneumonic complications. From 1935 to 1938 admissions averaged about 1,300 of which only fifteen died. During an outbreak foot-baths of 2 per cent. copper sulphate for affected animals and 2 per cent. cresol for the remainder were used and fresh chlorinated lime (90 grains per 100 gallons) was added to the drinking water; this appeared to have considerable curative effect and curtailed spread. In one outbreak among 300 cattle only eleven developed clinical symptoms.

Glanders was an ever-present menace owing to its prevalence among equines in the surrounding civilian areas. The number of cases occurring annually—clinical or detected by mallein—varied from two to thirty. Eternal vigilance was essential—the disease could appear without warning anywhere and at any time—and the relatively small number of cases, and the rapidity with which their spread was checked, reflects great credit on all concerned. The value of this constant observation by the A.V.S. is illustrated by an incident in Burma in 1936. Tonga ponies were suspected of being extensively affected with the latent form of glanders and, by arrangement with the Civil Veterinary Department, 1,396 of them were malleined. No less than 175 reacted.

Influenza constituted, at times, a major problem owing to its rapid spread with consequent immobilization of large numbers of animals and the care required to avoid fatal complications. In 1934–35, for instance, 3,468 horses were affected of which five died. In 1936–37 there were 829 cases among horses involving twelve deaths. The following year there were 7,002 cases in horses, 296 in mules and 226 in camels, the malady assuming the form of a coughing epidemic with only two fatalities.

Equine piroplasmosis was successfully treated with intravenous injections of quinine acid hydrobromide. In the early part of the inter-war period some 300 cases were recorded annually but this number steadily diminished as sanitation and anti-fly measures improved. The "graduated tube" as an aid to diagnosis and prognosis was successfully introduced in 1927.

Rabies claimed, on average, eleven victims annually among army horses, mules and camels. In view of the prevalence of this terrible disease among pariah dogs over enormous areas it is surprising that more cases did not occur. In one instance a rabid dog made three separate attacks on mules in infantry lines. Twice it was beaten off and the third time it was destroyed. Nine mules were badly bitten but they were inoculated with anti-rabic vaccine (the routine preventive procedure) and none were affected. For veterinary officers rabies was a constant menace owing to the number of privately-owned dogs which contracted it. Although treatment of such animals by officers of the R.A.V.C. was discouraged it was obviously impossible to refuse a request from a personal friend whose dog was "off colour"; and this was the dangerous case. In forty-eight hours symptoms of rabies might be only too apparent and if the veterinary officer had not taken every precaution when examining the dog he had to decide whether he would undergo a course of anti-rabic treatment or "take a chance". Those who chose the latter alternative often repented later when, during the long incubative period, they developed some potentially suspicious symptoms such as a sore throat!

Rinderpest was one of the diseases which were brought under complete control by the Army Veterinary Service in India. By 1937–38 it was possible to record, for the second year in succession, that no outbreak had occurred among cattle of the Military Farms Department. Yet in 1931–32 outbreaks in Quetta, Cawnpore, Ambala and Jubbulpore claimed 208 victims. The success which had attended the programme of immunization, so carefully developed and carried out during the earlier years, was well illustrated in two outbreaks among civilian slaughter-cattle in Razmak involving seventy-nine deaths. Despite the fact that the Military Dairy Farm premises adjoined the slaughter-pens not a single one of these animals contracted the disease, all having been protected prior to dispatch to this area of operations. In that year 2,630 cattle were immunized using one c.c. of goat virus alone except in the case of pure-bred imported stock which received serum simultaneously. Up to 1935 serum was used for all classes; pure-bred, cross-bred and indigenous. This new method was far more effective in addition to the fact that it saved much time and money.

Surra was one of the most serious veterinary problems in the early nineteen-twenties. The "Cross" treatment for camels by tartar emetic intravenously was admittedly a great improvement on any previous form of therapy but even so the losses among camels amounted to hundreds every year—an average of 313 from 1922 to 1928. For horses and mules there was no effective treatment at all. In Chapter XI a detailed account is given of the steps taken to find a satisfactory method not only of curing surra but of protecting animals against the disease.

Strangles throughout the inter-war years continued to be an immense problem, the vast majority of cases occurring in the Young-Stock Depots at Mona and Sargodha. Despite the most careful investigations, with the full co-operation of the Imperial Veterinary Research Institute, Mukteswar, and a host of different methods of treatment and control, the situation in 1937 was still most unsatisfactory. In these depots, that year, 1,030 horses and 756 mules were admitted of which 79 horses and 10 mules died.

From 1933 to 1938 the percentage of deaths to receipts was about 4 per cent. and to affected about 30 per cent.

Although the problem of strangles was still baffling the united efforts of veterinary officers in field and laboratory to bring it under effective control the veterinary situation in India at this period was, on the whole, excellent. As indicated, the general position regarding control of contagious disease was very satisfactory and the health of those animals for which the A.V.S. was responsible had never been better. The many veterinary hospitals and units were working smoothly and satisfactorily; the introduction of Indian officers had got into its stride after a few initial difficulties, and the Corps had a useful part to play on the North-West Frontier, where a large part of the Army was stationed to block the invasion routes and to deal with border raids.

In recorded history over thirty invasions have been made through the main passes—Khyber, Kurram, Tochi, Gomal and Bolan—which lead from the north through a tangled mass of mountains into India. As recently as 1919 the Amir of Afghanistan had made an abortive attempt to force the Khyber with his troops.

Tribal raids into British territory were common. Not infrequently the tribes would gather in considerable force and have to be dispersed by a punitive column of British and Indian troops. The tribesmen were clever guerrilla fighters and could seldom be brought to battle. They relied on harassing tactics, ambush and sniping; and were quick to take advantage of tactical errors. In opposing them our troops had to move over very rough broken country. Much of the transport was on a pack basis and mules were needed to carry machine-guns, mortars and mountain guns.

During 1937, 10,000 horses and mules and 800 camels were employed continuously in Waziristan on this type of mountain warfare.

Veterinary units had been equipped with mechanical transport since 1929. Motor horse-ambulances and trailers had been in use for a number of years. But until now there had been no opportunity to test out the serviceability of the motorized veterinary evacuation system under field conditions.

In this campaign two mobile sections between them collected over 1,300 sick and lame animals in lorries and trailers. Serious cases were treated in hospitals established at base. Returning lorries took up the remount replacements.

Gunshot wounds accounted for 248 casualties. Much of the veterinary work was related to the prevention and treatment of injuries to the feet and back.

Veterinary care was also extended to 600 dairy cattle and buffaloes which provided fresh milk for the troops; and slaughter stock, amounting during the year to 101,000 cattle, sheep and goats, had to be inspected and kept healthy.

But there was a cloud on the horizon—mechanization. The recommendations of the Chatfield Commission involved an eventual reduction of upwards of 40,000 animals and it was obvious that the A.V.S., which had been built up with such patience and skill over the years, could not escape drastic cuts in all directions. And so began the most distasteful task of drawing up a programme which would result in something like a 40–50 per cent. overall reduction covering a four-year period, to cater for an establishment of about 27,000 animals which included some 10,000 cattle of the Military Farm Department. But the labour over long lists of cuts in personnel, equipment, units and stores, revised again and again in attempts to "lighten the blow", was to be wasted. War was imminent and the A.V.S. far from being reduced, was to be called upon to expand to an extent totally unforeseen in any mobilization scheme. And when peace came the Army Veterinary Service was to hand over to our Indian colleagues, but of what it handed over it had good reason to be proud.

At home it was planned to complete the mechanization programme by 1939; leaving horses with only two Household Cavalry regiments, three line regiments of cavalry and one battery R.H.A. There were to be no mounted units abroad except in India and Hong Kong. However, in the event of mobilization it was estimated that up to 10,000 horses would be required by the Field Force.

During 1936 and 1937, committees under the chairmanship of the Financial Secretary to the War Office, Sir Victor Warrender, considered the position of the veterinary and remount services in the reorganized Army.

It was decided to retain both services on reduced establishments. The Corps had, in addition to its normal duties, to be responsible in future for the shoeing of all army animals.

A minority report went further and strongly recommended that, in the interests of economy, the two departments should be amalgamated. This was unacceptable at the time but only a year later No. 1 Cavalry Mobile Veterinary Section was formed to provide both veterinary and remount support for the Royal Scots Greys and the Royal Dragoons in Palestine.

The committee felt that the Corps would be an insurance against the danger that in the process of mechanization the Army would lose much of its skilled knowledge of the management of animals in the field which might prove indispensable should troops have to fight away from the roads in jungle or mountains: "We consider that the R.A.V.C. should be preserved in order to conserve the experience of the past against possible future needs and to modify and enlarge this knowledge by study and practice under changing conditions."

It was generally thought there was still a place for horses and mules in modern armies. The Italians in the Abyssinian campaign of 1935 had shown how essential it was to organize the use of animals in war on a rational basis. Marshal Emilio de Bono stated "But no amount of mechanical transport would enable us to dispense with pack animals. The pack animals are only one of the many components of a baggage train. Such a column requires, in addition to the animals, a commandant, veterinary officers, farriers, drivers and saddlers."

Soon after the start of the campaign he reported to Mussolini—"The greatest deficiency is in the baggage trains. Lissona has offered to have mules sent me. The mules we have would be sufficient but more than a third of them through organic deficiency or because too young or because their pack saddles do not fit because of lack of saddlers to adapt them and because of the incapacity of drivers and officers, are lying brutally exhausted in the animal hospitals."

The German Army, influenced possibly by experiences in the Spanish Civil War, when motorised units were frequently handicapped by mechanical breakdowns, was vigorously importing horses from Ireland and elsewhere. Its equine establishment rose from 35,000 in 1933 to over 100,000 in 1938. It had a strong and well-organized veterinary service which was showing a marked interest in chemical warfare.

In the event of war Britain expected to be raided from the air with high explosive, incendiary bombs and poison gas. It was anticipated that blister gases would be used against military targets in the field by shelling, bombing or spraying from aircraft. Although unlikely to be primary targets animals would be involved in such attacks. In 1936 a veterinary officer (Major R. M. Bamford) was attached to the Chemical Defence Experimental Station to study chemical warfare agents and their effects on horses and mules. His work led to the production of veterinary anti-gas chests, eye shields, respirators and anti-gas covers. He also evolved a procedure for the decontamination and treatment of affected animals which would have saved untold suffering had the threat of chemical warfare materialized.

CHAPTER III

The United Kingdom Base and the Campaigns in France and North-West Europe

I N September 1939 the embodiment of the Territorial Army and the recall of selected members of the regular reserve raised the Corps home establishment from eighteen officers and sixty-eight other ranks to forty-two officers and 441 other ranks. This cadre was sufficient for immediate needs; including veterinary services for the 1st Cavalry Division, whose formation increased the horse strength from 2,600 to 11,600. Further recruitment was necessary to meet the expected expansion of Corps commitments in other parts of the world.

A few days after mobilization commenced the Director of Veterinary Services, Brigadier C. A. Murray, convened a meeting of the Presidents of the Royal College of Veterinary Surgeons and the National Veterinary Medical Association, the Principal of the Royal Veterinary College and the Chief Veterinary Officer of the Ministry of Agriculture and Fisheries to discuss the respective claims of agriculture and the Army upon the man-power of the profession.

Veterinary practice was at first reduced by the war but it was thought that eventually the civilian service would have to deal not only with the increased demands of war-time agriculture but also with enemy attempts to sabotage the livestock industry by means of biological warfare. In addition, a veterinary air-raid precautions organization was needed for every large town and city in the threatened areas. Urban animals populations were considerable—Greater London had 50,000 horses and cattle, 24,000 sheep and pigs and 2,000,000 dogs and cats—and heavy casualties were expected.

It was foreseen that the conflict would be long and arduous. In World War I few officers over forty-five years of age could stand up to the strenuous conditions which prevailed in the forward areas. Most of the reserve officers were older than this, and many of them could be ill-spared from their civil duties.

As a general principle, therefore, it was decided to grant emergency commissions to young veterinary surgeons rather than call upon the reserve officers of the Regular and Territorial Armies. Already there were 247 volunteers to choose from, and the number of volunteers for commissions in the R.A.V.C. remained sufficient until 1943.

By then the limitations of mechanized vehicles in mountain, snow and jungle warfare were well recognized, and the provision of animals and veterinary establishments had been raised to a high priority. A modified form of conscription was imposed upon the profession and the Army Service Veterinary Selection Committee was set up to direct suitable veterinary surgeons into military service.

Besides veterinary surgeons, the officer establishment included quartermasters, practically all of whom were commissioned from the ranks of the R.A.V.C., and also a small number of non-professional officers who were mostly cavalry reservists selected for their knowledge of horsemastership and remount duties. In all, 519 officers served with the R.A.V.C. during the war.

The recruitment of other ranks with previous experience with animals was easy at first. Veterinary students, hunt servants, grooms, stable lads and farm workers eagerly came forward. While considerable numbers of cavalry reservists were transferred to the Corps. Later the demand for this type of recruit exceeded the supply, and throughout the war there was a shortage of farriers and saddlers. It takes at least two months to learn the rudiments of these trades, and instructional courses in farriery and saddlery had to be run almost continuously in veterinary units at home and abroad to meet the requirements of animal-transport units. During the war period 3,839 men served with the R.A.V.C.

Basic training for both officers and men was given at the Depot which, early in 1939, had been moved from Woolwich to Aldershot, and again in October, 1939 to Doncaster where it was more centrally placed for the units of the 1st Cavalry Division which was being prepared for dispatch to Palestine.

The Depot, subsequently called No. 1 Reserve Veterinary Hospital, Depot and Training Establishment, was situated throughout the war on the racecourse at Doncaster. It had stable-room for 600 animals and could train up to 175 men at one time. All veterinary units raised in Great Britain, whether for service at home or overseas, originated there. These included four hospitals, seven mobile veterinary sections, four veterinary and remount conducting sections, two remount depots, four store depots, one convalescent horse depot and a veterinary evacuating station.

In the House of Commons in March, 1939 the Secretary of State for War was asked whether mechanization had not gone too far and whether he knew that the German Army was buying up the surplus British cavalry horses. He replied that two regular and sixteen yeomanry cavalry regiments were to be retained as horsed units in addition to the Life Guards and the Royal Horse Guards.

In fact, on the outbreak of war only eight yeomanry regiments were horsed and sent overseas in company with one composite regiment of Household Cavalry to join the Royal Scots Greys and the Royal Dragoons. The provision of horses for the other yeomanry regiments was countermanded at an early stage of mobilization.

The formation of the 1st Cavalry Division, its preparation for overseas service and its movement across France to Palestine gave the Corps its first major war-time task.

To maintain the division in the field the following units were raised between 1st November and the end of December, 1939:—

> No. 1 Veterinary Hospital,
> No. 1 Convalescent Depot,
> No. 1 Veterinary Evacuating Station,
> Nos. 4, 5 and 6 Cavalry Mobile Veterinary Sections,
> No. 1 Base Depot Veterinary Stores,
> No. 1 Advanced Depot Veterinary Stores.

The overall control of these units and the responsibility for the veterinary services of the division lay with the A.D.V.S. at divisional headquarters.

To meet the increased veterinary commitments the Laboratory stepped up its production of mallein, and the Army Veterinary Stores issued field equipment to the new units. Three months reserve of veterinary stores for 15,000 horses was sent to the Middle East. The equipment, drugs and dressings essential for the treatment of animals in the field were supplied in standardized chests designed for carriage on pack saddles, and to withstand rough handling and climatic changes.

The purchase of the 9,000 horses needed for mobilization was made by a Remount Department working against time and reduced by recent establishment cuts.

Experienced remount and veterinary officers had in the past carried out the routine army instructions to buy suitable animals over five years old which were fit for one month's service in the field knowing that the stresses of war could only be borne by sound mature horses. By 1939 men with this background were scarce and some buyers fell into the error of thinking that practically any horse was fit to do a month's active service. Units were soon complaining about the numbers of aged, unsound and otherwise unsuitable animals reaching them; many of which had to be sent almost immediately to hospital.

The Director of Veterinary Services instigated an immediate amendment to current regulations. As a result buyers were instructed to accept only seasoned horses, aged from six to fifteen years, free from any defect likely to impair their capacity for work during the ensuing twelve months.

Most of the horses had been either running at grass or standing in good stables. Now the majority of them were on breastlines in the open, though, where possible, use was made of local stabling, cow byres and other suitable buildings. In these circumstances feeding required careful attention if debility and intestinal troubles were to be avoided. A daily ration scale of oats twelve lbs. and hay twelve lbs. per horse was authorized. On the whole the horses needed hard standings and shelter from the wind rather than overhead cover, but in very inclement areas large circus tents were erected over standings of sleepers or rubble and gave excellent service.

At first, veterinary officers were principally concerned with the treatment of kicks and other injuries, and the incidence of both was high during the confused early days before men and horses had adapted themselves to the rough conditions of camp life. There was also a small outbreak of stomatitis affecting some 200 horses. Of greater importance was a strangles epidemic, which by 12th October was affecting nearly every regiment. Fresh cases exceeded 200 per week on several occasions. Vaccination of the 12,000 horses on the home establishment was completed within seven weeks, by then the outbreak had passed its peak and the sick rate decreased rapidly. In all 1,431 cases occurred with a mortality of 2.6 per cent. Recovered horses showed a marked loss of condition and vitality which was serious in animals confronted with a difficult journey of 2,500 miles.

The division was sent overseas in four flights, each of about 2,000 horses. The first flight left England on 22nd December, 1939 and the other flights followed at intervals of two to three weeks. The move involved a train journey to Dover, a Channel crossing to Dunkirk, a train journey of about forty-eight hours to Marseilles and a sea voyage of six days to Haifa. Twenty-four trains carried the 7,900 horses across France and sixteen shiploads conveyed them to Palestine. The embarkation of the division at Marseilles began on 1st January and was completed on 18th March, 1940—the last shipload consisted of sick and convalescent animals which had been detained under treatment. During the move there were 722 casualties, of which 140 died or had to be destroyed. The principal causes of sickness were exhaustion, transit fever, injuries, pneumonia and relapses from strangles.

Considering that the horses were not yet in hard condition, that many of them had recently recovered from serious illness; together with the inevitable delays and difficulties involved in a large-scale war-time move and the very severe winter conditions prevailing both in England and France, the total loss of only 1.7 per cent. was unexpectedly small.

The success of the move owed much to careful planning. Veterinary staff accompanied all trains and ships, and detachments to intercept and deal with casualties were established at Dover and Dunkirk. At Marseilles, No. 2 Cavalry Mobile Veterinary Section set up a hospital, making use of available stabling augmented by circus tents. All the animals were very tired when Marseilles was reached. They were rested for at least two days before embarkation but horses showing symptoms of exhaustion or fever were detained, together with other sick and injured animals, to sail with later flights. Many animals from the first flight arrived at Marseilles with pneumonia. On later flights, on reaching Dunkirk, a check was made on all horse temperatures—a nasty job at night in the freezing cold. Every horse with a temperature was held at Dunkirk until fit to move. That stopped the train pneumonia.

The Marseilles camp was located at a disused chateau—Château Reynarde—about four miles from a railway station and twelve miles from the docks. Rain and snow had reduced the camp—normally a very pleasant spot—to a morass and No. 2 C.M.V.S. was called upon to handle large numbers of sick animals requiring cover and shelter from the intense cold—it was the worst winter France had experienced for forty-eight years.

Four horse-transport vessels were employed on each flight and sailed in convoy. For the first flight they were *Talamba*, *Tairea*, *Ragula* and *Rhona*. These ships of the British India Line had been fitted out in Bombay. There was great lack of headroom in many places while the width of the stalls was insufficient to allow a horse to come in and out without removing a stanchion. The greatest fault was that many fittings were fastened with nails instead of bolts and were incapable of bearing heavy strain. Throughout the series of voyages these defects and others resulted in injuries to the animals. With the quick turn-round in Marseilles only a certain amount of patching was possible and the ships were never in a completely satisfactory condition.

As it would have been foolish to ship the large horses of the Household Cavalry in these vessels a well-fitted horse transport, the *Quiloa*, was substituted for the *Tairea* after the first flight.

On the second flight the *Talamba* suffered badly. The convoy ran into severe gales with heavy rain. The vessel's scupper pipes were still blocked with dung from the previous voyage with the result that the after well-deck became awash and the nailed floor battens tore loose as the horses tried to retain their footing. During that night the veterinary escort had to raise to their feet some thirty or forty horses which had slipped or fallen from exhaustion, and at one period had to secure several panic-stricken horses which were loose on the open deck.

The V.O., Captain J. Clabby, reported: "By midnight the wind had increased to gale force and the ship was rolling badly. Most of the men were very sea-sick. It was raining and bitterly cold. The open decks were ankle-deep in water. Horses were down in all parts of the ship. The stalls, made in accordance with Indian regulations, were too narrow and the only way to get a cast horse out of them was either to dismantle the stall or saw down the stanchions. By 05.00 hours the situation was in hand and the horses were quieter and getting their sea-legs. At 06.30 hours the O.C. Ship reported a dozen horses loose on the after well-deck—he thought they should be shot as they were liable to go overboard probably taking a few men with them.

"The deck was a shambles. Loose horses were skidding about on their haunches; one horse had been flung into the donkey engine and sustained multiple fractures; two horses had broken their legs and one had fractured its ribs. Having disposed of the badly injured we tied the legs of the remaining loose horses and lashed them to the rails or mast with sacks under their heads to keep them from drowning. That cleared things a bit. But on this deck and the after tween-deck, which was also flooded, horses went down as fast as one got them up. On the other decks they could be kept on their feet by putting hay down under them; here it was simply washed away and gave no foothold."

There was little rest for any Corps personnel on these trips and it was largely due to their untiring efforts that losses were so slight. In all the ships it was necessary to keep up a constant patrol of the decks and holds in order that immediate attention might be given to cast horses and to those showing signs of pulmonary distress. It was seldom possible to get the latter out of the holds on to the open deck but the oxygen cylinders carried by the horse transports provided an excellent substitute for fresh air and revived many horses in the early stages of pulmonary congestion.

On the conclusion of the move the divisional commander paid a well-deserved tribute to the A.V.S. "I feel I must express my appreciation of the work of the A.D.V.S. 1st Cavalry Division and the whole of the personnel who came under his orders for the move. Their preparation for the move was exceedingly thorough and both before, during and after, their energy, enthusiasm and professional ability have been of the greatest assistance to all ranks in the Division. It must be remembered that this report is written about a Division which was chiefly made up of Territorials whose training in camp can be no preparation for a move such as this. Therefore the load on the R.A.V.C. was even heavier than it would have been if regular soldiers had constituted the main part of the Division."

Whilst the 1st Cavalry Division was moving south to Palestine an Indian mule-transport contingent named Special Force K6 was travelling north to join the British Expeditionary Force in France. At times during January, 1940 the Château Reynarde camp held around 4,000 animals.

In October, 1939 it had been decided that the B.E.F. would need 500 pack animals to each front-line division to carry ammunition and supplies to forward positions where approaches had been made impassable to wheeled traffic by heavy shelling.

India provided four fully-equipped animal-transport companies and a remount unit and mules for two Cypriot pack-transport units—a total animal strength of about 2,700. These units travelled in the same five horse transports which were later used for the Cavalry Division. Casualties were negligible—the mule is a hardy beast and these had the added advantages of being seasoned animals in charge of experienced men.

There were two veterinary assistant surgeons I.A.V.C. to each Indian A.T. company and one with the remount unit. The Cypriot companies each had a R.A.V. officer. The veterinary services, and also the remount service, were organized by Major J. J. Plunkett, the Senior Veterinary Officer at General Headquarters. With the departure of the last flight of cavalry horses No. 2 C.M.V.S. moved to G.H.Q. Troop Area to establish a hospital.

By the end of January the mules were at work and widely distributed with the B.E.F. Despite the severe winter the sick-rate never rose above 2.4 per cent. Great difficulty was, however, experienced in keeping the mules from slipping on the paved ice-bound roads. The unusual winter had not been foreseen when the mules left India and the A.T. units were without field forges and tools for hot shoeing; frost nails were scarce and the mules had to operate as best they could with unroughed shoes.

One Indian company together with a temporarily-attached R.A.V.C. officer (Major F. J. Eardley) were captured in the *blitzkrieg* of May 1940. This unit had been doing excellent work in the Saar position carrying supplies through thickly-wooded areas almost to the front line. The other animal units were able to withdraw to Dunkirk and St. Nazaire but no ship could be spared for mules and evacuation was confined to the troops.

No. 2 C.M.V.S. after a narrow escape got away from Boulogne.

In the prevailing chaos the S.V.O. could only assume that the animal units were marching towards the Channel ports. As his normal duties were in abeyance he assisted in the emergency measures set up at Calais for the loading and unloading of ships and the urgent carriage of supplies to troops withdrawing to the coast. On 24th May Calais was surrounded and all except the essential fighting garrison were evacuated. After two weeks in England Major Plunkett returned to the B.E.F. to make contact with the veterinary personnel and animal units left in France. Soon after his arrival the final evacuation of France was ordered and he embarked at St. Nazaire in the *Lancastria*. He had the good fortune to survive the disaster to that vessel in which 3,000 lives were lost and was landed in England in a destroyer on 18th June.

Several hundred dogs returned with the B.E.F. They were mostly homeless animals befriended by the troops on the Dunkirk beaches. In view of the risk of rabies they had to be traced and dealt with by the civil authorities and the R.S.P.C.A.

Another unexpected event was the arrival in British ports of two shipments of French Army remounts from North America which had been dispatched before France had asked for an armistice. In all some 1,600 French Army horses and mules were taken over.

There was little scope for the Corps in the brief campaign in Norway during the spring of 1940. A pack-transport company R.A.S.C. which began training in Scotland with 240 garrons rendered surplus from the Lovat's Scouts never became operational. It was intended to rely mostly on locally-hired transport, but the intelligence reports that considerable numbers of ponies were available proved false. Troops were at times immobilized by soft deep snow, and the lack of skiers and shortage of snow-shoes severely handicapped movement; later, the thaw made the rough roads impassable to wheeled traffic.

At home, the remainder of 1940 was a period of reorganization for the Corps during which it prepared to carry out the additional duties resulting from the Army Council decision that on 1st January 1941 the Director should become responsible for both the veterinary service and the remount service and entrusted with all matters concerning the supply, care and maintenance of army animals. Soon after its formation the office of the Veterinary and Remount Directorate was partially wrecked by bombing and it was moved to Droitwich on 30th May 1941.

The R.A.V.C had always had much to do with the purchase of animals and was as competent as the Remount Department at training and conditioning horses and mules before issue. The amalgamation of the two Services resulted in a considerable saving in staff appointments, units and man-power. The Remount Depot, Melton Mowbray; No. 2 Remount Squadron, Derby; and No. 1 Remount Squadron, Palestine were taken over, and their personnel made a valuable addition to the Corps establishment.

Mobile veterinary sections could now be redesigned to hold a reserve pool of twenty-five remounts to replace casualities on the spot. This sensible economy led to the replacement of the veterinary evacuating station by a new unit—the veterinary and remount conducting section—designed to relieve mobile sections of their sick and to provide remount replacements. These units could hold 100–200 remounts and with their six lorries and trailers lift up to 120 animals at one time. Ten were formed during the war and proved particularly valuable during the Italian campaign for the evacuation of casualties to advanced hospitals and the supply of remount replacements to the forward areas in the absence of rail transport.

Between 1941–1945 the Corps purchased some 31,000 mules, horses and camels, chiefly for use overseas. In India Command, however, the veterinary and remount services remained separate until after the war. The Indian Remount Department bought widely in U.S.A., South Africa and South America.

In U.S.A. a mule purchasing commission, consisting of Brigadier R. S. Scott, late Director of Remounts in India and Major D. A. Green, R.A.V.C., was attached to the India Supply Mission in Washington in October 1943. Prior to this the procurement and shipment of animals had been carried out by Major R. F. Wall, R.A.V.C. (retired); his shipments to the United Kingdom during 1941–1943 included 778 mules, and sixty-four sledge dogs for the Snow and Mountain Warfare Training Centre.

The commission during 1943–1944 obtained some 3,000 mules under the lease-lend scheme. Shipment of the animals to India was arranged by the India Supply Mission. Four shiploads were conducted by officers and enlisted men of the American Quartermaster Corps and Veterinary Corps. For a fifth ship the Canadian Army provided the conducting party.

During 1943 it was arranged to exchange one officer each from the R.A.V.C. and the Veterinary Corps, U.S.A. to compare ideas and pool information. In April 1944 Major Green was attached to the Training and Liaison Pool of the British Army Staff, Washington with the local rank of Lieutenant-Colonel and at the same time an American veterinary officer left the U.S.A. to carry out liaison duties in England, the Middle East and India. A good deal of useful information was exchanged. Particular attention was paid to the employment of dogs for the detection of non-metallic mines.

During September–November 1944 Lieutenant-Colonel Green assisted by Major W. B. Bamber, R.A.V.C., bought a further 755 mules for India. The British commission accompanied the American mule purchasing officers on their routine tours in the central and south-western remount areas. This arrangement worked well and saved a lot of time. In the mule centres dealers could deal with the British and American buyers

CHAPTER IV. Cavalry operating in the Syrian Campaign, 1941. After the etching by Major W. P. Moss.

CHAPTER V. The farrier had an essential part to play.

CHAPTER V. No. 6 C.M.V.S. ambulances with extension ramps, Cassino Front, 1944.

CHAPTER V. No. 3 V.R.C.S. near Cassino, 1944. Dressing a casualty.

CHAPTER V. Mine detector adapted for locating shrapnel, No. 4 V.H., Italy, 1944.

CHAPTER V. Cargo net. From merchant ship to L.S.T.

CHAPTER V. Remount purchasing. Italy, 1944.

CHAPTER V. No. 1 Field Remount Depot, Apricena. Neck branding was used to identify animals in C.M.F.

CHAPTER V.　On the way to Ravenna.

CHAPTER V.　Casualties returning from forward area to No. 4 C.M.V.S., 1944.

CHAPTER V. Disembarking loaded mules from L.C.T. into three-and-a-half feet of water.

CHAPTER VI. Bullock shoeing, R.A.V.C. Officers' Training Course, Ambala, 1944.

CHAPTER VI. Ambala. Demonstration of methods of loading animals into M.T.

CHAPTER VII. Crossing the Irrawady —
a 500-yard swim.
Imperial War Museum photo.

CHAPTER VII. Pack mules, Burma, 1944.

CHAPTER VII. A Chindit mule goes aboard a transport plane.
Imperial War Museum photo.

simultaneously and there was never any trouble. In fact throughout the war the mule purchasing commissions enjoyed the greatest co-operation both from the U.S. War Department and from individual quartermaster and veterinary officers. All shipments were made from the port of New York; of the eight shiploads, totalling 3,401 mules, dispatched to India between February 1944 and April 1945 only one fatal casualty occurred en route.

From 1941-1943 the numbers of army horses and mules in Britain gradually increased to a peak figure of 5,450 partly because pack transport and mountain batteries might be required for Norway—then regarded as a possible theatre of opertaions—and partly because a start had been made with the use of horse transport to save petrol, vehicles and rubber supplies. The horses used by the Home Guard for hill and moorland patrols were private property and are not included in the military statistics.

Field Force units for the Norwegian project trained for snow and mountain warfare in Wales and Scotland. They included three Indian companies of Force K6, two companies of which had been converted to motorized transport after Dunkirk and then back again to animal transport; three further companies sent from India, and four R.A.S.C. pack companies. These units were designed to carry the essential equipment of infantry battalions and their animals were surplus cavalry horses and cobs bought in all parts of the United Kingdom. The men and horses of the pack-transport companies were trained in the use of snow-shoes. In addition, there were two Mountain Regiments R.A. provided with mules bought in America, and a Norwegian contingent, giving a total establishment of 3,700 animals. The veterinary support was provided by Nos. 10 and 11 mobile detachments and the veterinary staff of units. The animals were in hard training and gave little trouble. In January 1942 the sick-rate was horses 7.8 per cent. and mules 2.8 per cent.

About this time the Quartermaster-General directed that every animal the Army possessed should earn its keep if at all possible and that full use should be made of animal transport. There were plenty of horses but a great shortage of wagons, and an even greater scarcity of drivers. Four hundred vehicles and 600 horses were employed on short hauls and barrack fatigues. Where possible R.A.S.C. horse transport companies were formed; but in Northern Command, No. 1 Reserve Veterinary Hospital, Doncaster supplied the drivers needed to start the scheme in York and Catterick and later trained a number of men from the Pioneer Corps in horse-transport duties.

In the same year the willing collaboration of the Royal Society for the Prevention of Cruelty to Animals was obtained in promoting an appeal for dogs for military employment. The Director also appealed to the profession to dissuade the public from having young healthy dogs destroyed owing to the food shortage or other difficulties of maintenance. The threat of bombing had led to many destructions in the early days of the war—over 400,000 dogs and cats were put down in London in the first week— and suitable animals were scarce.

It was estimated that the Army required 2,000 dogs, a figure which was beyond the capacity of a small War Dog Training School established in Aldershot in 1941.

In March 1942 the War Dog Training School was moved to larger premises at the kennels of the Greyhound Racing Association, Northaw, and a veterinary officer, Captain D. Danby, and three R.A.V.C. dressers were added to its establishment to deal with the preliminary examination and immunization of dogs and to care for their general health.

At the same time the Ministry of Aircraft Production required large numbers of dogs for the protection of airfields and set up its own Guard Dog Training School at Cheltenham. The Admiralty also needed about 200 guard dogs.

To prevent useless competition between the Services the responsibility for the supply of dogs was placed under the centralized control of the A.V.R.S.

The War Dog Training School received some 2,000 dogs in the first year of the scheme. On arrival each animal was carefully examined prior to immunization against distemper and isolated for ten days. Meticulous care was taken with feeding, exercise and kennel management. The average number of dogs receiving hospital treatment did not exceed 7 per cent. and epidemic disease gave no anxiety.

Altogether 6,000 dogs were loaned by the public and allocated to the War Dog Training School and the Guard Dog Training School. Of these approximately 55 per cent. were successfully trained and issued to units at home, in North Africa and in North-West Europe.

Other canine matters in which the Corps became involved at this period were the import of teams of husky dogs from America for the snow-warfare training units, and the shipment of a pack of beagles to the isolated garrison of the Falkland Islands.

The threat of gas warfare was always present and the veterinary establishment of the Chemical Defence Experimental Station was increased to a total of two officers, thirty-seven other ranks and fifteen civilians to meet the demand for animals for biological and physiological experiments. The primary task of the section was to devise means for counteracting the effects of poisonous gases on animals, but it also managed two farms accommodating some 15,000 to 20,000 animals with eight main species— monkeys, goats, dogs, cats, rabbits, guinea-pigs, rats and pigeons. A further six species were also bred for experimental purposes including hamsters, locusts and mosquitoes. Major W. P. Blount, writing in the *Veterinary Record* of 1st December 1935, states "From 1941 until the end of the War we weaned, bought or issued for experiment over one-third of a million animals. Our object has always been to see that the needs of the scientific officers concerned have been met with the least delay and greatest accuracy possible—sex, age, weight, colour, maturity, virginity and the like have been complied with as far as possible, although we did fail on one occasion to provide an elephant required for certain anti-Japanese activities." He goes on to mention "the willingness of certain members of the Corps who volunteered to breed, on themselves, hundreds of lice for weeks on end—work necessitated when anti-vermin experiments concerning the impregnation of shirts and allied A.T.S. underwear were in progress. The irritation was great, but the scab formations even more remarkable for their pigmentation and persistency."

The veterinary section of C.D.E.S. co-operated with the Royal Navy in trials on under-water blast resulting from the explosion at sea of depth charges, which later provided a means for protecting submarine personnel; with the Army Pigeon Service on disease matters generally, from which arose an interesting investigation into psittacosis and a successful trial of homologous vaccines against pigeon pox; and with numerous other organizations on a variety of matters such as toxicity experiments in cattle with the components of the German V.1 bomb, the treatment of lungworm in goats by means of the inhalation of supposed anthelmintic substances, and high-frequency radiation tests.

From 1942 onwards No. 1 Reserve Veterinary Hospital became increasingly concerned with the training of sufficient Corps personnel for employment with the expanding animal-transport formations in the Mediterranean area, India and Burma.

The Central Veterinary Stores, which remained at Aldershot throughout the war, found that war-time shortages of supplies and shipping space made it necessary to arrange for overseas commands to obtain as much as possible of their drugs, dressings and instruments locally or, in the case of the Middle East theatres, from India.

In a small way this change of tempo reflected the position of the whole United Kingdom Base which, by early 1943, was preparing to re-deploy its resources now that the invasion of Britain was less likely and the enemy halted and on the defensive in nearly every theatre abroad.

The planning for the Allied invasion of Europe was most detailed. The only animals included in the order of battle of the British invasion force were the guard dogs of the Corps of Military Police vulnerable point companies, the mine-detecting dogs of the Royal Engineer dog platoons and a few patrol dogs of the Parachute Regiment; but the Corps was represented at Headquarters 21st Army Group by a nucleus staff of two officers and three other ranks which dealt with veterinary and remount matters as they arose. Even in this campaign involving a mechanized army operating in a fully-developed country there was a considerable build-up of Corps commitments during 1944 and 1945 arising not only from the number of war dogs employed with the Allied Forces but also from the need to form horse-transport companies to ease the strain on motor transport, to take over captured animals (many of which were severely wounded) and to advise on civilian veterinary affairs in the occupied areas.

The first problem arose when 400 Russian and Polish ponies were captured during the initial landings. They were disposed of to local farmers.

Further captures of animals were expected and a veterinary and remount conducting section was called for to deal with them and also to serve as a hospital for war-dog casualties. Before it had time to arrive 5,000 horses were taken at the Seine crossings. At this phase of operations the French Forces of the Interior were much in evidence and were able to take over the animals for distribution to farmers. Later the movement of captured horses was stopped as they were going largely to black-market butchers and the Army now needed horse transport.

No. 6 V.R.C.S. took up its position south of the Seine in early September 1944 and began the collection of captured horses including many wounded animals. With the help of the French remount authorities, it started to register all horses in the liberated areas and to retrieve for army transport purposes horses previously disposed of to local farmers.

A month later No. 5 Veterinary Hospital and No. 2 Field Remount Depot arrived to take over the work begun by No. 6 V.R.C.S. This enabled No. 6 V.R.C.S. to move forward to Bruges to collect sick and wounded horses and to register fit animals in the area.

We raised the horse-transport companies entirely from captured horses and equipment with the exception of harness and some farriery tools which were flown out from England. Local French and Belgian civilians were employed as drivers under R.A.V.C. supervision. When the units were in working order they were transferred to R.A.S.C. administration and did invaluable work in the docks and the rear maintenance areas, particularly in the Port of Antwerp where, in the first half of December, they lifted a total of 9,500 tons of stores from the quays to the supply depots. The units remained in operation so long as captured forage was available, but when this became short they had to be reduced. In all about 1,000 horses were employed on these duties. The Antwerp company had the misfortune to be hit by an enemy long-range missile which killed four R.A.V.C. men and thirty-nine horses.

The next task was to plan for our part in the initial occupation of Germany. It was estimated that 250,000 *Wehrmacht* horses would be taken over and there was much to do concerning the supervision of German veterinary and remount units, the disposal of surplus animals, the collection of captured stores, and inquiry into the general state of the civil veterinary organization.

To deal with these matters R.A.V.C. officers were placed on the headquarters staff of the 2nd British Army, the 1st Canadian Army, and all Corps; plus a pool of six V.Os. under the control of A.D.V.R.S. 21st Army Group. Also orders were given for the dispatch of three conducting sections and two base stores from England. Pending their arrival No. 2 Field Remount Depot was split into two detachments and placed under the command of the A.Ds.V.R.S. of the 2nd British and 1st Canadian Armies.

The first German remount depot to be captured was at Mecklenhorst, near Hanover. This unit was taken over by No. 6 V.R.C.S. and subsequently handed to a detachment of No. 2 F.R.D. It remained a R.A.V.C. unit until disbandment in 1955.

In April 1945 it was decided to bring out the War Dog Training School to train personnel and dogs on the spot. The school brought ninety dogs with it and further supplies were obtained by requisitioning dogs in France and Germany. The Corps provided the usual veterinary and remount cover for the unit and also lent veterinary assistance to the R.A.F. and to the United States Armies, neither of whom had any organization for the treatment of serious war dog casualties.

By the end of May 1945 all the units requested had arrived from home to complete the veterinary and remount organization of the British Occupation Force in Germany. The official animal strength of 21st Army Group at this period was 1,652 horses and 509 dogs. There was little sickness and much of the Corps' effort was directed into the sorting and disposal of captured horses and the supervision and reorganization of the civil veterinary service as described in Chapter VIII.

CHAPTER IV

The Middle East Base (including Persia and Iraq)
The Campaigns in Eritrea, Greece, Syria and North Africa

FTER Dunkirk the Middle East Command was for eighteen months the only
theatre where there was any land fighting of note and for the rest of the war it
remained one of the most important overseas bases. Its veterinary and remount
services played an active part in the operations in East Africa, Greece and Syria, and
provided R.A.V.C. units for the campaigns in North Africa, Sicily and Italy. The main
remount purchasing areas were situated in the adjacent Persia and Iraq Command.

Early in 1940, on the arrival in Palestine of some 8,000 horses of the 1st Cavalry
Division together with its A.D.V.S., Lieutenant-Colonel E. S. W. Peatt, twenty
officers and 386 other ranks R.A.V.C. and eight veterinary units; a D.D.V.S., Colonel
G. A. Kelly, was appointed to Force Headquarters, Jerusalem. The following year the
appointment was redesignated D.D.V.R.S., and transferred to General Headquarters,
Cairo, where Colonel Kelly became responsible for both the veterinary and remount
services of the Middle East Command.

After a brief rest period the Cavalry Division went into intensive field training and
the constant movement of its patrols across country and through remote areas did
much to maintain local peace and security.

No. 1 Veterinary Hospital, No. 1 Veterinary Evacuating Station and No. 1 Base
Depot Veterinary Stores were located at Ramle with No. 1 Convalescent Depot at
Sarafand. Nos. 4, 5 and 6 Cavalry Mobile Veterinary Sections were attached to their
own cavalry brigades and relieved regimental veterinary officers of the more severe
casualties. In order to keep the units mobile and unburdened with useless animals it
was the policy to evacuate sick horses unlikely to be fit for work within two weeks;
a few cases were retained for treatment by the mobile sections and the remainder sent
to Ramle.

As the horses became acclimatized and improved in condition there was a waning in the incidence of diseases brought from England such as strangles and ringworm, but endemic diseases, kicks and injuries kept the sick rate at the abnormally high level of 13 per cent.

Lice and a mild form of tick fever, which responded well to acapron injections, were minor nuisances. Injuries and sand colic, both to some extent due to faulty animal management, were the main causes of inefficiency. Sporadic cases of glanders and encephalomyelitis provided additional problems, and the incidence of anthrax was such that 5,000 horses were inoculated with a type of spore vaccine used for the routine immunization of goats in Cyprus. This vaccine proved to be insufficiently attenuated for horses and was responsible for sixty-seven deaths.

The hospital at Ramle under the command of Major C. H. S. Townsend, was a model of its kind and representatives from all units of the division attended there for courses in animal management and first-aid. During 1940 it held an average of 550 sick animals and achieved excellent results in the treatment of both medical and surgical cases. On the lighter side, its week-end gymkhana meetings were tremendously popular and everyone from the Divisional Commander downwards attended regularly to watch and compete in the show-jumping and donkey-racing.

When Italy declared war in June 1940 the Middle East Command had to expand and reorganize. Events directly affecting the Corps were the mechanization of the 1st Cavalry Division, the move from India of several animal units, the formation of numerous mule companies and the revival of horse transport for use in base areas and on the lines of communication.

In August 1940 it was anticipated that the services of the Bikaner Camel Corps or Bikaner Ganga Risala (an Indian State Force unit) might be required for operations in British Somaliland and the Director of Veterinary Services in India was instructed to supply veterinary personnel and stores to accompany the unit to Aden.

This unit had on its strength only 200 camels when mobilization orders were received. A further 400 camels had to be obtained by local purchase in Bikaner State and blood tested for surra at very short notice. The entire executive work in connection with this project was carried out by the Army Veterinary Services.

Six hundred camels were entrained in Bikaner State and sailed from Karachi during August. Despite a monsoon voyage and a three-day delay for disembarkation at Aden, consequent upon enemy bombing at the port, only five casualties occurred which could be attributed to the effects of the journey. This was considered to be a remarkably low casualty figure and reflected great credit on the conducting R.A.V.C. officer and other veterinary personnel, especially as camels are known poor travellers in ships and many of these animals were in soft condition having been purchased recently.

The 27th Mountain Battery, Royal Artillery, was dispatched from India to Aden with 175 mules and thirty horses during September 1940. A veterinary assistant surgeon, with six months' supply of veterinary stores, accompanied the unit. The Jammu and Kashmir Mountain Battery (an Indian State unit) was originally earmarked for dispatch to Aden but in September 1940 was sent direct to the Sudan and participated in the Eritrean campaign. This unit had on its strength a similar number of veterinary personnel and animals, and an equivalent amount of veterinary stores to the 27th Mountain Battery.

The veterinary staff originally sent to Aden was augmented in January 1941 by the arrival of No. 1 Veterinary Detachment I.A.V.C., consisting of two R.A.V.C. officers, one veterinary assistant surgeon and eight Indian other ranks. A year later India provided an A.D.V.S. for Headquarters 10th Army to direct veterinary work in connection with the thirteen animal-holding units—two A.T. companies, one draught camel company, eight cattle stock sections, one advanced remount depot and one mobile veterinary section—sent from India to Iraq. Two R.A.V.C. officers, twelve V.A.Ss. and forty I.A.V.C. other ranks accompanied the units, and a six months' supply of veterinary stores was provided. The responsibilities in this theatre included the examination of camels and mules obtained by purchasing commissions in Iraq and Persia (operated that year by the Indian Army Remount Department), the inspection and supervision of many thousands of locally purchased slaughter stock, and the control of surra and mange in camels.

The progressive mechanization of the Cavalry Division freed R.A.V.C. units for tasks outside Palestine. Towards the end of 1940 No. 1 C.M.V.S. moved to Egypt with the Polish Carpathian Brigade, a formation which was later to distinguish itself at Tobruk and in Italy. At this time it consisted of a regiment of Uhlans, mounted on ex-Cavalry Division horses, as well as artillery and other arms employing large numbers of animals. Following the success of Wavell's offensive in the Western Desert No. 1 C.M.V.S. was sent to the Sidi Barrani—Buq Buq area to salvage abandoned Italian army mules, many of which were *in extremis* having been without food or water for days.

At the same period No. 1 Veterinary Evacuating Station moved to the Sudan to serve as the base hospital for the East African campaign and, after a lapse of sixteen years, the Sudan Veterinary Service was temporarily reunited with the Corps, its chief, C. P. Fisher, being granted the rank and title of A.D.V R.S.

Some thousands of camels and mules were employed in carrying arms and supplies from the Sudan to aid the rebellion against the Italians in Abyssinia but it was not until the 4th and 5th Indian Divisions had the enemy at bay in an immensely strong natural defensive position at Keren that organized pack units were needed.

Nos. 1 and 2 Cypriot Pack Transport Companies R.A.S.C., after their escape from France earlier in the year had been re-equipped in Egypt with 800 mules, or rather jennets, bought in Cyprus. After a short training period and the immunization of the animals against African horse sickness, the two companies moved up the Nile by cattle barges to Wadi Halfa and from there by rail to the Eritrean border. From railhead at Kassala across country to Keren was a twelve-day march through arid bush country full of game. The length of each day's march depended upon the distance between water-holes. The one and only road to Keren was avoided as it was reserved for motor transport busy building up the ammunition and supply dumps for the assault on that place.

In the absence of the R.A.M.C., the V.O., Capt. J. Clabby, combined medical and veterinary duties. Serious casualties were few though both men and animals were in soft condition and sore backs in the mules and sore feet in the men were the rule. Marching up at the same time was the Kashmir and Jammu Mountain Battery.

On arrival in February, 1941 the mules were put to work at once to supply the forward positions and build up dumps for the attack, climbing two or three times daily about 2,000 feet up precipitous hills. Sometimes the tracks came under shell-fire and often the journeys were made during the night. The mule lines of one company were shelled out of several positions until a fairly safe place was found for them. The other company was several miles away and also came in for a good deal of shelling. An Italian pack battery was particularly annoying, lobbing in shells from unexpected angles. Luckily many of these were duds and animal gunshot casualties averaged only two a day. The mules appeared quite unperturbed while under fire.

The nearest R.A.V.C. unit, No. 1 V.E.S., was 700 miles distant so an improvised hospital was established out of artillery range. The veterinary staff for the two companies totalled only two sergeants, one corporal and four privates and they coped gallantly with a vast amount of work carried out under most difficult conditions. The hospital cared for about a hundred sick and injured animals. Captured animals were also collected there, most of them requiring veterinary attention, being badly galled and in a shockingly debilitated condition. At the end of the action there were some 200 captured mules of which about seventy could be patched up sufficiently to replace casualties amongst our own animals.

Due to a shortage of shoes and casualties amongst the farriers it was impossible to keep all the mules shod and many became foot-sore. Saddle galls were also a continual source of trouble but animals could only be laid off work for really serious injuries as it was vital to maintain supplies to the forward troops and the only practical method of doing so was on mule-back.

Soon after the fall of Keren Capt. J. H. McGhee took over as V.O. of the two companies and later returned with them to Egypt. On the march back to the Sudan border an outbreak of a disease with the local name of *nigma* caused the death of seventeen mules. It was probably African horse sickness, though this was never established. Despite this, and the long journey to Egypt by rail and river, the mules arrived in excellent condition. The D.D.V.R.S. even remarked upon the fatness of some of them.

Meanwhile the campaign in Greece was developing and it was obvious that first-line pack transport would be required for operations in the mountains. The veterinary and remount organization was under the control of a D.A.D.V.R.S., Major J. Bell. It consisted of No. 3 Veterinary Hospital (formed from the disbanded No. 1 Convalescent Horse Depot), No. 5 C.M.V.S., No. 3 Advanced Depot Veterinary Stores, and No. 1 Remount Squadron. At this time the amalgamation of the two services was not officially effective in Middle East Command but the position was quickly regularized after landing in Greece and by 15th April 1941 all the veterinary and remount units were encamped close together at Stephani, about ten miles south-west of Athens.

The first consignment of mules arrived from India in the *Quiloa*. She was unable to dock at Piraeus as the port had been put out of action by bombing and the blowing-up in harbour of a ship carrying explosives. The need for pack animals in the north was now urgent and, making the passage of the heavily-mined Salamis Straits, the *Quiloa* landed her cargo of 830 mules and quantities of saddlery at a small quay near the remount camp. Soon after she was holed by bombing and had to be beached.

Two hundred and fifty fully-equipped mules were sent to the front as soon as possible. At this stage there were no trained pack-transport personnel in Greece and they had to be found by the fighting units themselves aided by detachments from the remount squadron. Events were moving so swiftly that evacuation of casualties was impossible and No. 5 C.M.V.S. was retained at base.

The mules and advance party for No. 3 Pack Transport Company R.A.S.C. were dispatched from Alexandria in the *Santa Clara Valley*, a ship which had survived Narvik and the evacuation of Norway. She carried 338 mules of which 200 had been recently salvaged from the Western Desert by No. 1 C.M.V.S., and fifty-nine horses. She was dive-bombed and sunk in shallow water near the Greek coast on 23rd April. In spite of continued bombing gallant attempts were made by the V.O., Capt. R. I. Macrae, and his assistants to put the animals from the upper decks overboard, in order that they could swim ashore. In this they were partially successful but nothing could be done for the mules trapped below.

On 23rd April orders were received at Stephani camp to abandon heavy equipment and to move down to the Peloponnese. All ranks were issued with hard rations for two days and fifty rounds of ammunition. The following day saw No. 3. V.H. and No. 5 C.M.V.S. dispersed in the neighbourhood of the small port of Nauplion. Enemy aircraft were continuously overhead during the day. Not far out in the bay lay the wreck of the *Santa Clara Valley*. Several animals which had swum ashore from her were found helpless and exhausted amongst some rocks under a high cliff where they had to be destroyed.

After an abortive attempt at evacuation on 26th April the two units marched to another beach at Tolon, ten miles away, but had no better luck on the following night.

Early next morning the O.C. No. 5 C.M.V.S., Lieutenant R. C. Crowhurst, set off with six volunteers to find a caique or other vessel large enough to take all the Corps troops. A few hours later the enemy appeared and the O.C. No. 3. V.H., Major J. Clabby, collected his scattered men and withdrew them to a position covering the embarkation beach. The small force at "T Beach" which included one officer and 112 other ranks R.A.V.C., held off the enemy for twelve hours, finally surrendering on the evening of 28th April. Lieutenant Crowhurst and his men after some hazardous adventures found their way to Crete: so did the D.A.D.V.R.S. and his staff. No. 1 Remount Squadron was captured on 27th April at Kalamai.

During 1941 the Cavalry Division in Palestine was being converted into the 10th Armoured Division and disposing of its surplus horses to remount depots. But before mechanization was complete its 5th Brigade, comprising the Cheshire Yeomanry, the North Somerset Yeomanry and the Yorkshire Dragoons, saw action as horsed cavalry in the short Syrian campaign of June-July, 1941, which was made necessary by the German infiltration of that area assisted by the Vichy Government and pro-Vichy French troops.

Besides the 5th Cavalry Brigade, other animal-holding units engaged were the Trans-Jordan Frontier Force with its own small modified mobile veterinary section, Colonel Collett's Free French Cavalry, the Jammu and Kashmir Mountain Battery and No. 4 Pack Transport Company R.A.S.C.; No. 4. C.M.V.S. provided the veterinary support, with No. 6 C.M.V.S. and an advanced remount depot in the rear at Acre.

At first opposition proved unexpectedly fierce and the Cheshire Yeomanry, in particular, suffered equine casualties which the V.O., Major W. P. Moss, found difficult to evacuate due to the rough terrain, the distances involved and the intense fighting. The troop horses had to be kept saddled-up for twenty-four hours of the day so as to be ready for immediate action. The C.M.V.S. mounted Hotchkiss guns on its vehicles to beat off machine-gun attacks by low-flying aircraft. Towards the end of the operations the mounted regiments were engaged on very active patrol work when saddle galls and bruised soles became the chief causes of wastage.

But it was not until the campaign had finished that the R.A.V.C. may be said to have really come into its own; for then the first opportunity was presented to undertake remount duties on a large scale. A little later it took an active part in livestock production, meat inspection and the provision of war dogs. Major A. V. Franklin, writing in the *Veterinary Record* of 18th November 1944 gives a good picture of this period "The French Army in Syria was not highly mechanized and numbered upon its establishment many thousands of animals of all kinds. There were barbs from regiments of Spahis; there were light and heavy draught horses and mules of various types. These were mainly concentrated in remount establishments in the Lebanon; at Beirut, Damascus, Baalbek and elsewhere. The task of taking over the animals from the Vichy French was undertaken by a Commission of Control Committee presided over by a senior R.A.V.C. officer. Later on, according to requirements, the animals were allocated between the Fighting French and the British Forces. This involved an immense amount of work such as classification, examination for disease, mallein testing, branding, shoeing and so forth, as well as the sorting out of masses of equipment, harness, saddlery, vehicles and veterinary stores, much of which proved to be very valuable when further horse-transport units were formed. Most of the draught horses other than those turned over to the Fighting French were issued through our remount depots to the British companies and splendid animals many of them were. Of the barbs, many were issued to pack-transport units as riders. In a large proportion of cases the horses and, to a lesser degree the mules, were originally found in a pitiable condition, their attendants having 'walked out on them', leaving them tied up without food or water. The mules, which included a large proportion of excellent type, were later issued to pack-transport companies. At last the task was completed and thousands of animals had been taken over, conditioned in remount depots and re-issued as required to units forming over a very wide area in Syria, Palestine and Egypt."

In the meantime the yeomanry and regular regiments of cavalry had either been mechanized or were destined to become so in the near future and their horses were handed in to our remount depots. In order to make the best use of these animals it was decided that all those of a suitable type and likely to prove useful for draught purposes should be trained as such for distribution to existing horse-transport companies and to assist in the formation of others in conjunction with the newly-acquired French animals. Men well equipped for this duty were forthcoming at the remount depots and very soon ex-cavalry troop horses were being issued, fully trained for their new but equally useful though more humble duties. At first, these companies were formed to save mechanical transport, petrol and tyres, at a time when anything on four wheels driven by petrol was at a premium. They were, as a rule, disposed of by sections, four or more to a company, at depots and establishments where transport was constantly required to undertake short journeys in which speed was unimportant. It was soon found that the load figures indicating material hauled over a comparatively short period by one of these sections reached large proportions. It can fairly be claimed that the R.A.V.C. was the progenitor of these invaluable units.

The year 1942 marked the advent of further important duties being assigned to the Corps: meat inspection and the administration of livestock depots. The time had come for the inspection of fresh meat now supplied to the troops (all of which was purchased through local sources) to be established upon a sound and scientific basis and the R.A.V.C. was asked to organize a programme of inspection both ante and post-mortem. This was done and before long (throughout the Middle East) an organization was devised whereby a high standard of inspection was initiated and maintained. Responsible N.C.Os. were trained to act as assistant inspectors of meat; they carried out general inspection duties in the slaughter-houses and were able to detect any abnormalities pending a decision by the veterinary officer in charge. Standards of hygiene in many local abattoirs left much to be desired; indeed, in certain of the smaller slaughter-houses conditions obtained which, according to western standards, were distasteful in the extreme both as regards the buildings them-selves and the methods employed by the persons engaged in them. Consequently, upon the advice of our administrative officers model abattoirs were built, equipped with ample lairage accommodation, and sited with a view to adequate rail and road facilities for the rapid distribution of meat by the supply services. It is well known that in the Middle East certain parasitic conditions communicable to man are widely prevalent in cattle and the Corps had the satisfaction of eliminating the danger from this quarter; although the work was not spectacular it was certainly not behindhand in relative importance. Later the actual selection of all livestock for army consumption was delegated to us and consequently the quality of the stock produced by the contractors rose at once by the simple expedient of our declining to accept anything which did not comply with a certain standard. This caused a temporary shortage of fresh meat until the contractors realized it was useless to offer for selection and trans-portation, frequently over long distances, inferior stock which would be rejected at the ante-mortem examination. At the same time, owing to prevailing local conditions whereby good grazing and a plentiful supply of foodstuffs were difficult to secure, it was often beyond the powers of producers to offer stock of the required quality. We, therefore, established our own livestock depots, run by our own people, to supplement supplies from civilian sources. The first of these depots was formed in Syria and so successful was the venture and so excellent the quality of its products, that it was rapidly succeeded by other depots throughout the Middle East, not only for the fattening of cattle, sheep and goats but also for the breeding and rearing of pigs. An interesting but less successful side-line run in conjunction with the pig farms were the rabbitries, organized in order to ensure a supply of white meat for patients in military hospitals on special diet. To command the livestock depots officers were available familiar with the various problems associated with the feeding and rearing of farm animals, assisted by R.A.V.C. personnel with an agricultural background in civil life and, in their hands, the project was an outstanding success. The idea, in so far as cattle were concerned, was to purchase and retain them for a period of about ten weeks and by a programme of intensive and scientific feeding to increase their weight to a maximum within a minimum of time. One depot alone, carrying a total stock of 1,500, was thus able to produce a weekly turnover of 150 beasts for issue. A careful system of grading was introduced according to breed and condition, and the stock distributed in separate kraals so that beasts commencing in the lowest or an intermediate grade upon purchase gradually worked their way up to the "fit for issue" grade.

It is interesting to record that the veterinary officer commanding this particular depot, Captain J. H. McGhee, observes that in Syria immense annual losses occur as a result of parasitic disease in civilian-owned sheep and goats, and that in one winter alone, aggravated by severe weather, no less than 1,000,000 head succumbed, representing a loss of £3,000,000 sterling or one-quarter of the annual budget of the country.

The employment of dogs on an extensive scale, both for guard duties and active operations, was now being considered. In the Middle East, it was found that properly-trained animals were valuable for guarding installations such as supply depots, especially at night, against the pilfering proclivities of the native inhabitants while special consideration had to be given to dogs living in a sub-tropical climate. In 1942, at the height of the desert war, thefts from military dumps and installations reached alarming proportions. Men could be ill-spared for guard duties at the base and on the lines of communication and it was thought that dogs would provide an economical and effective security system.

A dog-training school was opened at Almaza, near Cairo, in June, 1942 and from there dogs and handlers were posted to Royal Military Police Dog Companies. During the first six months in the Suez Canal Zone they made 308 arrests and recovered property worth £3,000. Within a few years the figures had risen to 3,398 arrests and £94,000 of recovered property.

The large number of animals of different species used by Middle East Command and the variety of their diseases called for an efficient laboratory service. The Chief Veterinary Officer of the Palestine Government, G. B. Simmins, gave most valuable assistance by placing his services and those of his laboratory at our disposal. The work carried out at the Tel Aviv laboratory, under the direction of the veterinary research officer, H. R. Binns, entailed the day-to-day examination of pathological specimens and in addition exacting research work in connection with anthrax, encephalomyelitis and epizootic lymphangitis in army animals. Without this voluntary effort it would have been necessary to send out a R.A.V.C. laboratory from England.

There was a great deal of movement of animals at this period both within the Command, and to and from the Middle East, P.A.I.C. and India. Three examples are given here of how these moves were made with the minimum of animal suffering and loss.

During 1942 over 1,000 mules were sent to India. The first shipment of 511 mules sailed from Haifa on 1st May and passed through the Red Sea at the hottest season. A R.A.V.C. officer, Captain G. D. Young, combined the duties of V.O. and O.C. ship. The transport, an old Greek vessel, was ill-equipped for the tropics and poorly ventilated. The mules were carried loose, seven to a pen. There was a most detailed routine—no animals remained in the hotter standings more than one day; all animals had a spell on deck during the afternoon; water was given five times daily and no wastage of water was permitted. The only casualties were a few mild cases of fever and all 511 mules were disembarked at Karachi on 18th May in good condition.

During the period 7th October to 28th November 1942 it was necessary to march seven Indian mule companies and one mountain battery by the cross-country route from Syria to Iraq. Some 3,000 horses and mules marched out of Aleppo on the 370-mile trek. Watering was carried out from wells and rivers. Nos. 1, 4 and 6 C.M.V.Ss. travelled with the force and evacuated casualties by lorry to veterinary detachments at Aleppo and the end point of the march at Qamichliye. The S.V.R.O. moved constantly up and down the route advising units and supervising the veterinary arrangements. Only 0.78 per cent. animal casualties occurred, comprising four dead and eighteen evacuated sick and lame.

On 1st July 1943 one of these mule companies, No. 6 Indian, sailed from Basra bound for the Middle East via the Persian Gulf and the Red Sea. The transport, the *Gazana*, was well fitted-out and had a satisfactory ventilation system on all decks save one—No. 5 "tween deck" where a number of cases of heatstroke occurred during the voyage. The veterinary staff consisted of an officer (Captain R. I. Macrae) and six men R.A.V.C., and an I.A.V.C. veterinary assistant surgeon. About forty cases of heatstroke and exhaustion occurred during the extremely hot humid passage through the Persian Gulf but all responded to oxygen inhalations—five minutes treatment was sufficient to bring round an unconscious animal and when necessary inhalations were repeated at half-hourly intervals. In the Arabian Sea a bad storm resulted in a number of injuries and cases of exhaustion. In the latter the respirations became very fast and weak, the membranes cyanosed and the pulse was almost imperceptible, but as in heatstroke, the administration of oxygen effected complete recovery. Through the Red Sea the weather was not as hot as anticipated but while the ship anchored at Suez for twenty-four hours the temperature aboard became very high and oxygen treatment again proved useful for the treatment of incipient heatstroke cases. Despite these extreme conditions there were no fatalities during the voyage and 404 horses and mules were safely disembarked at Kantara on 21st July.

Captain Macrae's own recollections of this voyage are of interest: "At the time of loading the shade temperature was close on 120 degrees and 'tween decks it was so intolerable that men could not stand it for more than about half an hour at a time. The conditions were of course quite abnormal. The convoy was attacked outside the mouth of the Persian Gulf and some ships were sunk and owing to complete black-out there was precious little ventilation. I was told before I started that I might expect to lose 25 per cent. of the animals but the urgency was such that this was a calculated risk. The oxygen treatment was a quite impartial effort to try anything. The oxygen cylinders were a standard medical issue pattern which I 'acquired' unofficially from the Base Medical Store and in fact for some years inquiries about disposal of them followed me about. To each cylinder I attached an ordinary stomach tube. The first day out animals started dropping to the deck apparently unconscious and with very rapid shallow respiration. Owing to the very high temperature it was impossible to record the blood temperature of the animals. After a few animals had tried to hang themselves, I left them all untied without any serious results even in some rather rough weather near Aden at the peak of the monsoon. My men worked in pairs. The drill was that as soon as an animal dropped one member of the team shoved the stomach pump into its nostril whilst the other connected the cylinder. Normally treatment lasted about five minutes but in a few cases it had to be continued for about fifteen minutes. The man on the tube also held the animal's tongue out of the side of the mouth. Recovery was measured by return of deeper and easier respiration, return of eye reflexes and the change in the colour of the conjunctival mucous membrane from a dirty dark colour to pink. No attempt was made to hurry the animals back on their feet. They usually required steadying and some assistance to regain their feet about five minutes after completion of treatment."

Perhaps the most important contribution by the Corps in the Middle East was the provision of a base for the supply of animals, personnel and units to meet the operational needs in North Africa and Italy for large numbers of ponies and mules for both pack transport and mountain artillery. Remount purchasing commissions were continually at work in Cyprus and the Sudan and a number of animals were bought in North Africa, but a large proportion of the remount requirement for the Italian campaign was met by Lieutenant-Colonel V. G. Hinds, A.D.V.R.S., Persia and Iraq Command, who used No. 3 (Indian) Mobile Veterinary Section and No. 12 Mobile Veterinary Detachment as remount collecting centres. The main base remount depots were located in Palestine and Syria. From 31st December 1943 to March 1945, 493 horses and 12,458 mules were shipped from Alexandria, Port Said, Haifa and Beirut in twenty-one consignments. The mortality rate *en route* was 1.46 per cent. in horses and 0.15 per cent. in mules.

Not only were our veterinary officers successful in the provision of suitable animals for the operations in Italy but they were soon called upon to deal with contagious diseases which, if uncontrolled, would have prevented many shipments. Practically without exception such important diseases as glanders, epizootic lymphangitis and African horse sickness in army animals can be traced to civilian horses. Of these the first two occurred sporadically in the Middle East but never reached serious proportions due to close veterinary inspection.

In July 1943 African horse sickness broke out in Upper Egypt and spread northward, reaching its maximum incidence in November and December and disappearing by April 1944 after causing 1,575 deaths amongst civilian animals. It recurred in May 1944 and spread throughout Lower Egypt, reaching the Canal Zone at the end of July, causing a further 3,062 deaths amongst civilian horses, mules and donkeys before disappearing in December. A few cases occurred amongst army horses before they could be protected with vaccine. The disease appeared in Palestine in August 1944 and took on a most virulent form, particularly amongst English and French horses, and not a single case recovered. Amongst army animals in Palestine 197 horses and twenty-eight mules succumbed to the disease. Fortunately mules showed a high degree of immunity and very few were affected but shipments of remounts from Palestine had to be suspended until November 1944 when the effects of a widespread vaccination campaign combined with stringent control measures and the onset of cooler weather brought the epidemic to an end. The premonitory symptoms were slight—a small swelling of the supra-orbital fossae, a rise in temperature, but still feeding—and then suddenly acute symptoms with death or *in extremis* in nine hours. Treatment was useless and the spread was unaffected either by the application of insect repellents to the horses' skin or by anti-mosquito precautions such as clearance of vegetation and the oiling of stagnant pools. It is no exaggeration to say that the energetic measures taken by the D.D.V.R.S., M.E.F., Colonel Glyn Lloyd, and the Palestinian Veterinary Service saved Italy from this scourge at a crucial time.

It was decided that the needs of the Central Mediterranean Force would be best served by transferring experienced and acclimatized men from the Middle East where an organized service was already available: this service included:—

D.D.V.R.S. at G.H.Q., M.E.F., Cairo

A.D.V.R.S.	A.D.V.R.S.	A.D.V.R.S.	A.D.V.R.S.
Syria and Lebanon	Palestine	Sudan	Persia and Iraq
No. 3 Vet. Hospital			
No. 1 Field Remount	No. 1 Vet. Hospital	No. 1 V.E.S.	No. 4 Vet. Hospital
Depot	Nos. 3 & 4 Remount		No. 4 C.M.V.S.
Nos. 1 & 6 C.M.V.S.	Squadrons		
No. 2 V.E.S./V.R.C.S.	Base Depot of		
Advanced Depot of	Vet. Stores		
Vet. Stores			

Units dispatched to North Africa and Italy during 1943 and 1944 were made up from these formations and comprised:—

No. 812 Base Remount Depot.
No. 1 Field Remount Depot.
No. 4 Veterinary Hospital.
No. 3 Base Depot Veterinary Stores.
Nos. 1, 2 and 804 Veterinary and Remount Conducting Sections.
Nos. 1, 4, 803 and 817 Cavalry Mobile Veterinary Sections.

The organization which remained after departure of units to the C.M.F. had to be reinforced from home in order to allow for the provision of remounts and the maintenance of horse-transport companies, cattle-stock sections, pig farms and war-dog sections; and also to carry out meat inspection duties.

The Anglo-American invasion of North Africa, Operation "Torch", took place in November 1942. The usual feature in any war is shortage of shipping, and ships have to be specially fitted to convey animals and then re-converted for ordinary cargo. Vessels were particularly scarce at this period and the only two pack-transport companies of the force were landed in cadre form and though complete with essential stores and saddlery, were made up to establishment with locally-requisitioned mules and muleteers. No shoeing equipment was provided but luckily the conditions were such that the mules could be worked unshod. Major I. McLaren was appointed D.A.D.V.R.S. Force Headquarters and made responsible for procuring the necessary horses and mules and for the organization of a veterinary service.

In conjunction with the French Army Remount Department the requisition of animals began in January 1943 in Tunisia and continued later in Algeria. After examination of some 20,000 animals, the majority of which were too young, unsound or of poor conformation, forty-five riding ponies and 922 pack mules were obtained.

Pending the arrival in May of No. 1 V.E.S., a combined veterinary and remount unit was improvised at Souk-el Khemis under command of one of the pack company V.Os. Sick were evacuated and remounts issued in three-ton lorries. The other V.O. had the difficult task of caring for the animals of both companies which were working in widespread detachments forward from their headquarters.

Although glanders and mange were endemic in the area, careful pre-purchasing inspection prevented their appearance in the animals employed by the Army, and the sole epidemic was due to strangles, or *gourme* as it was known locally. This was confined to mules and its spread was controlled by routine measures. Another trouble was the prevalence of horse-flies which made the animals very restless. The standard of horsemastership was high and, in spite of bad weather, long marches, journeys in lorries and pack loading at night, the majority of injuries were due to gunshot wounds, which is not always the case in animal units.

The two companies acquitted themselves well in the operations preceding the final offensive which took place in mountainous country covered with dense scrub while all the time rain fell in torrents. In one instance pack transport was used, perhaps for the first time, to supply tank crews with rations, and, in areas unfit for motor transport, mule cacolets and litters were employed for the evacuation of wounded men.

Following the enemy collapse the collection of captured animals proved unexpectedly easy, for, though the Germans had used pack transport on a considerable scale, most of their animals had by the end been lost, stolen or eaten. Approximately 250 horses and mules scattered on farms over a wide area were recovered and assembled in the old German remount depot at Djedeida.

By 13th May 1943 the whole of the North African coast was in Allied hands, the isolation of Gibraltar and Malta was ended, the Mediterranean was open and the way clear for the invasion of Southern Europe.

CHAPTER V

The Campaigns in Sicily and Italy

THE long campaign in the Western Desert and North Africa had been a mechanized war, yet during the ultimate battle in the Tunisian mountains, two British pack-transport units had played an invaluable part in carrying supplies for troops of the Allied Forces.

In the preparatory stage for Operation "Husky"—the invasion of Sicily—Allied Force Headquarters had planned to embark pack companies and veterinary and remount servicing units soon after D-Day because of the mountain barriers to be overcome between the landing beaches and the final objective, the port of Messina close to the Italian mainland.

The need for pack animals soon became evident after the landings on D-Day (10th July 1943) because the narrow beaches quickly led to mountainous country, and by the time that the approaches to Mount Etna (10,741 ft.) were reached, the Allied advance in this sector had lost its impetus. Here the Germans had established their main defensive positions and inflicted heavy casualties on our forces.

The alternative staff plan for improvised pack transport using local animals and saddlery resulted in an urgent call for R.A.V.C. assistance. At Ramle in Palestine, two detachments each comprising a R.A.V.C. officer, a farrier-sergeant, a farrier-corporal and four farriers were hastily assembled and dispatched to Sicily. The first to arrive, on D-Day + 3, was in the charge of Captain D. C. Henderson, accompanied by Farrier-Sergeant Simpson, Farrier-Corporal Thurlow and Farriers Jones, Dennis and Duffy. By the time they arrived, units of the Canadian Division which had landed equipped with 200 sets of pack saddlery, were already requisitioning a motley collection of horses, mules and donkeys of all ages and degrees of unsoundness, many of which soon became useless. Besides battle casualties, many animals escaped and others became ineffective from injuries sustained during transport in unsuitable vehicles, from foot soreness, and from the effects of saddle galls. A lot were old while others were immature and quite unable to cope with their work. There was also a shortage of experienced men, and the Canadians who had by then left the roads in the Regalbuto area had selected a number of ex-cowboys as muleteers. The farriers were invaluable in maintaining mobility, since the Sicilian mule cannot work in the mountains unless shod all round. The farrier's traditional rôle of auxiliary surgical dresser also proved very useful, but there was an obvious need for the resources of a suitable unit—a veterinary and remount conducting section—designed for the dual purpose of requisition of remounts as well as attendance to any sick. As it was, the shortage of M.T. to assist these *ad hoc* R.A.V.C. detachments and the A.T. cadres of the R.A.S.C. could also have been avoided if a V.R.C.S. or C.M.V.S. had been on the spot to help.

Captain Henderson, besides organising the selection and supply of local mules in the 30th Corps sector, was ordered by 8th Army H.Q. to make veterinary arrangements at the municipal abattoir at Syracuse for the supply of beef and mutton. Standards of hygiene were very poor and trichinosis, cysticercosis, brucellosis and anthrax were prevalent. Nevertheless, suitable arrangements were made with the Italian authorities and a supply of meat arranged to augment the tinned variety and save shipping. Besides this logistical saving, experience in war has shown that the morale and vigour of troops in the field improve when supplies of fresh rations—especially meat—are available during strenuous operations.

The Canadian infantry brigades became greatly attached to the R.A.V.C. farriers and consistently refused to release them for other sectors while operations were in progress. Two R.A.S.C. pack cadres by this time had arrived from North Africa to assist the formations which were organising improvised pack transport. Wastage, nevertheless, was very high and of 700 mules obtained locally, 50 per cent. became casualties within a fortnight.

The second R.A.V.C. detachment to be sent to Sicily arrived on D+20 and reported to H.Q. 30th Corps that evening. It comprised Captain J. P. Wilmot-Smith, Farrier-Sergeant Russell, Farrier-Corporal Webb, and Farriers Gray, Pitt, Clifford and Lockett. The farriers were distributed to the artillery who required mules for taking wireless sets to observation posts and to the 11th, 36th and 38th Infantry Brigades, who, between them were using 250 pack animals in the Caternouva area. Contact with R.A.V.C. staff was difficult to maintain since the needs of the brigades necessitated frequent interchange of animals. Mules often travelled in trucks with only a piece of string as a halter and consequently many casualties occurred on the mountain roads and tracks while others jumped out and were lost owing to shortage of trained muleteers and from lack of line gear. Here again the farriers did vital work in keeping mules in a serviceable state for duty and shoes were requisitioned locally by Ordnance. The old story of shortage of shoes, nails and, to some extent, farrier's tools, occurred yet again as it always does in war-time; and in retrospect, it is fair to say that non-bulky items such as horse-shoe nails must always accompany farriers sent on urgent missions of this sort, since there is no effective substitute for them. Unfortunately, the senior

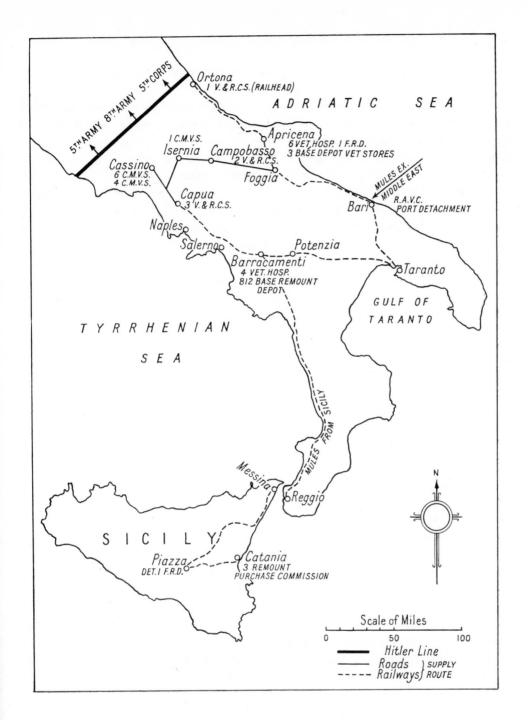

ADRIATIC SEA

Ortona
1 V. & R.C.S. (RAILHEAD)

5TH ARMY 8TH ARMY 5TH CORPS

5TH ARMY 8TH ARMY

Apricena
6 VET. HOSP. 1 F.R.D.
3 BASE DEPOT VET STORES

1 C.M.V.S.
Isernia   Campobasso
2 V. & R.C.S.

Foggia

MULES EX.
MIDDLE EAST

Cassino
6 C.M.V.S.
4 C.M.V.S.

Bari   R.A.V.C.
PORT DETACHMENT

Capua
3 V. & R.C.S.

Naples

Salerno   Potenzia

Barracamenti
4 VET. HOSP.
812 BASE REMOUNT
DEPOT

Taranto

GULF OF
TARANTO

TYRRHENIAN

SEA

MULES FROM SICILY

N

Messina

Reggio

SICILY

Piazza
DET. 1 F.R.D.

Catania
3 REMOUNT
PURCHASE COMMISSION

Scale of Miles

0   50   100

━━━ Hitler Line
───   Roads   } SUPPLY
- - - Railways } ROUTE

VETERINARY AND REMOUNT SUPPLY ROUTES

May 1944

farrier, Farrier-Sergeant Russell, was wounded in the back by mortar fire while assisting the Argylls and was evacuated to hospital.

It is interesting to record an "on the spot" assessment made by the young veterinary officer of this detachment: "It is clear that improvisation is a complete myth. It is not practicable to take the equipment off a soldier and it is found that the numerous blankets, ropes, pickhelves required for pack improvisation are not to hand in the field. At best, they are a very inferior substitute for real saddlery which should always be available". The only formation which, in fact, brought pack saddlery on D-Day was the Canadian Division, and it was found that the local Sicilian pack saddle in any case, was quite unsuitable for military loads; numerous mules were badly galled by them and many were discarded, lost, and permanently damaged through lack of the appropriate fitments to keep them in position. In so far as local procurement was concerned, there had been in Sicily at the beginning of the war some 250,000 mules. A great number had been removed by the Germans by the time the Allies landed, but sufficient were found in the operational areas to enable some form of pack supply to be organised, and they achieved useful results.

Although a comprehensive veterinary and remount organisation with staff representation and units existed in the Middle East Base when "Husky" was launched, there was only the Deputy Director Army Veterinary and Remount Services at Allied Force Headquarters in Algiers with dual administrative and executive functions, and much of his time was spent buying remounts. Also, when the operation was planned there was no staff on the establishment of 8th Army H.Q. at a particularly vital time. This was remedied when Lieutenant-Colonel A. P. MacDonald and his clerical staff of Sergeant J. Wild and Private R. A. Foster, were appointed to Rear H.Q. 8th Army arriving in Sicily in the D+14 convoy. MacDonald subsequently held this appointment during the northerly advance up Italy, and finally handing over after the cessation of hostilities in June, 1945 to Lieutenant-Colonel D. F. G. Smith at Udine, close to the Austrian frontier.

Three pack-transport groups with their pack companies together with one pack troop Indian field ambulance (mule) had been included in the original order of battle for "Husky". Also, there was the R.A.V.C. backing of one C.M.V.S. and one V.R.C.S. for each group and a field remount depot and a veterinary hospital were earmarked for calling forward at a later stage in the operations. Owing to shipping priorities, however, the original plan could not be adopted, and instead, Group H.Qs. and the personnel of two companies from North Africa commanded by Lieutenant-Colonel J. Hume Dudgeon R.A.S.C. arrived without their animals and were employed with locally-obtained mules for a short time at the later stages of the operations in Sicily.

Operation "Husky" lasted only thirty-eight days until the 17th of August when the Allied Forces entered Messina. The improvised pack experiment, although wasteful in terms of animal life and injuries, had materially assisted formations but there was an element of luck that made this possible.

There were enough mules conditioned and used to the pack saddle in this part of Sicily because the mountain inhabitants regularly used pack animals as in the Southern Provinces of Italy. Operations were not prolonged and animals were fairly easily replaced, so that organised veterinary services were not so vital at this early stage. Furthermore, forage was plentiful at this time of the year, water presented no problem and the climate was kind. Nor was disease a hazard with indigenous mules; Southern Sicily was very malarious during the invasion period but there were no equivalent insect-borne diseases causing animal wastage. Parasitic skin bleeding (cutaneous filariasis), although endemic in Southern Italy and Sicily, did not have any significant constitutional effect.

Numbers 1 and 4 C.M.V.S. arrived in Sicily within a few days of each other. Captain B. C. M. Edmonds was in command of No. 1 C.M.V.S., and had embarked at Kantara with his unit and 690 mules and thirty horses belonging to the 13th and 34th Indian Mule Companies. Five hundred tons of reserve forage was off-loaded when they disembarked at Syracuse on the 20th August. A week later they were established in the malarious area around Lentini and were providing the necessary services for the Indian pack group. Captain R. I. Macrae in command of No. 4 C.M.V.S. had by then, travelled many thousands of miles. He left Basra on the 1st July and sailed through the Persian Gulf and Red Sea in a "blacked-out" mule transport carrying mules and horses. He disembarked at Kantara in Egypt, on 21st July and the unit, less animals, completed the journey to Tripoli by road. Eventually he reached the port of Augusta in Sicily on the 25th August. This C.M.V.S. was allotted to No. 4 Pack Group to provide the necessary services to keep the two North African pack units operating smoothly.

When the operations in Sicily ended, 549 mules were accounted for; of these, 315 serviceable ones were transferred to No. 4 Pack Group; the rest including two and three-year-olds were handed over to A.M.G.O.T. (Allied Military Government Occupied Territory) for disposal to farmers or were destroyed. The horses were a very poor lot and only four out of fifty-two were retained. The estimated fatal animal casualties were 150.

Large quantities of Italian pack saddlery including a thousand saddles were captured intact and were very useful when Italian pack companies reformed under Allied control.

Another month elapsed before the pack groups with their mules and the mobile veterinary sections embarked on landing craft for Reggio, situated on the Italian side of the straits. During this period the equipment and transport of our units was over-hauled, the men received further training in their future veterinary and remount rôle and there was a fillip to morale with the arrival of mail after long delay consequent upon changes of theatre.

This marked the beginning of a period of close and friendly association between the R.A.S.C. and R.A.V.C. at all levels; it prospered, and this extract taken from a letter sent by Brigadier H. M. Hinde, D.D.S.T., H.Q. Allied Armies in Italy to the D.D.V.R.S. towards the end of hostilities illustrates how closely the two Corps co-operated on animal matters.:

"One of my Staff Officers has recently conferred with a number of Pack Officers, including two Group Commanders. These officers had come straight from the line on the 13 Corps front.

"It will be of interest to you to hear that quite spontaneously they all emphasized the efficiency of the Remount Service. They expressed themselves full of admiration for the way mules were replaced immediately they were demanded—very often the same day after heavy casualties.

"I pass on this commendation to you and would like to add to it my appreciation and thanks for the assistance you are giving to my Corps. The co-operation which has always existed had done much to enable the companies successfully to surmount their many difficulties!"

The 8th Army crossed the Straits of Messina on 3rd September 1943. Five days later Italy surrendered unconditionally but any hopes of a rapid occupation of Italy were quickly shattered by the swift and effective measures taken by the Germans to retrieve the situation. It was going to be a hard fight.

The campaign in Sicily had provided some insight into the terrain and conditions likely to be encountered when the Allies invaded the Italian mainland. At War Office and at A.F.H.Q. the planning staffs were anticipating a substantial demand for pack mules to equip the mountain divisions being formed. It was by no means certain early in October 1943, that sufficient mules of the right stamp would be found in Sicily and Southern Italy because the Germans had requisitioned many animals, and so on the 1st October, Lieutenant-Colonel C. H. S. Townsend and Captain W. J. B. Watson were sent from Middle East to Algiers to investigate possible sources of supply of mountain artillery mules in the Mediterranean area, especially in Southern Spain and Spanish Morocco. Although by this time contact had been made with the British Ambassador in Madrid neither territory was visited because surveys of Sicily and Southern Italy revealed the existence of suitable mules in the remoter mountain districts. Furthermore, many mules were to be handed over soon after the Italian Army surrendered.

The principal need early on was that an effective directorate be established at A.F.H.Q. to co-ordinate procurement, delivery and veterinary arrangements for the many thousands of pack animals now needed and to plan the phasing in of more veterinary and remount units and officers for the formations of the 8th Army and the 5th (U.S.) Army employing pack transport. This was achieved in November when Colonel Townsend was appointed D.D.V.R.S. with a subordinate staff of one A.D.V.R.S.

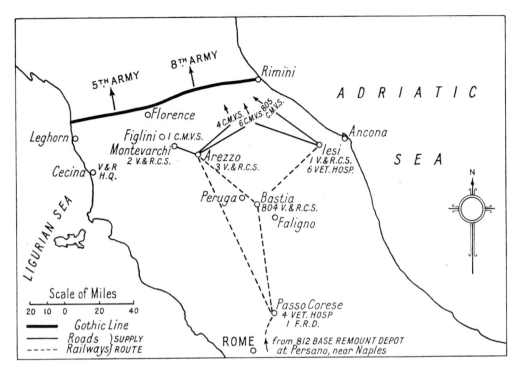

VETERINARY AND REMOUNT SUPPLY ROUTES

August—September 1944

(Lt.-Col. J. C. Rix) for the advanced administrative echelon of A.F.H.Q. located in Naples, and a staff captain (Captain G. S. Mason) and clerical staff.

During this time preparations were being made to establish a remount purchasing commission in Sicily to be commanded by Lieutenant-Colonel J. Bell, and the A.D.V.R.S. 8th Army began requisition and purchase of mules in the southern provinces of Italy. Although a remount depot was not yet positioned to receive them, No. 2 V.R.C.S. was by now located in Foggia and had assumed dual duties as an advanced veterinary hospital, and remount collecting and distribution centre. With British 10th Corps under command of the 5th (U.S.) Army, D. F. G. Smith was appointed liaison A.V.R.O. with the American Army in the rank of Lieutenant-Colonel.

Early in December, the D.D.V.R.S. decided that the time had now come to establish himself and his staff at Naples nearer the hub of events; his appointment was therefore interchanged with the A.D.V.R.S. post which remained at Algiers, Lieutenant-Colonel Rix continuing from there the necessary periodic surveys of North Africa, Sardinia and Corsica, where known resources of mules, riding ponies, and "meat on the hoof" existed.

After preliminary conferences with the British and American staffs in Naples, a policy statement was issued by A.F.H.Q. making the D.D.V.R.S. the responsible adviser on veterinary and remount matters for both the 8th and the 5th (U.S.) Armies. Remounts were to be treated as a common user pool allocated between allied forces according to operational requirements. An animal provision board was to be set up at once under the direction of Colonel Townsend; this staff was to be integrated with the U.S. Army to facilitate planning, and a few days later Major Lehane from the Quartermaster Branch, U.S. Army joined as liaison officer. The main terms of reference were control and co-ordination of local purchase in Italy, the assessment of the numbers of remounts of various categories for procurement in other countries and the arrangements for disembarkation and reception of animals imported into Italy through the heel ports and Naples.

The conclusion after further meetings with the U.S. Army was that an adequate (30 per cent.) reserve was available for existing British pack units, but that the U.S. Army situation was not as good. Meanwhile, following the landings in Southern Italy, the A.D.V.R.S. 8th Army had been able to requisition and purchase 951 mules and forty-six horses, while Lieutenant-Colonel Bell's No. 3 Remount Purchasing Commission team at Catania, comprising Captain W. J. B. Watson (2 I/C), and Captain J. Hart in command of the holding section of No. 1 Field Remount Depot at Piazza Armerina, had been busy since October with a procurement target being achieved of 500 mules a month. Already, the common user remount concept recently enacted at A.F.H.Q. was being complied with by No. 3 R.P.C. when the U.S. Army collected 150 mules at Catania on the 16th December.

The remount estimates of December 1943 visualized a requirement of twenty-one pack companies for the 8th Army and 10th Corps, and twelve for U.S. 5th Army. In sight were thirty, comprising seven Indian, four North African, five Cypriot, six Italian and eight French, amounting to just over 10,000 animals. Additional provision —which was very difficult indeed to predict accurately—was needed for the improvised pack units, and their wastage rate was wisely assessed at 17 per cent. per month compared to 10 per cent. for organized pack units. It was also foreseen that a force of over 13,000 mules might have to be attained and maintained, and about 1,000 mules per month produced to cover wastage and any further possible build-up. Four thousand mules or thereabouts were in units by this time, and a further 6,000 trained pack mules complete with saddlery, had to be shipped with their units from Syria, Palestine and Egypt. There were another 3,000 or more with French units in North Africa and Italian companies in Sardinia; the Sardinian animals were in bad condition and had to be omitted from the earlier operations. An urgent and special requirement for 3,000 mountain artillery mules for allied units arose at this time which necessitated a substantial contribution from the remount purchasing commissions in Italy and Sicily.

Such was the urgency for delivery of pack units and mules by the middle of November that 15th Army Group signalled A.F.H.Q. requesting assistance in the following terms: "Request you increase earliest date of shipping of animals to total of 4,500 per month from all sources. Will accept if unavoidable, the consequent reduction in vehicle lift of 1,000 vehicles per month".

With remounting plans on a more organized footing, other problems had to be tackled. Chief of these were the shortage of R.A.V.C. units and officers for staffing formations using improvised pack transport. A special establishment designed to meet this need, and designated "Corps Detachment R.A.V.C.", was therefore authorized as a temporary measure until trained pack units arrived. This establishment comprised a V.O., one farrier-sergeant, one farrier-corporal, four R.A.V.C. privates, a driver batman, and one 15 cwt. truck. A British cadre of one veterinary officer and one sergeant R.A.V.C. was also sanctioned for Italian pack companies to provide a more effective means of controlling contagious diseases, especially epizootic lymphangitis.

The units which the D.D.V.R.S. particularly needed towards the end of 1943, were a remount depot, a hospital, a laboratory, a base depot veterinary stores, and three more conducting units to facilitate casualty evacuation and the delivery of remounts to field units; without sufficient mobile units, the turn-round between C.M.V.Ss., V.R.C.Ss. and pack units became excessively long and produced tremendous wear and tear on vehicles and fatigue in the drivers. During December, furthermore, the animal casualty rate rose above the predicted figure and resulted in the V.R.C.Ss. having to act as advanced hospitals. This imposed rôle was to be repeated on other occasions during the campaign, and it appeared to work efficiently.

The arrival in January 1944 of a comparatively large R.A.V.C. unit, No. 1 Field Remount Depot, provided a better organization for assisting the remount purchasing commissions in Sicily and Italy. No. 1 F.R.D. eventually moved into half-built premises at Apricena, a compact area with small paddocks which proved suitable in the summer but extremely muddy and difficult to run in the winter. A detachment from this depot had already been posted permanently to No. 3 Remount Purchasing Commission from North Africa to facilitate preparation and initial training of remounts before their ultimate transfer to the remount holding depot at Persano and another detachment of 1 F.R.D. was to be located for most of the campaign, at Bari. This was the "Port R.A.V.C. Detachment" responsible for the reception and care of a great number of mule and horse shipments from Middle East which were unloaded at this port.

No. 812 Base Remount Depot which arrived early in February 1944 was luckier than 1 F.R.D. moving to a pleasant rural area on the west coast, sixty miles south of Naples. This was the pre-war Italian remount depot of 10,000 acres at Persano, laid out in well-fenced paddocks of twenty-five acres with stabling for 2,000 animals. Accommodation was divided into three self-contained centres, each between two and three miles apart. The area was administered by the U.S. Army who allotted one centre each to the British and French, and one for themselves. In view of its roomy paddocks and grazing, it proved valuable as a convalescent and conditioning depot because quite a number of the recently purchased mules in Italy and Sicily needed two months preparation before being fit to issue to field units.

No. 4 Veterinary Hospital also had premises at Persano, and had in fact moved there some weeks before No. 812 Base Remount Depot. The environment and accommodation at Persano were good, and it became in some ways a second Ramle for officers and men on leave and in need of a rest and change, also for periodic departmental conferences held by D.D.V.R.S., A.F.H.Q. There were race meetings and other distractions, a delightful country setting, with a river nearby, which showed promise of containing trout but proved barren when the A.V.R.Os. of the 5th and 8th Army fished it together one day. In command of these two units for an appreciable part of their existence in Italy, were Major R. C. Crowhurst (veterinary hospital) and Major G. Newport (remount depot). Both units could accept and accommodate very large numbers of horses and mules and not infrequently held over 3,000 animals between them.

The identification and branding system for mules was reviewed in 1944. As in World War I, foot numbering proved useless because the mud defeated this system and foot numbers also grew out; there was also some duplication in the foot numbers of remounts sent from North Africa. The U.S. Army peace-time system of branding numbers on the neck was successfully adopted, using the right side in contrast to the Americans who branded on the left. The custom of identifying the purchaser of the mule by his surname initial branded under the broad arrow was also enforced, and this at times evoked cryptic comments where the brand had been lightly applied.

As might be expected with a sudden and large expansion in animal strength, serious shortages of animal equipment occurred. During the first winter, mule rugs were very difficult to obtain and many units had to delay clipping for indefinite periods. Ordnance were able to make arrangements for some equipment such as rugs, line gear and nose bags, to be manufactured locally, and the R.A.V.C. were instrumental in providing supervisory farrier staff to run a horse shoe and nail factory in Naples on behalf of Ordnance. This was in the charge of Farrier-Quartermaster-Sergeant Siely, assisted by Farrier-Sergeants Simpson and Thurlow. Thirty Italian blacksmiths worked in this factory which was able to turn out shoes at the rate of 500–600 a day. Such was the shortage of shoes during the earlier operations that C.M.V.Ss. had to salvage all shoes from dead mules.

Possibly the most urgent need of all in the early months of the campaign on the Italian mainland was for pack saddles. Captain B. C. M. Edmonds reported that when he was O.C. No. 1 C.M.V.S. in the first winter in Italy saddlery was so precious that even if badly smashed in action it had to be salvaged. Military pack saddles were in fact less easy to replace than the mules themselves, and a dead mule with its saddlery floating downstream out to sea was a tragedy mainly because of the serious loss of saddlery. The mule being useless without a fitted military saddle, it became the custom for V.R.C.Ss. in the first winter to receive large consignments of pack saddlery from Ordnance, assembling this and fitting it to the individual mule before issue and transfer to C.M.V.Ss. The system was very wasteful indeed with units employing pack on an improvised basis, and O.C. No. 1 C.M.V.S. records one batch of 200 mules and saddles issued originally through No. 2 V.R.C.S. and No. 1 C.M.V.S. to the 1st Canadian Division at Ortona. Of that batch only ten saddles were ever recovered. Although this might be considered an administrative problem not relating to R.A.V.C. responsibility it so happened that A.V.R.Os. were very intimately concerned at the various headquarters throughout the war in representing to the staffs and services the need for correct provisioning of equipment according to animal classifications and sizes.

As the campaign progressed in April and May 1944, and pack units increased in number, a shortage of farriers occurred, and it became necessary for a school of farriery to be formed, the original establishment consisting of four farrier-sergeants, one corporal-clerk and one Italian cook. This unit was originally attached to No. 3 V.R.C.S. at Capua and was designed to train twenty-four pupils at one time.

During May also, an Italian hospital unit, 125 Infirmeria Quadrupedi, with four officers and ninety-one other ranks arrived from Sardinia and was posted to Persano to assist and release No. 4 Veterinary Hospital for its move to Passo Corese. During previous months it had been possible to replace some civilian labour working in R.A.V.C. units by Italian soldiers and the results were better, although administrative difficulties and the language barrier were problems at times. After the capture of Rome (5th June 1944), the premises of the second of the large Italian remount depots and veterinary hospitals became available for the R.A.V.C. This was located twenty-five miles north-east of Rome at Passo Corese. Though smaller than Persano, it had an area of five to six thousand acres with stabling for 1,500 animals. Some of the paddocks were heavily mined and an Indian Sapper unit was employed for some weeks in clearing the area before it could be used by No. 3 V.R.C.S. This unit had to function as an advanced hospital and No. 804 V.R.C.S. as an advanced remount depot until the arrival from Persano of No. 4 Veterinary Hospital, and from Apricena of No. 1 F.R.D.

There was a period of difficulty in obtaining veterinary stores during the first winter until No. 3 Base Veterinary Stores was properly established at Apricena. This unit, like No. 1 F.R.D., became separated from its equipment and stores when it moved to Italy. The main shortages were lack of anti-tetanic serum, in the face of many cases of tetanus following gunshot wounds; a great lack of bandages and cotton wool; and the absence of ready-prepared ampoules, especially stimulants for hypodermic use on the many exhaustion cases among animals in transit. Both the German and Italian veterinary chests were better supplied in that respect than the British, which relied on compressed tablets of adrenaline and strychnine. The Germans used cardiazol (Leptazol) a powerful medullary stimulant, and the Italians camphor and ether, or caffeine and sodium benzoate in ampoules.

We were fortunate to have an administrator of the calibre and experience of Colonel Townsend during the first year in Italy with much planning and reorganization required to establish the R.A.V.C. as a going concern when resources in trained units and manpower were small. He was a quick thinker whose mind focused clearly on the practical aspects of any problem, with that invaluable flair in war-time of being able to achieve successful improvisations when temporary shortages occurred. He was a master of the short concise letter and made a significant contribution towards the smooth running of the veterinary and remount services by a series of some forty-five rapidly-issued administrative instructions; these embraced a wide variety of subjects intimately concerned with the day-to-day functioning of the R.A.V.C. in Italy, such as effective sign-posting of R.A.V.C. units ("It is essential that all V. & R. units should be properly sign-posted as a lorry conveying sick animals does not want to spend half the day looking for them".); correspondence and returns; documentation; issue and delivery of veterinary stores; branding systems for remounts; forage and substitutes; moves and transfers of units; disposal and sale of cast animals and carcases; the training and re-training of mules and how to deal with vice; administration of Italian dilutees and civil labour; and a number of concise and practical instructions on the control of endemic diseases. One rather minor instruction titled "The Supply and Use of Magnesium Sulphate" (Epsom Salts, that universal veterinary and medical panacea) was not without humour. The first sentence read, "Magnesium sulphate is a veterinary store supply and not part of the forage ration. Supplies from veterinary stores are limited and will not be used as a weekly ration to all fit animals as is sometimes asked for".

Very large animal holdings began to accumulate in the base hospitals and remount depots from about March, 1944 onwards, and the original forecast of two hospitals, each designed to treat 250 animals, being enough to cope with the two lines of communication behind the 5th and 8th Armies proved incorrect. The two remount depots as well, were on a restricted R.A.V.C. cadre basis, and their average animal holdings were greatly in excess of their establishment and the equipment scales to maintain them. Their manpower resources were also attenuated at the headquarter end by frequent road and rail conducting parties and by dispersion. No. 1 F.R.D. for example, had a permanent detachment in Bari for port reception duties, and in Sicily another larger permanent detachment functioning as a collecting centre for No. 3 Remount Purchasing Commission. The civilian local labour increments had proved insufficient and very unsatisfactory for the most part, and it was not until July 1944 that these four installations were reorganized to enable them to hold 500 sick or 1,500 fit animals. This was regularized by a theatre establishment amendment upgrading the ranks of R.A.V.C. N.C.Os. to improve supervision, and two additional officers— an adjutant and a quartermaster—were added to each veterinary hospital as they were undoubtedly under-officered. To each hospital was added an Italian Army increment of two officers and 191 other ranks and to each remount depot four officers and 276 men. The basis for estimating the number of extra men was in the proportion of one man to three mules in stables, and one to nine for those accommodated in paddocks. Experience in Italy had also shown that the transport allotment was greatly under-assessed to cover all duties, and the degree of dispersion to which these units were liable; the remount depots were therefore allotted ten vehicles including seven three-ton lorries, one car, an animal trailer, and a motor cycle. The hospitals were allotted four three-ton lorries, one car, and three motor cycles.

The shortage of V.Os. in the early days was acute, with frequent alterations in the priorities as to where their advice and assistance was most needed. These were for the supervision of improvised pack units as well as the trained, for Italian pack units being formed, for animal surveys and sheep procurement in Sardinia and North Africa, for veterinary supervision at the ports where animals were regularly disembarked, for C.M.P. Dog Sections and R.A.F. dog detachments, and for special forces like No. 1 Forward Base in Yugoslavia. This difficulty was partly resolved by the formation of a "Pool of Officers R.A.V.C.", which included two majors, three captains, and two lieutenants, to which was added later, one lieutenant-colonel. This arrangement provided some flexibility and security at a time when the R.A.V.C. needed every available officer for service in the Far East; all bids therefore had to be fully justified on a British manpower ceiling based on authorized establishments, the figures for which in May, 1944, were sixty-three officers and 584 men. Included in the British other rank establishment were thirty-seven clerks, sixty-one farriers, and fifteen saddlers. There had been considerable difficulty in supplying enough clerical personnel to the earlier units and H.Q. staffs in Italy, and O.C. No. 3 Remount Purchasing Commission had complained repeatedly of the difficulties in carrying out his work without a full-time clerk. Few of our men had former clerical experience or were endowed with the qualities needed to make good clerks, although it is interesting to record that quite a number of jockeys and apprentices, seemed to have a flair for Orderly Room routine and trained on as useful office workers.

It is doubtful whether there have ever been enough farriers in war-time where armies move on an animal basis, and it was only a matter of time before expanding commitments in Italy resulted in a large demand for farriers. The School of Farriery which had started in a fairly small way with four instructors, at No. 3 V.R.C.S. in Capua, was not the first installation to start such training, and records showed that the O.C. of No. 1 V.R.C.S. had commendably started an unofficial school of instruction for one of the pack groups early in the campaign. After the move of No. 3 V.R.C.S from Capua to Passo Corese the scope of this school enlarged very considerably. The premises were more suitable in an animal depot of this size, and with the large numbers of animals requiring attention to their feet and shoeing, it was found quite practicable to train farriers to third-class standard in two months. The students were British, Cypriots, Indians, Basutos and Italian and the language difficulties were successfully overcome by including a full-time Italian interpreter who was especially needed because of the high proportion of Italians under training. Some Basutos showed rather little promise early in the course, but their keenness substantially made up for this and they generally made good third-class farriers in eight weeks. Northern Italians were good pupils and Sicilians were probably the worst. In December 1944 an enlarged instructional establishment was authorized comprising one officer, one W.O. II, twelve sergeants and one sergeant-clerk, two cooks, one batman-driver and two orderlies. The parent unit was by now, No. 1 F.R.D. and a deficiency of R.A.V.C. instructors necessitated posting in four R.A.S.C. farriers to help, and with the arrival of more students, three Italians were co-opted as instructors enabling this unit to train approximately eighty men at one time. Premises were improvised under the supervision of Lieutenant W. H. Cliff, F.Q.M.S. Siely and his N.C.O. staff which included Farrier-Sergeant R. Walmsley and Farrier-Sergeants Carter, Brooks, Budd, Goodchild and Bennett. Later F.Q.M.S. G. Moore was to succeed F.Q.M.S. Siely. The premises erected were corrugated lean-to sheds with concrete floors which covered quite an area because of the many classes under training, and two Nissen huts were built for housing stores, the office, and mess rooms with a separate cook-house. The School became almost self-contained and ultimately 218 farriers were to graduate, as third and second-class farriers. The exact figures were 131 Italians, fifty-seven British, fifteen Basuto, eight Indian and seven Cypriots.

One of the first tasks of Lieutenant-Colonel D. F. G. Smith, on leaving the 5th (U.S.) Army for H.Q. No. 2 District in Bari, was to act as the administrative link between A.F.H.Q. and Force 266, on the remounting of pack and mountain artillery units for the partisans concentrated at No. 1 Forward Base on the island of Vis, a few miles from the mainland of Yugoslavia. A series of visits by sea and air were made to the island including a journey to Marshal Tito's headquarters in a heavily guarded cave in the mountains, to discuss mule provisioning, animal management, training and veterinary arrangements. He accompanied Lieutenant-Colonel Geoffrey Kup, R.A., who was in charge of the Balkan school of artillery, a part of the military mission on the island, and met Tito's chief of staff at that time, General Arso Iovanovic. The A.D.V.R.S. accompanied the first shipment of mules to Vis and had the misfortune en route to be caught unequipped to deal with a bad case of tympanitic colic. Fortunately, some R.E.M.E. technicians travelling on the ship were able, in the space of an hour, to produce from a drawing a fearsome eighteen-inch long trocar and cannula, and the mule was successfully deflated and survived. The partisan army were

CHAPTER VII.   Pack Transport, Burma, 1944.

CHAPTER VII.   Indian Mountain Battery.

Opposite page :

CHAPTER VII.   Elephants captured from the Japanese and used by the 14th Army in the Kalewa battle, 1944.   *Imperial War Museum photo*

CHAPTER VII.   The Chindwin crossing, December, 1944. Mules disembarking on the victory side. *Imperial War Museum photo.*

Below :

CHAPTER VII.   Veterinary inspection in the jungle. The Arakan front. *Imperial War Museum photo.*

CHAPTER VII.   A bullock about to be flown into one of Wingate's strongholds behind the Japanese lines in North Burma.

CHAPTER VIII.   Surrendered horses of the Cossack Corps, Austria, 1945.

CHAPTER VIII. Surrendered steppe-bred ponies of the Cossack Corps, Austria, 1944.

CHAPTER VIII. Cossack Corps horse, an Anglo-Donetz with English thoroughbred blood.

CHAPTER IX.   The unveiling of the R.A.V.C. War Memorial, Melton Mowbray, July, 1951.

CHAPTER IX.   R.A.V.C. Crest in Khyber Pass, 1961.

CHAPTER X.   Western Front, 1918. Messenger dog showing the metal cylinder in which the message was carried and, *below*, a messenger dog in action.   Both *Imperial War Museum photos*.

CHAPTER X.   Bully, a cross-bred labrador dog trained to retrieve concealed arms and ammunition, Cyprus, 1956.

CHAPTER X.   Labrador and Alsatian tracker dogs in training at Troodos, Cyprus, 1956.

tremendous enthusiasts and impressed everyone by their keenness to learn every possible detail about the techniques of using pack-artillery mules under load, and were particularly thrilled with the U.S. Army pattern mountain artillery gun with its excellent range. It was a great pleasure therefore for the R.A.V.C. to assist these forces when it could be seen how very seriously they noted all details and advice on animal management and concerning the loading limits of the individual mule according to its size and bodyweight. Not only were remount aspects studied carefully but it was impressive to see one partisan veterinary officer who had already been running a one month duration course consisting of eight hours daily of lectures and practical demonstration on veterinary first aid and animal husbandry. He had no books of reference to consult except for some lecture notes retained at the time of his graduation from Zagreb University. His delight on receiving a gratuitous copy of the H.M.S.O. publication *Animal Management* was quite unbounded. The partisan veterinary service as it was, came under the overall direction of their army medical service. A substantial proportion of the Yugoslav army were women who wore battle-dress and marching boots and carried arms and a girdle of grenades—their favourite weapons—just like the men. Their medical orderlies were powerfully-built girls, who trudged behind the marching columns; they were enormously strong and were said to be quite capable of carrying a wounded man single-handed. In rather curious contrast it was stated quite definitely that partisan women troops should not be involved in the duties of veterinary orderly or muleteer in view of some of the more distasteful duties involved! It was not difficult to make suitable arrangements for training and indoctrination of the partisans and a few of their veterinary officers were sent to our base units in Italy for training. It was also planned that a R.A.V.C. detachment would be made available for instructing their personnel in saddle fitting, shoeing, and animal management; there were very few partisan farriers on the island and one of the tasks of this unit was to train them.

By June, 210 mules and twenty horses had been delivered to Yugoslavia and the plan was that the strength would ultimately rise to 900 mules and sixty horses. Major A. K. Kirkwood who had been in charge of the port detachment, Bari, for some time, ultimately assumed all local responsibilities for this force and had much to do with the subsequent transportation of mountain artillery mules and their equipment by air in C 47 aircraft to the Yugoslav mainland, in July 1944; this was done by the Balkan air force. Four mules were carried in each plane with one of our men in charge, and Major Kirkwood in one of the planes. No incidents occurred except slight trouble in take-off due to breaking of some of the rather flimsy wooden crossbars behind the mules. This possibility had been foreseen and roped attachments to the breeching prevented displacement of the mules. The planes arrived at the airstrip in darkness and unloaded the mules without difficulty by jumping them out. Experience gained earlier in Burma proved useful for those responsible for assembling the plane fittings.

The following extract of a report from the Brigadier in charge Administrative Echelon, Headquarters Special Operations Mediterranean, addressed to D.D.V.R.S., suitably acknowledged the contribution made by the R.A.V.C. "This was the first operation of its kind to be carried out in the Mediterranean theatre, and I feel that the fact that the mules were safely delivered without a hitch can in no small measure be attributed to the help and advice rendered by Major A. K. Kirkwood and his staff. I should like to express my thanks and appreciation to you for allowing this officer and R.A.V.C. personnel to take part in the operation".

To return to the animal units of the 8th Army: The invasion of Italy was planned to commence on the 3rd of September 1943 with the landing of the 8th Army at Reggio to be followed up by the landing of the 5th Army (U.S.) at Salerno on 9th September. This latter army included the British 10th Corps.

Both armies were now under the operational and administrative command of A.F.H.Q., but the 8th Army was not entirely divorced from G.H.Q., M.E.F., on which it still partially depended for maintenance. Also, there remained in the Middle East many units in the 8th Army Order of Battle which had not yet been called forward.

In the original planning it was anticipated that the four pack companies which had been called forward together with two C.M.V.Ss. and one V.R.C.S., would meet the operational demands of the 8th Army during the first phase of the campaign on the mainland. Two troops of No. 574 Pack Company and No. 4 C.M.V.S., were committed in the landing operations and got ashore on the mainland by D+1. The remaining troops of No. 574 Company followed shortly afterwards. All the animals were carried across the Straits of Messina in landing craft without incident.

"A" Group H.Q., with No. 13 and No. 34 Indian Mule Companies, and No. 1 C.M.V.S., remained in reserve at Lentini.

There was little demand for pack transport in the first phase of the operations. The 8th Army seized Calabria against weak opposition and having made contact with the 5th Army at Salerno, pushed rapidly northwards along the Apennines and up the eastern half of Italy. The ports of Crotone, Taranto, Barletta and Bari were quickly occupied and the advance continued through Foggia to Termoli, and the Trigno River, and in the centre towards Isernia. The 5th Army captured Naples and continued to the Volturno River. This, roughly, was the position towards the end of October when bad weather and more stubborn defence slowed down the advance.

While all this was taking place No. 574 Pack Transport Company was collecting its scattered troops, and, together with No. 4 C.M.V.S., was following up the advancing Army. No. 573 Company together with the ambulance troop of No. 27 Indian Company and some spare remounts, landed at Crotone on 20th September in S.S. *Nirvana* from North Africa. No. 1 C.M.V.S. arrived by road, and took over the remounts at Crotone. "A" Indian Group remained in Sicily.

Italy now became a co-belligerent and though the Italian Army was somewhat disorganized it was known to hold large numbers of pack animals. These could be used to form new companies or to provide remount reserves for existing allied units, and with this object in view the A.D.V.R.S., 8th Army made a survey of the Italian 7th Army which was then located in Calabria. Accurate information was difficult to obtain from the Italian authorities but it was estimated that the equivalent of two pack companies could be found either as remounts or fully equipped for operations. Complete pack companies did not exist in the Italian Army but these could be formed by the amalgamation of artillery and infantry transport sections. It was estimated that the 7th Italian Army had, in all, a strength of approximately 6,000 mules but these were scattered in the various garrison towns of Calabria, and were essential for Italian Army maintenance.

Towards the middle of October it became clear that the number of allied pack companies available would not meet the operational needs of both armies. All formations called for pack transport about the same time. No. 4 Pack Group with Nos. 573 and 574 Companies and No. 4 C.M.V.S., were allotted to 13th Corps in the central sector. "A" Indian Group with Nos. 13 and 34 Mule Companies and No. 1 C.M.V.S., were called forward from Sicily and allotted to 5th Corps on the eastern coastal sector. No. 2 V.R.C.S. arrived and took over from No. 1 C.M.V.S., forming an advanced remount depot and hospital at Foggia.

This distribution met the immediate needs of the 8th Army, but at the same time urgent requests were made by the 5th Army for two pack companies. In view of these demands, and also because the 8th Army had no reserve pack company, it was decided to form two Italian companies, from the resources of the 7th Italian Army.

The first Italian mule company arrived at Foggia on time and was dispatched immediately by M.T. to the 5th Army. The second company arrived later and was retained by the 8th Army.

During October and November 1943, both No. 4 Pack Group and "A" Group were fully committed with the 8th Army, and the latter group suffered heavy casualties at the Trigno River. Nos. 1 and 4 C.M.V.Ss. allotted to these groups were fully committed but were adequate to meet demands for the evacuation of casualties and the supply of remounts. No. 2 V.R.C.S. was established at Foggia with approximately 200 mules and was in a suitable location to accept casualties from and supply remounts to both C.M.V.Ss.

With the gradual arrival of more pack and R.A.V.C. units the situation eased considerably, and with an effective Directorate at A.F.H.Q. the veterinary and remount organisation of the 8th Army could confine itself to its own responsibilities. Furthermore after crossing the Sangro River, owing to the stabilisation by the enemy of the Hitler Line, operations on the 8th Army front at the end of 1943 became static.

Reference must be made here to the conditions under which units were operating during the winter of 1943. The pack-transport requirement had been underestimated and the mule companies had no rest, ordinary formations were relieved at regular intervals but the pack companies supplying them had to remain in the line. The weather conditions were appalling and the fact that animals maintained their condition speaks highly for the animal management of the companies. Likewise, our units were, at times, extended beyond the capacity for which they were intended. No. 2 V.R.C.S., acting as a remount depot and hospital, at one period held over 1,000 animals. The vehicles of the C.M.V.Ss. were continually on the road, owing to the long lines of communications, the absence of railways and the inadequate main roads.

During the early part of 1944, five more Indian companies had arrived from Middle East and two companies from North Africa. Five Cypriot companies arrived during the early spring.

Animal casualties were high during and immediately prior to the battle for the Hitler Line. Actual battle casualties for the worst period of six days amounted to 266 animals. Our units were worked to full capacity, but they were able to meet all demands. All animal casualties of operating units were replaced in less than twenty-four hours after their occurrence.

The distribution of pack and R.A.V.C. units in the 8th Army prior to the assault on the Hitler Line was:

Directly under H.Q. 8th Army—H.Q. No. 20 Group Italian mule companies
          —Four Italian mule companies
          —No. 3 V.R.C.S.
          —No. 2 Corps Detachment R.A.V.C.
under 10th Corps—H.Q. No. 4 Pack Group
          —Four pack transport companies (North Africa)
          —Four troops of Nos. 3 and 4 Italian Pack Companies
          —No. 1 Razziupamento Motorizzato (869 mules)
          —No. 1 C.M.V.S.
          —No. 2 V.R.C.S.
          —No. 3 Corps Detachment R.A.V.C.
under 13th Corps—H.Q. B Group Indian mule companies
          —Four Indian mule companies
          —No. 4 C.M.V.S.
          —No. 6 C.M.V.S.
under Polish Corps—H.Q. No. 1 Group pack transport companies
          —Four Cypriot pack transport companies

The animal strengths of these units totalled 7,300.

Towards the end of May 1944, the Hitler Line finally collapsed and both the 8th and the 5th Armies advanced rapidly until the enemy became established on the

Rimini-Pisa or Gothic Line. Pack companies followed up the advance but, except in the central sector around Arezzo, were not heavily committed. Nos. 7 and 85 Mountain Artillery Regiments were called forward and were in action in the central sector.

R.A.V.C. units moved forward and conformed to the disposition of pack groups and mountain regiments, both of which had appreciable casualties north of Perugia towards the end of July. No. 3 V.R.C.S. was called forward to take over the Italian remount depot at Passo Corese, pending the arrival of base veterinary and remount units.

Various changes of command occurred during the advance until the final re-grouping for the battle for the Gothic Line, towards the end of August. The 8th Army Order of Battle then included the following units:—

Nos. 803, 4 and 6 C.M.V.Ss.

Nos. 2 and 804 V.R.C.Ss.

Nos. 7 and 85 Mountain Regiments R.A.

H.Q. and five companies of No. 1 Group, Cyprus Regiment.

H.Q. and four companies of No. 4 Pack Group R.A.S.C.

H.Q. and three companies of "A" Group R.I.A.S.C.

H.Q. and four companies of "B" Pack Group R.I.A.S.C.

The animal strength of these units totalled 8,116, which was the greatest number so far employed with the 8th Army. Casualties were not, however, as high as expected, and no difficulty was experienced in providing veterinary and remount services for units in the line. Everything connected with animals was now on an organized basis. There were adequate reserves at the base. Forward R.A.V.C. units were well placed to deal with any emergency and to maintain pack units wherever they were operating. Railways were working and tonnage bids for movement of animals were accepted without question. The Army as a whole had become accustomed to animals and above all their operational importance throughout the campaign was fully understood.

Between the end of January and the end of March 1944 a major transfer of British and Italian pack units occurred from the 8th Army to the 5th Army to cover U.S. Army operations in the mountainous Cassino sector. This also involved the transfer of four R.A.V.C. units—No. 3 Corps Detachment and No. 3 V.R.C.S. to Capua, No. 4 C.M.V.S. to Cervaro and No. 6 C.M.V.S. to Sessa Aurunca.

The A.D.V.R.S. appointment to the 5th Army had been planned some months previously but was not implemented until February when it was temporarily filled by Major A. M. Bain until the arrival of Lieutenant-Colonel D. F. G. Smith early in March. The rear headquarters of 5th Army at that time was at Caserta Palace and moved later to tentage at Sparanise. This British increment included a "Q" branch headed by a brigadier, with major "Q" services such as Ordnance and Supplies and Transport represented at brigadier level; its chief task was to organize the maintenance of British formations operating under the 5th Army.

In February, Major K. G. Comrie, R.A.V.C., the executive veterinary officer of "B" Group Indian mule companies was killed at San Michele near Cassino while assisting the officer commanding No. 17 Indian Mule Company to re-organize his unit while under heavy shell fire. About a month later, on the morning of the 17th March, No. 17 Mule Company and No. 14 Gruppo Cavalero, sustained heavy animal casualties at San Michele during an attack by bombers, despite their mules being well dispersed in small groups in the woods. This incident provided a good illustration of the capabilities of R.A.V.C. conducting units for evacuation and replacement. Six hundred and fifty mules were dispersed in the woods, of which one hundred and twenty-one (18.6 per cent.) became casualties with thirty-six killed, thirty-six seriously wounded, and forty-eight with minor wounds. All the wounded were evacuated by Nos. 4 and 6 C.M.V.Ss. on the 17th and 18th March, and in answer to urgent demands from B Group for replacements, eighty remounts were delivered from No. 3 V.R.C.S. at Capua, using the pooled transport supplied by three R.A.V.C. mobile units in the vicinity. All mule casualties were replaced within twenty-four hours, and the wounded that could be saved were evacuated farther south to No. 4 Veterinary Hospital. The majority of the wounds were caused by shrapnel from anti-personnel bombs and involved the shoulder and hindquarter regions.

In March 1944, all pack and veterinary units returned under command of 8th Army prior to the final assault on the Hitler Line in May. The British increment at 5th Army Headquarters was reduced and the A.D.V.R.S. moved to Headquarters No. 2 District at Bari to administer his base units, organize further mule purchase in the southern provinces of Italy and to assist Force 266 in providing veterinary and remount services for animals due for shipment to Yugoslavia.

In August of the same year, 5th Army again took over command of a large proportion of the British pack companies and R.A.V.C. field units, which necessitated the re-installation of the A.D.V.R.S. appointment at Rear Headquarters (British Increment). Lieutenant-Colonel A. D. Seton was nominated for the post and held it until the end of hostilities. During this time the animal strength rose to 323 horses and 7,108 mules. During active operations it was impossible to rest pack companies which were working full capacity under extremely difficult conditions; with the arrival of snow and heavy frost in January an additional ration of 2 lbs. of grain per day was authorized. Mules were ever prone to slip in the icy conditions in the Apennines and the practice was to shoe with caulkins fore and hind; after the thaw, the front shoe caulkins were dispensed with.

Clipping was done up to the beginning of November and then the coat was allowed to grow. This proved a much better arrangement than no clipping at all, otherwise the long coat became encrusted with a cement-like mass of Italian mud, of a particular variety found in these mountains which was almost impossible to remove. As regards R.A.V.C. units, the largest number of mules evacuated sick during any week by a

C.M.V.S. was one hundred and sixty-eight during October 1944. During the same period this unit (No. 1 C.M.V.S.) issued 310 remounts to pack companies as reinforcements. The peak figure held by No. 2 V.R.C.S. during these U.S. Army operations was twenty-six horses and 559 mules issued in February 1945. Further statistics concerning the field veterinary and remount units are given in Appendix XI.

The Italian campaign is the only one in which there was an organized combined veterinary and remount service working over a considerable period. It was necessary to re-design the equipment and transport for our field units so that either a dual veterinary and remount rôle or specialized rôle could be carried out according to the requirements of the prevailing situation.

The C.M.V.S.—a proved veterinary unit of the World War I—became a self-contained mobile veterinary and remount section in World War II, and although the R.A.V.C. complement remained roughly the same (one officer and nineteen other ranks) its attached element was increased with R.A.S.C. drivers to enable it to operate four three ton lorries adapted as animal carriers and a 15-cwt. truck and motor cycle for intercommunication. Emergency increments of Italian civilians or soldiers were authorized for short periods when animal holdings were exceptionally large. The C.M.V.Ss., six of which were utilized in Italy, were located well forward, often where the roads were bad or snowbound; they were placed as close as possible to, and with not more than twenty miles turn round between themselves and the pack groups for which they provided services. Often C.M.V.Ss. during active and mobile warfare established small veterinary collecting posts (V.C.Ps.) consisting of a N.C.O. and a few men alongside one of the pack units of the group; to accelerate evacuation and to move animals cross-country to and from the mobile veterinary sections when transport could not get through. Sometimes this movement had to be carried out in darkness because of shelling and enemy air attack during day-time. In the Cassino area, the *Luftwaffe* had a typically regular time-table for attacking animal convoys, and the V.C.P. of No. 4 C.M.V.S. at San Michele became quite cunning in timing their movements since besides having to trek on foot to and from Cervaro, some of the drinking water had to be collected by pack mule. Nos. 1 and 4 C.M.V.Ss. were the only R.A.V.C units available during the early advance through Southern Italy and bore the full brunt of animal maintenance and veterinary aid until the early part of November 1943 when No. 2 V.R.C.S. arrived at Foggia. Early in the advance through Calabria when the animal commitment was not too heavy, No. 1 C.M.V.S. had held the anomalous responsibility of arranging forage contracts on behalf of the R.A.S.C. pack group. This apparently worked well and was much appreciated while pack units were re-organizing and training for their future rôle.

O.C. No. 1 C.M.V.S. records that no organized supply as such occurred until the River Sangro was reached. Hay and straw stacks or tibben were obtained as required on the normal army requisition forms signed by an officer, and later when he was a staff officer at H.Q. A.A.I. at Caserta Palace he had to process some of these forms which he had himself signed well over a year before. Even as far forward as Lanciano in February 1944, the mule companies had to live off the land and the C.M.V.S. staff would act as scouts for the packs units if any suitable sources of forage were found. The grain supply was sporadic and scanty in the early months of the campaign but the mules did pretty well on fodder which was of exceptionally good quality compared to Middle East standards. There is a story told of No. 34 Indian Mule Company which illustrates some of the repercussions of local requisition. The unit moved close to the top of a hill overlooking Orsogna which was strongly held by the Germans. A Bofors gun had been concealed behind a haystack near the summit; when dawn came there was no haystack, only an irate brigade major. No. 34 Pack Company had passed that way!

C.M.V.Ss. were normally designed to hold twenty-four remounts ready for immediate issue, as well as sick animals awaiting evacuation to the V.R.C.S. In this connection, where transport was dispersed or under strain priority was always given by C.M.V.Ss. to the sending forward of remounts, the casualties being sent down the line as soon as possible, or, by asking V.R.C.Ss. to collect them when delivering a consignment of fit mules.

The siting of the V.R.C.Ss. was to some extent conditioned by their distance from the C.M.V.Ss. which had to be located close to the pack groups; generally speaking, this distance did not exceed forty miles though there were exceptions when it was necessary to position V.R.C.Ss. close to railhead, so that they could have effective communication with veterinary hospitals and remount depots in the base areas. If C.M.V.Ss. seemed likely to remain in position for an indefinite period, an attempt was always made to find and use farm buildings with roofs and hard standings—especially for the sick awaiting transit.

V.R.C.Ss. required much larger premises since they had to hold not less than 150 to 200 mules plus the sick sent down by at least two C.M.V.Ss. When located in or near railhead towns such as Capua it was sometimes possible to requisition Italian barracks and stabling in varying conditions of serviceability. Excess holdings in animals, however, were necessarily accommodated in adjacent paddocks and temporary increments of civilian labour or soldiers authorized for care and maintenance. The British manpower of a V.R.C.S. provided two officers—the C.O. being a V.O., and the second officer normally a V.O. though sometimes a quartermaster. There were forty-eight R.A.V.C. other ranks plus attached R.A.S.C. drivers for seven vehicles, six of which were three-ton lorries adapted with long extension ramps and internal fittings, for the carriage of horses and mules.

In April 1944 an excellent trailer with high sides and a towing bar was improvised by R.E.M.E. from disused Bedford chassis. These trailers, after modifications, permitted carriage of twelve small or eight large mules, it was found quite practicable for a full load of twenty small mules to be conveyed along many of the main highways of the Apennines by the ordinary three-ton lorries, although the Dodge lorries with their suitable gear ratios and four-wheel drive were to prove the most suitable of all. No V.R.C.S. was able to acquire its full complement of six trailers though No. 3 V.R.C.S. held three of them. To give some idea of the additional lift which these trailers could provide for the V.R.C.Ss., two examples are quoted:—

In July 1944, No. 3 V.R.C.S. using its lorries and three trailers were able to move 300 remounts, their personnel and equipment from Capua to Passo Corese (140 miles) in four days besides evacuating the sick animals to Persano (80 miles) and collecting an equivalent number of remounts. With the same equipment, in August 1944, 1,400 mules were moved by road from Littoria and Minturine to a remount depot 125 miles distant without a casualty.

V.R.C.Ss. were equipped to deal with surgical and medical cases until they could be moved back to hospitals which could be as much as one hundred miles away. If required to do so they could undertake longer-term hospitalization pending the arrival of a hospital unit, or alternatively function as an advanced remount depot if suitable paddock accommodation and local labour was available. During the first winter, No. 2 V.R.C.S. while at Foggia awaiting the arrival of No. 1 Field Remount Depot from Middle East, held over 1,000 animals, functioning in three rôles as a remount purchasing and collecting centre for locally procured mules, a remount depot and as a hospital.

The V.R.C.Ss. proved outstandingly useful units for this campaign, and although the principle of avoiding contact between fit remounts and diseased could not always be meticulously enforced in such a small unit, there were no serious repercussions because equine epidemics of high infectivity and rate of spread did not occur in Italy and Sicily during the war.

The base R.A.V.C. units—the hospitals and remounts depots although under district or area control for local administration were able to have direct access through A.D.V.R.S. to Rear Headquarters Army on matters of veterinary and remount significance. This system worked well and it was to become the boast of the R.A.V.C. that no animal reinforcement was delivered to any pack unit outside twenty-four hours from the time of demand.

This chain of supply and evacuation, however, could not be effectively maintained without suitable base hospitals. Although their work in some ways was less spectacular, it was here that the technical skill of officers was brought to bear in restoring to active-service fitness 46 per cent. of the seriously sick and badly injured horses, and 68 per cent. of the mules. Cured animals unlikely to withstand field service conditions were returned to civil life. No. 4 Veterinary Hospital (West Coast) and No. 6 (East Coast) were equipped as hospitals for 250 animals but with labour increments and adjustments to the N.C.O. content of the establishment were able to deal with very much larger number than originally thought possible.

In World War II, the mule rather than the horse occupied the stage and being a comparatively hardy animal, seemed to require less surgical interference than the horse, and was less prone to lameness. However, some interesting investigational work on obscure high lameness was done, using injections of local anaesthetic into the joint cavities of the shoulder and stifle. Many hoof sections were also carried out for foot lameness using all the well-known methods, with careful records maintained. The final conclusion was that hoof sectioning was useless as a permanent cure. In so far as open wound treatment of mules was concerned, it was an outstanding fact proved by clinical trial in one hospital, that healing was quicker and with less complications if not repeatedly dressed or irrigated after the initial debridement and cleaning up had been done. Many wounds were caused by shrapnel and mines, and X-ray and mine-detection apparatus proved very useful for locating fragments. Major A. M. Bain, O.C. No. 2 V.R.C.S., had an exhibit of three sackfuls of metal which he had removed from wounded animals after the first fortnight of the Sangro River battle. Fistulous withers due to neglected saddle injuries were frequent and although no new surgical techniques were developed, sulphonomide proved useful in shortening the healing period; old scars on backs were removed by surgical operation. Quittor cases were extremely rare, a striking comparison with World War I, which was strange, bearing in mind that mules were shod all round, including with caulkins in front, and often had to be kept on muddy and foul picket lines. Muting operations were carried out on a certain number of mules required for special operations but the numbers were small compared to those in Burma; a fair number of ovariotomy operations were done in vice cases, and very large numbers of castrations.

No. 4 Veterinary Hospital at Persano had ample and good paddock accommodation and was able to restore many debilitated and war-worn animals to health before re-issue, in its capacity as a convalescent depot. The paddocks were extensively covered to a depth of one inch with "fall-out" conveyed by a south-west wind from the big eruption of Mount Vesuvius in 1944. It was an amazing sight to see the amount of contamination, bearing in mind a distance of over forty miles from the eruption. The dust was very fine and with subsequent high winds, conditions like a sandstorm occurred which eventually dispersed the volcanic dust completely. Traces of this ash were subsequently said to have been detected as far away as Constantinople. Incidentally animals in paddocks suffered no discomfort or illness during the contamination period.

No. 6 Veterinary Hospital, serving 8th Army units in the eastern sector, lacked comparable grazing facilities at Apricena, and was situated roughly two miles from No. 1 Field Remount Depot. No. 6 Veterinary Hospital later was to move forward on the east coast to Jesi near Ancona. It fulfilled an unusual rôle for a purely veterinary unit during the last two months of the war as a combined remount depot and veterinary hospital, holding 1,200 animals to free No. 1 V.R.C.S. and enable it to participate in the final advance. By the end of the campaign the third British veterinary hospital (No. 7) had been formed and earmarked for Yugoslavia, and two Italian Army hospitals were already assisting with the treatment of veterinary casualties for both the 5th and the 8th Armies. One diagnostic laboratory had been brought over from Middle East in the early days to assist in the identification of epizootic lymphangitis, mange and other equine and canine diseases and was located to begin with at Apricena.

The key to the remount situation was the establishment in rearward areas of two large remount holding depots, one on the east coast at Apricena within easy distance by rail and road from the port of Bari, and at Persano close to the railhead of Barracammenti, with good communications with the ports of Salerno and Naples. Of these two, No. 812 Base Remount Depot on the west coast had by far the largest and most suitable premises for holding an animal reserve, and although many thousands of remounts were shipped from Middle East to Italy most of which were unloaded at the east coast port of Bari, yet a considerable proportion of them were railed via Taranto and Potenza to Persano. No. 812 B.R.D. remained on its pleasant location throughout hostilities since its supply line was closely associated with our main source of mules provided by No. 3 Remount Purchasing Commission in Sicily, from which 7,000 animals were ultimately received. This depot seldom held less than 2,000 animals, and was ably run by Major J. H. McGhee, followed by Major G. T. Newport, with a small R.A.V.C. cadre establishment, assisted for some months by a Basuto increment for the care and training of mules to the pack saddle before issue. No. 1 F.R.D. acted similarly as a remount collecting centre for mules bought on the mainland in the provinces of Campobasso, Foggia and Matera and received upwards of 3,000 mules from the remount purchasing commission in Italy later operated by various officers and latterly by Lieutenant-Colonel R. K. Kent. Apricena did not prove a good location for remounts because it lacked roomy grazing paddocks; the artificially constructed ones on the sports stadium of the town were small, cramped and became very muddy and foul in winter. This was an added complication when an outbreak of epizootic lymphangitis occurred during the first winter of the campaign. It was not possible to vacate this location until Rome fell a few months later, after which No. 1 F.R.D. was moved forward to the Italian Army remount depot of Passo Corese.

No. 3 Base Depot Veterinary Stores staffed by one officer and seven other ranks was attached to No. 1 F.R.D. at Apricena and later at Passo Corese and proved sufficient for the campaign.

The mules which accompanied British units from Middle East and North Africa had been bred in various parts of the Middle East and Africa. Chief of these were Iraq, Persia, Cyprus, South Africa, Abyssina, Morocco, and Tunisia. In addition the 5th Army imported from U.S.A. some large mules of 15 to 15.2 hands for mountain artillery and ambulance duties.

It was fortunate that occupied territories in Sicily and Southern Italy were able to provide perhaps the most suitable types of mules of any for operations in the Apennines. The need in winter was for pack mules of the "leggy" type known in India as equipment mules, because the smaller Middle East breeds from Cyprus and Iraq, were unable to cope as effectively with deep mud and snow as the indigenous types. Nevertheless, besides the mules that accompanied the pack units from Middle East, many thousands of remounts were sent from Middle East to provide the required 30 per cent. reserve for the build-up that occurred in the 5th and 8th Armies' pack companies, between 1943-45, and they performed very useful services indeed. Some of the smaller tough Iraqi mules later found their way to Yugoslavia and were greatly liked by Marshal Tito's partisan forces due to their ability to withstand hardship and heavy loads. The Cyprus-bred mules reared in a kinder climate than Italy, were in fact mostly jennets; although they appeared better in quality than some of the other breeds, they did not withstand the effects of transit and shipping, took longer to acclimatize, and did not endure privation and sustained work so well; neither did the dimunitive Abyssinian mules which made up the entire complement of No. 6 Indian Mule Company, go through the winter mud satisfactorily although their ability, relative to their bodyweight to carry exceptionally large loads was unquestionable under dry conditions. The remounting of this particular company presented a special problem since it was equipped with the small size Indian pack saddle and the smallest size Iraqi mules had to be found as replacements. By way of comparison, the hardy type of small pack mule most suited to conditions in the North-West Frontier of India, proved on the whole unsuitable for the mountains and mud of southern Europe.

Amongst the remounts from Iraq and Persia were a large number of grey mules. The Americans were never keen on accepting greys and there was some divergence of opinion in the 8th Army on whether grey animals were more easily observed than those of any other colour. In the early stages of the campaign a brown dye ("Durafur", I.C.I.) was found to give a persistent stain for as long as three months. Later on, whether due to faulty material or to some peculiarity in the animals' coats, all efforts to produce a stable colour failed. The final verdict seems to have been that animals of any colour if employed in daylight within enemy observation are easily detected; that greys are not more obvious than other colours by night, and in snow are less obvious; any advantage to be gained by dyeing is out-weighed by the reduced visibility of greys under snow conditions.

The earlier surveys had shown that Sicily and parts of Italy could produce fine specimens of mountain artillery mule, and these were urgently needed in 1943-44 to equip British mountain artillery regiments as well as American units equipped with the large and heavy Phillips cargo saddle. Additional mules of the best mountain artillery specification possessing good temperament were required throughout the campaign as ambulance mules for carriage of stretchers and cacolets. These were readily produced by No. 3 R.P.C. in Sicily and also were found in Matera province in the vicinity of the commune of Alberona which had an unusually big number of large mules.

As in other mountainous regions such as Corsica, the pack mule and local saddle had always been used by the inhabitants of villages sited on hill-tops with bad road communications, so frequently observed in provinces in the south of Italy. Mules procured in such districts were already conditioned physically and temperamentally to pack and were therefore much easier to train than some from other territories. Although the Italian peasant was accustomed to working a mule after it was three years of age, the Army found that the conditions of active service were not tolerated until a mule was fully five years old. The majority of debilitated animals that were evacuated to rear depots for convalescence were the young rather than the aged, and a surprising number of broken-winded three-year-olds were found when the remount purchasing commissions were inspecting mules in the communes. As a working rule no mule under the age of four and over twelve years was bought by the Army. The conditions under which purchase and requisition were carried out in Italy, and particularly in Sicily where banditry and intimidation has always been prevalent, were far from easy for the R.P.Cs. and the Allied Military Government in Sicily was not so effective as in Italy in obtaining compliance with requisition orders perhaps because most Allied units had by then left the island. Nevertheless, Taffara Giovanni proved a valuable mule agent to the commission in Sicily until his death in 1944, after which one of his relations carried on until the work finished at the end of hostilities. The prices paid for mules in Italy and Sicily were much higher than elsewhere and rose from an average of £75 for A.T. mules and £87 for the M.A. variety in 1943 to £146 for A.T. and £156 for M.A. after November 1944. In Italy the prices paid by the Army were a little lower than in Sicily and though they were roughly 25 per cent. below the market prices of mules which had soared due to the needs of agriculture and because of their value as carriers in illegal black market activities—there were rich rewards for those able to transport grain and olive oil over the Apennines from the fertile eastern provinces to the depleted western regions of Italy.

By the end of hostilities, No. 3 R.P.C. had been able to procure in nineteen months 6,770 mules, 5,343 of which were purchased through agents and dealers, and the remainder by requisition. On the Italian mainland, the equivalent contribution obtained mostly by requisition and purchase amounted to just under 4,000 mules. Here it should be mentioned that on average, only 6 per cent. of the total mules presented for inspection were found acceptable, so that very large numbers indeed were seen and rejected by the commissions. The mileages covered by the R.P.C. on bad roads in Sicily were large, anything from 2,000-2,500 miles per month, and it was not uncommon experience to travel 200 miles in a day to find that some flagrant and deliberate mis-interpretation of the requisition order had occurred—with no animals presented for inspection and much waste of time incurred.

It was the duty of the remount depots to try out all animals before issue to ensure that only workable animals reached the field units. But sometimes there was trouble. During the period of the assault on the Hitler Line, one A.V.R.O. reported: "Companies are now operating at night. Any disturbance by difficult animals draws enemy fire. Animals which are difficult to handle invariably escape during operations". Colonel Townsend summed up the situation in a typically terse instruction to his officers: "All V.Os. are reminded that the Base Depots and Hospitals have a hard task to keep up the supply of mules to the front. Mules are purchased with every care to see that they are the best available. The supply is running short. We cannot in future afford to be so particular. Complaints sometimes are made that mules are not quiet enough. On investigation of such cases that are sent down it was found that such mules were much above themselves, short of work and too well fed. The remedy was successful. I request all V.Os. especially at the front not to accept it as a fact when a mule is described as 'vicious'. It may be fairer to say 'mischievous' and a great endeavour should be made to subdue his spirits and sober him down with the obvious remedies. It is often the toughest and best working mules who assume this mischievous attitude when they are too long hanging about perhaps in Base V & R Units or perhaps in forward V & R Units awaiting their turn to join in the battle. The work of the army mule was never more valuable than today and it is becoming harder to find the right mule. Let us not cast him out until he has been given a thorough try out".

With few exceptions all English horses employed in Italy were selected from those of the 1st Cavalry Division in Palestine. They were mature, strong, serviceable animals, well-trained and steady rides. They stood up to the work well under the severest conditions.

A variety of North African Barbs and Syrian and Iraqi Arabs was also used. These were, generally speaking, equal to the work. Several of the North African horses had not been castrated and were, for this reason, intractable, and in some ways, difficult to handle.

A number of Italian and Sicilian horses and ponies were acquired. Some were good strong animals but almost without exception these were bad movers and indifferent rides. The smaller type of Italian horse and the Sardinian pony were better bred. A proportion of these were too small and light for the work required, but the stronger and bigger ponies were acceptable.

Some Sudanese ponies accompanied units from the Middle East. These were hardy little animals, and almost all good rides. Like the Abyssinian mule they were unable to negotiate deep mud.

When the Italian campaign began there were uncertainties about equine contagious diseases which, it was thought, could adversely influence the forecasted wastage rate as soon as the numbers of remounts started to accumulate in the base remount depots of southern Italy. The mule and horse remounts had been bred in territories as far distant as Persia, Iraq, America, North and South Africa, Cyprus and Abyssinia. At some time or other concentrations from these various territories would mix with the steady flow of indigenous remounts arriving from No. 3 Remount Purchasing Commission in Sicily and from the purchasing commission operating in Italy. Such conditions could well be the precursor of rapidly spreading epidemics which might have impeded operations. Already African horse sickness had broken out in Upper Egypt in July 1943, at Komombo—situated on a caravan route in the upper Nile Valley—and the disease was rapidly spreading northwards amongst civil animals in the narrow desert-flanked Nile Valley to the Delta 400 miles away. Here there were a few army animals in the vicinity of Cairo and Alexandria and not so far distant, large numbers of remounts in our depots in Palestine and the Lebanon. Also ascending this narrow Nile route at the time were regular consignments of thousands of Sudanese sheep for the cattle stock sections in Italy and elsewhere.

African horse sickness was very much in the minds of the senior officers of the Army Veterinary and Remount Services early in 1944, as G.H.Q. Middle East had undertaken to send to Italy most of the trained pack and mountain artillery units then ready and waiting in Syria, and at a later stage a 30 per cent. reserve of remounts to maintain them. The short campaign in Sicily had revealed a serious lack of anti-malarial readiness among many allied formations that had participated in the invasion, and the casualties amongst soldiers from this disease were heavy. There was every reason to suppose, therefore, that suitable insect vectors for spreading African horse sickness would exist in Italy and Sicily, as in other countries bordering the Mediterranean. It was very fortunate indeed for the equine population in Europe that African horse sickness did not enter Italy as serious outbreaks of the disease occurred in our depots in Palestine in 1944 causing a delay of six weeks in the remounting programme. With this single exception, the prospect of spreading African horse sickness to Italy, the disease problem never became a really serious factor in the campaign and the only diseases of any significance encountered were tetanus and epizootic lymphangitis. Tetanus took toll of badly wounded animals undergoing hospitalization particularly in the province of Foggia. Thirty-six fatal cases occurred up to May 1944 and tetanus toxoid was eventually obtained for active immunization. Every mule in the force could not be protected and cases continued to occur throughout hostilities (a total of 99).

In the past there have seldom been campaigns in the Middle East or Far East where animals have not at some time or other been affected with paraplegia or suspected encephalomyelitis. In Burma there had been outbreaks of so-called kumri in the last year of the war and many cases were seen in the mules and horses during disposals of surplus army animals in 1947. Throughout the northern coast of Africa, sporadic cases of encephalomyelitis have occasionally been known to occur, and this was army experience in Egypt and Palestine before and during the war. Nevertheless, despite the very large numbers of mules and horses that were imported into Italy from territories where this disease sometimes occurs there were no official records of mortality from paralysis.

The prospect that glanders might be introduced to units by infected captured animals was always considered a strong possibility, since there was evidence from the branding of some of those captured that they had previously come from the Balkans and other parts of Europe where the disease was prevalent. The first of a series of administrative instructions issued by Colonel C. H. S. Townsend on veterinary and other matters dealt with this very pertinent question of the method of disposal on the battle field of captured animals, and about mallein testing procedures. Very many thousands of doses of I.D.P. mallein produced at the R.A.V.C. laboratory in Aldershot, were used for testing animals obtained by the commissions and from other sources. No cases of glanders occurred throughout the campaign and it should also be mentioned that no cases were ever detected among the 60,000 or so captured animals concentrated in Austria at the end of the war, some of which had come from Hungary, Russia and other parts of Eastern Europe.

The equine disease of primary importance in Italy was epizootic lymphangitis. Italy and Sicily had always been the home of this insidious disease and the civil and army veterinary authorities rather accepted it as something that would always remain with them. They did not destroy clinically affected animals but attempted to treat them in isolation clinics and hospitals. The R.A.V.C. had previously encountered epizootic lymphangitis in the Abyssinian mule remounts introduced from the Sudan to our depots in Palestine. It had been a somewhat latent form of disease, often difficult to identify from the clinical symptoms alone and requiring microscopic verification. Some were cases of catarrh and conjunctivitis yet provided positive microscopic smears without showing enlargement of the lymphatic vessels of the head and face. No. 3 R.P.C. in Sicily was the first R.A.V.C. unit to report cases of epizootic lymphangitis among civilian-owned animals. Open cases with the typical chain of lymphatic nodules and ulcers were encountered in some of the cities and communes during purchase operations, and the local authorities had to be shaken out of their apathy by the officer commanding the commission through direct contact with the G.O.C., H.Q., No. 1 District since the provincial officials of the Allied Military Government at that time seemed unable to exert the necessary authority over the Sicilians. The Italian regulations for this disease were that all equine animals showing clinical symptoms had to be brought before a veterinarian who would arrange quarantine and treatment until the animal succumbed or was fully recovered, and under no circumstances would diseased animals be permitted on the streets. This rule was being completely disregarded especially during the sowing and harvesting months and several cases were seen in transport animals in the larger towns. The R.A.V.C. made strenuous efforts to keep the disease clear of army units and the orders were that suspicious clinical cases would be destroyed if necessary, for the safety of other animals, before confirmatory diagnosis had been provided by the R.A.V.C. laboratory at Apricena—under wartime conditions this might take ten days. Although regarded as a chronic disease there were several instances quoted in the reports of R.A.V.C. officers, where recently purchased and apparently healthy animals, as well as healed gunshot wound cases, suddenly broke out with the fulminating lymphatic form of the disease in various parts of the body, within seven days of passing a weekly routine veterinary examination. These experiences showed that a very strict inspection drill had to be adopted in all units. This was one of the principal reasons why the D.D.V.R.S. decided to have a R.A.V.C. cadre of one officer and one N.C.O. posted to the establishment of every Italian pack unit, because he believed that the animals of the Italian Army were the most likely source for disseminating the disease through R.A.V.C. units when their casualties had to be evacuated. The most serious outbreak to occur was in a batch of mules (healed gunshot wound cases) which were discharged as cured cases from hospital to No. 1 F.R.D. when this unit first occupied the muddy and half-completed paddocks in Apricena. Under the prevailing congested conditions, the disease was not spotted and it became necessary to evacuate the paddocks and place all animals on picket lines on the roadways, and to close the depot for issues and receipts for a few weeks until the disease had been eradicated. Nevertheless, epizootic lymphangitis did not at any stage of the campaign interfere with operations. In the first eight months, 105 mules and horses had been destroyed as clinical cases and by the end of hostilities rather over twice this number had been disposed of. A puzzling feature of epizootic lymphangitis as seen in units in Italy, was its uncertain rate of spread and infectivity. Italian Army veterinarians considered that the British, if they insisted on slaughtering all suspected and confirmed clinical cases, would find themselves having to destroy up to 50 per cent. of the mule population in the Army. Their forecast, happily, was far from correct, for the disease did not spread rapidly although it was usual to see more cases between May and December. It was thought possible also that the summer condition of parasitic skin bleeding (filariasis) might readily create some of the possible points of entry for the cryptococcus into the body. Epizootic lymphangitis clinics or hospitals, were a feature of the Italian military organization and one of these was located on the outskirts of Bari. It was claimed by Italians, that cures could be obtained with various lines of treatment. The Italians placed most emphasis on the combination of excision, autogenous vaccination, non-specific protein therapy, and mercury preparations administered topically and parenterally. The D.D.V.R.S. felt in these circumstances that opportunity should be taken to run a small epizootic lymphangitis experimental treatment centre; this was to be the task of Major R. C. Crowhurst, commanding No. 4 Veterinary Hospital. The conclusions arrived at in the comparatively short time available were indefinite since experience showed on more than one occasion that a flare up of lymphatic lesions would occur after an apparent complete cure. The R.A.V.C. method of control was substantially the same as in World War I, and it was insisted that the only wound dressing to be used where outbreaks occurred should be oily dressing applied by the flit syringe; bandages and dressings had to be dispensed with in such circumstances and results achieved justified this procedure.

Early in June 1944, the first of a few cases of ulcerative lymphangitis caused by *Corynebacterium ovis* (Preisz-Nocard's bacillus) was diagnosed at No. 4 Veterinary Hospital and confirmed by laboratory examination. A few cases had been seen earlier in the war in 1941 in Beirut among captured French-bred draught horses of the Vichy forces, and with the prevalence and similarity in symptoms of epizootic lymphangitis, careful examinations had to be made to distinguish them from this disease as well as glanders. It was ascertained that ulcerative lymphangitis was well known in certain provinces of Italy, lesions usually being confined to the fore and hind legs below the knee and hock. Cellulitis and gross enlargement of the leg was a feature plus some budding and ulceration along the lymphatics of the affected limb, whereas epizootic lymphangitis lesions tended to be centred on the lymphatic vessels without undue swelling of the affected limb. This disease, said to be mud-borne and known to be capable of causing considerable losses in wartime when large numbers of horses and mules are congregated together, never spread and multiplied as it did in France in the summer of 1916 when many hundreds of cases developed, with an accumulation of over 2,000 under treatment in veterinary hospitals by December, 1917. The mud conditions of Italy were described by the D.D.V.R.S. as "worse than he had ever seen in France in the first world war". In certain parts of Italy the mud had a depilating effect, and there is a record of the mules of one North African pack company having lost all the hair on their legs after prolonged work in the mire.

The prevailing seasonal disease, or perhaps clinical state, affecting nearly all mules bred in Sicily and Southern Italy was cutaneous filariasis (parasitic skin bleeding) caused by *Filaria tropicalis*. There was no loss of bodily condition or apparent discomfort, but it was most unsightly with many bleeding points and a cumulative loss of several ounces of blood per day. The disease usually made its appearance in the middle of March, and the incidence was high from about May onwards during the summer, and diminished considerably by the onset of autumn. The blood and its decomposition products were found to have a destructive effect on the numnah pannels of the pack saddle and this predisposed to saddle galls. The most common sites of the bleeding points were the withers, shoulders and back, and along the upper ribs. Swellings usually appeared in the morning and their rupture seemed to be hastened, and the symptoms accentuated by a strong sun. Risaldar Kartar Singh, I.A.V.C., a Viceroy's commissioned officer with one of the Indian pack units, made a detailed study of the condition having as he said, seen somewhat similar symptoms in cattle in India caused by the larger *Filaria haemorrhagica*. He claimed that intravenous tartar emetic gave complete relief in doses of 100 cc of a 1 per cent. solution, repeated three to five times at intervals of three to five days; that is for mules of about fifteen hands stature, with a proviso that weaker or debilitated animals and the smaller pack mules should receive a suitable reduced dose. His results are recorded in the *Journal of the R.A.V.C.* of May 1945. For those unfamiliar with cutaneous bleeding in the equine, it should be mentioned that no cases were ever seen in mules or horses imported from other parts of the Middle East between the years 1943-45, despite the longish periods that some of them would have spent in various parts of Italy. As might be expected, this condition is not confined to Italy and was previously encountered during World War I in Greece, and in a batch of Turkish Army animals captured near Baghdad. The R.A.V.C., however, never encountered parasitic skin bleeding in North Africa or elsewhere in the Middle East.

It was expected that protozoal diseases might appear during the summer, and it transpired that the mule was more resistant than the horse to piroplasmosis, cases of which started to occur in imported horses and war dogs in May 1944. The highest incidence was sixteen equine cases during one week in June, and the overall number of cases slightly exceeded one hundred. The principle chemotherapeutic drug used was pirevan (quinuronium sulphate), and dips were constructed in some of the guard sections for the elimination of ticks.

No cases of rabies occurred among army animals in Italy, although some cases of the disease did occur in privately owned animals; in one incident, a R.A.V.C. officer was the subject of a disciplinary investigation as a result of his having to undergo a course of anti-rabic vaccinations through a technical error he made. This incident resulted in yet another administrative instruction issued by the D.D.V.R.S. for the benefit of his officers and men, instructing them to dissociate themselves from the handling of the pet animals held by some units.

Skin disease, often coupled with debility, has caused appreciable wastage in wars of the past. In Italy, the majority of the indigenous mules purchased by the commission were heavily infested with lice, and in winter could not be effectively treated owing to their long coats; R.A.V.C. units, therefore, were busily employed in clipping out prior to treatment with derris preparations or A.L. 63 (D.D.T.)—the latter preparation being extensively used for treating lice-infested refugees and displaced persons. Veterinary officers, however, were warned of previous occasions when lice and mange were found to be co-existent, and so not to expect without further close examination that lice were the sole cause of any skin irritation. Officers commanding advanced R.A.V.C. units which were prone to frequent changes of location, were also instructed to disinfect any farm premises before occupation by army animals. Mange, like epizootic lymphangitis, was of fairly common occurrence in civilian owned animals in the towns and countryside, but it never became a significant military hazard. When the disease was diagnosed, affected animals were invariably evacuated direct to one of the base hospitals where they were treated in mange clinics some miles away from the main hospital premises. The old-fashioned treatments of sulphur and bunker oil and freshly prepared calcium sulphide solution were effectively used; the latter gave rather better results with debilitated animals.

Ringworm was of common occurrence during the second winter in Italy, and one outbreak originated in a large consignment of mules transferred from Middle East. It was a benign form of the disease and caused no particular problems.

Respiratory diseases, despite two very severe winters in the Apennines, never obtruded unduly into the veterinary picture. Catarrh was a common seasonal complaint, pneumonia was rare, and comparatively few strangles cases occurred among young remounts.

Digestive complaints among equines were conspicuous by their absence in this campaign and this was undoubtedly a tribute to the excellent quality of the forage supplied in Italy—better than any seen elsewhere in the Middle East. Colic cases were such a rarity that O.C. No. 1 C.M.V.S. made especial reference to it in his report when a single case occurred during the first advance in 1943 to the winter line. The veterinary authorities had been warned that anthrax was of common recurrence in the spring and early summer in the province of Campobasso and near Isernia, which was the area of much activity by pack units; no cases or anything remotely suspicious of anthrax was recorded.

Such was the demand for V.Os. for pack formations and R.A.V.C. units, and for veterinary supervision of sheep purchase in North Africa and Sardinia—demands which came at a time when there was a competing requirement for R.A.V.C. officers in Burma and India—that the veterinary coverage needed to improve animal health and to control epidemics among civilian-owned livestock behind the advancing 5th and 8th Armies, could not be provided from our resources. The American Army however, was able to provide some public health veterinary officers for staffing the Allied Control Commission and they were responsible for ensuring that the Italian veterinarians were supplied with the materials and equipment, plus the necessary degree of direction for complying with their pre-war regulations on control of animal disease.

Despite this the needs of agriculture and of foodstuffs were such at that time that enforcement rules were seldom adhered to in the proper way, and the violation of the regulations on the movement of livestock in infected areas resulted in widespread outbreaks of foot-and-mouth disease among sheep in Sardinia and in epidemics of swine fever and swine plague on the mainland. Fairly close liaison was maintained by R.A.V.C. officers, particularly in the rearward areas, with American public health veterinary officers, on questions of this sort, which was necessary because the R.A.V.C. was responsible for importing meat on the hoof from territories far from Italy. It was indeed fortunate, and a tribute to the British Colonial Veterinary Service staff in the Sudan, that none of the many thousands of Sudanese sheep that made the long journey to Italy for military consumption were the cause of introducing any African diseases, especially rinderpest, to Southern Europe where a highly susceptible animal population existed. The same might be said of our more junior veterinary officers who worked alongside the R.A.S.C. in the screening and purchase of sheep in North Africa for shipment to Italy.

To conclude this section on the main problems encountered by the R.A.V.C. in Italy it would be accurate to say that the principal causes of wastage in transport animals were battle casualties, chief of which were gunshot wounds and those that occurred in minefields. Battle casualties were rather higher than expected whereas wastage from contagious and infectious disease, and from lameness, was lower than originally predicted. The overall wastage estimate for provisioning had been assessed by the D.D.V.R.S. at ten per cent. per month, and only in the first winter in Italy before sufficient R.A.V.C. units were available, did the figure exceed this by a small margin. The total number of deaths and destruction of mules and horses caused in battle between September, 1943 and April, 1945 was 2,725, and the peak figures for operational losses were 337 animals in December, 1943 and 394 in October, 1944. Detailed statistics are given in Appendix X.

In August 1944 Colonel J. J. Plunkett took over the appointment of D.D.V.R.S. from Colonel Townsend. He came at the moment when further expansion in the numbers of pack and R.A.V.C. units was being considered for the winter offensive in the Apennines and for operations in Yugoslavia. It was known that difficulties were likely to occur in the next few months because of the start in the repatriation scheme, called "Python", for men with continuous service overseas exceeding four years. One hundred and seventy of our men (about one-third of the R.A.V.C. establishment in C.M.F.) had been abroad over four and a half years; and a few officers previously in Egypt and India before the war who had not seen England for seven or eight years. It was vital that replacements from home should arrive in time to fill the gaps. However, there was a delay until January 1945, before the main draft of 119 reinforcements arrived.

In so far as the expansion in pack was concerned, the U.S. Army authorities were making immediate preparations to form another five pack companies before winter— this gave us fifteen American pack companies to service. Animal wastage due to fatal casualties was unusually high in the last week of October with 149 killed and missing, and 208 evacuated sick. No. 3 V.R.C.S. had by now moved from Passo Corese to Arezzo after replacement by No. 1 Field Remount Depot, and was providing remounts and evacuating sick for both the 5th and the 8th Armies. The strain on unit M.T. was exceptionally heavy with the onset of appalling weather which disorganized the rail system between Passo Corese and the front. The work performed by the R.A.V.C. units was suitably recognized by a visit made to No. 3 V.R.C.S. by General Alexander the Commander-in-Chief, Allied Armies in Italy, on the 1st December 1944.

Although we were better equipped and organized to deal with casualties and their replacement in the second winter, animal transport units were working at high altitudes in very rigorous weather indeed. This and the extension of R.A.V.C. activity on a larger scale than originally contemplated for the Yugoslavia front, called for five new units—No. 8 C.M.V.S., No. 7 V.R.C.S., No. 601 Italian Veterinary Hospital, No. 2 Veterinary Laboratory and the last R.A.V.C. unit sent from Middle East, No. 817 C.M.V.S., commanded by Captain D. Burgess, also arrived about this time, to look after the newly formed No. 252 Italian Pack Group and its four companies. The Corps were now responsible for the veterinary and remount services for 22,168 mules and horses, with a further thousand in Yugoslavia; this required an all-out effort by the remount purchasing commissions which included No. 5 R.P.C. commanded by Lieutenant-Colonel R. K. Kent in South-East Italy, No. 3 R.P.C. in Sicily now in charge of Lieutenant-Colonel D. A. Gillmor, and, with the hold-up of remounts from Middle East due to outbreaks of African horse sickness in Palestine, Major K. Cabban, R.A.V.C., was sent to North Africa to undertake further surveys of mule resources in that territory. Plans were afoot to establish No. 6 R.P.C. there, if sufficient mules could be obtained. The French authorities, however, did not agree to provide the numbers required.

With the progressive increase in the animal strength the formation of another veterinary hospital for 500 animals became necessary; this was staffed by a Basuto increment with a R.A.V.C. cadre in charge.

Our last field unit formed in Italy was No. 8 V.R.C.S., in February 1945; its rôle was to replace the detachment of No. 1 F.R.D. at Piazza Armerina in Sicily.

The tempo of animal procurement by the R.P.Cs. had been unrelenting throughout the campaign but by the end of March 1945, with the imminent signs of the German surrender, purchasing was slowed down on instructions from War Office. Already No. 7 Mountain Regiment had been ordered to move with its mules to India to participate in the Burma campaign, and plans were in being for large numbers of mules that would become surplus in C.M.F. to be shipped to the Far East.

In April the D.D.V.R.S. issued provisional instructions to the 5th and 8th Armies outlining the scheme for collection and disposal of large numbers of enemy animals that it was believed would be surrendered in Northern Italy and Austria. The plan was that the majority of V.R.C.Ss. and C.M.V.Ss. would be released from their normal duties with the pack formations as soon as hostilities ended. Reconnaissance teams of one officer and three other ranks were to be formed to undertake surveys and census' of animals in German and other units. The C.M.V.Ss. were to function as far forward as possible collecting all enemy animals; these were to be sorted and then evacuated to V.R.C.Ss. after branding with the broad arrow on the near quarter and the "C" (captured) on the off shoulder. The V.R.C.Ss. were to open temporary collecting centres and would prepare spacious paddocks for reception, arranging for the best of any captured mules between 13.0 and 15.0 hands, plus all riding horses, to be evacuated to remount depots or other permanent collecting centres, with the sick transferred to veterinary hospitals. Mules and horses considered unsuitable or unserviceable after initial examination would be disposed of under arrangements with the Allied Military Government and local mayors of towns and villages, who would hand over any serviceable animals on receipt to needy farmers.

Such was the forecasted demand for transport animals not only for rehabilitation of the depleted Balkans and Northern Italy but for assisting the war effort on the Burma front, that the Director of the Army Remount Department in India, visited Italy in April to tour Indian pack units and remount installations. In these circumstances it was considered necessary to enlarge the port reception facilities at the Bari Mule Camp where most animal shipments had staged during the war, and No. 7 V.R.C.S. was posted there to look after the animals awaiting shipment. By the 10th of May, 3,500 A.T. and 580 M.A. mules had been selected for transfer to India and 2,000 of these arrived at the port reception centre by the end of that month. Shipping priority was allotted to the Far East mule consignments though, on the 11th of July, the first consignment of the 7,400 mules for U.N.R.R.A. relief work in Greece were leaving on the s.s. *Fanny Brunner*, a ship destined to deliver all these mules to Piraeus in batches of 600 at one time. The R.A.V.C. found itself very busy during the next six to eight months arranging for the disposal of captured animals—8,000 were taken in Italy, a large proportion of which were draught horses, and some 60,000 were surrendered to the 5th Corps in Austria.

The disbandment of pack companies proceeded steadily after the surrender, and the surplus, including many from the U.S. Army, were moved to our remount depots which by July and August 1945, were holding over 14,000 animals, and No. 7 Veterinary Hospital assumed the temporary rôle of a remount depot until the concentrations were dispersed. U.N.R.R.A. had by now increased the original bid for mules to cover Yugoslavia as well, and by the end of October, the 7,400 animals for Greece had been delivered with an additional 4,600 for Yugoslavia. It is fitting to record here a particularly appreciative letter sent by the U.N.R.R.A. Liaison Office at A.F.H.Q. to the D.D.V., R.S. "The provision of draft animals to the war-stricken Greek farmer is of the greatest help. The food and clothing, which U.N.R.R.A. and other agencies are distributing in Greece will soon be forgotten, but these mules will be remembered for years to come by every Greek farmer who was given the opportunity of having one, as British Army mules given him by U.N.R.R.A. Your office has made it possible for the mules to be shipped into Greece in time for the autumn planting of cereals. This will enable the Greek farmer to produce more food, while the lack of them might have meant still more suffering from lack of food."

Passing reference has been made to administrative and veterinary problems relating to the supply of sheep for the Indian troops. It was well-known that the Gurkhas and other races preferred to have their meat delivered "on the hoof" for ritual slaughter. The morale and fighting qualities of these warriors was undoubtedly influenced by factors such as a regular fresh meat supply, and A.F.H.Q. therefore arranged a comprehensive system of provision from the Middle East, North Africa and Sardinia. The Corps had in its ranks veterinary officers and men experienced in the husbandry and diseases of sheep and they were busily employed for over two years at procurement centres, and as conducting staff for shiploads from the Middle East and elsewhere to Bari. From Bari they were dispatched to holding units, some of which were Indian cattle/sheep stock sections with veterinary supervision provided by the I.A.V.C. During 1944 and 1945 some 8,000 sheep at a time were held in the principal centres in C.M.F.:

Sheep Collecting Centre at Bone N.Africa.
,,   ,,   ,,   Sardinia.
,,   ,,   ,,   52 Area Cozena (Calabria)
,,   ,,   ,,   56 Area Cancello
No. 2 Indian Cattle Stock Section RIASC
No. 22   ,,   ,,   ,,   ,,   ,,
No. 33   ,,   ,,   ,,   ,,   ,,
No. 5 Indian Field Butchery.

There had been rather heavy mortality in shipments of Sudanese sheep around February 1944 with 75 dead out of 1,000 in one particular consignment. In succeeding shiploads, a R.A.V.C. N.C.O. Corporal Willey (a farmer and sheep expert) accompanied by a very good Indian N.C.O. from one of the cattle stock sections supervised the sheep en route and only two out of 1,000 died in the next shipload sent from Middle East. The R.A.V.C. officers most concerned with sheep procurement and investigation of disease outbreaks which periodically occurred, were Captain T. Stewart in North Africa and Captain J. B. Abbott in Sardinia.

Some mention should be included of the contribution made by war dogs. The R.A.V.C. was responsible for their provision from the Middle East and England and for the veterinary supervision of a small number of C.M.P. Guard Dog Sections dispersed in North Africa and Italy for protecting installations against pilfering and theft. The strength in Italy never exceeded 155 dogs although there were some R.A.F. guard dogs in addition requiring regular veterinary inspection. The sickness rate was never serious, but piroplasmosis caused some wastage during summer. Army dogs remained in Italy after the war ended as they were needed just as much in the unstable conditions of military occupation for controlling illegal entry into depots and other installations, and the canine establishment was slightly augmented by eight captured German dogs. There was a small C.M.P. training section in Italy which for a time was close to the foothills of Mount Vesuvius and the R.A.F. equivalent was located near the beautiful coastal resort of Sorrento. It should be mentioned that specialist dogs for infantry patrol and other purposes played no part in the Italian campaign although four infantry patrol and liaison dogs were sent from home in 1943 to assist infantry in the Tunisian mountains. They comprised two Alsations and two collies; one of them, named "Scruff" (actually an Alsatian-Airedale-cross), and his handler achieved some prominence as a result of a rather poignant letter which by-passed staff channels and was written after the North African campaign by his handler and sent direct to the O.C. War Dog Training School at Potters Bar in London. It read as follows:—

> "E" Company, 4 Battalion,
> No. 1 I.R.T.D.,
> B.N.A.F.
> *Date:* 16.9.43.

To: Officer Commanding,
    War Dog Training School.

Sir,

Could you please send me instructions as to what is to happen to my Patrol Dog "Scruff" No. 582 and myself. He is the only dog left out of the four that was sent to the Inniskilling Fusiliers. "Gyp" was killed in action on patrol. "Ben" and "Glen" the two alsation dogs have both died within the last two months. The dogs were not used much in the North African Campaign. The conditions were seldom of any use to work the dogs but what work they did do was done well. I am at the base now, having been graded unfit for a fighting unit and no-one seems to know what to do about myself or the dog so perhaps you could inform me Sir. If there is any dog training schools out in this country, I would be glad to be sent there having gained valuable experience under battle conditions with the dogs which can be passed on to other handlers.

> I am,
> Sir,
> Your Obedient Servant,
> 5335487 Fusilier Winlow, J.

Six months after the end of the war when the R.A.V.C. quarantine scheme for pet dogs was functioning at Chilbolton, the D.D.V.R.S. made arrangements for issuing military licences to applicants of the Navy, Army and Air Force who wished to take their pet dogs home. The scheme was of sufficient dimensions to justify the establishment of a Corps Detachment at Milan. Here the dogs were taken over in batches of between ten and twenty at one time and were sent under escort by rail in a fitted railway truck to Antwerp where they were handed over to another R.A.V.C. unit before being delivered to England. The turn-round period for the fitted truck was about seven days. By February 1946 one hundred dogs had been sent home and there were still in Italy 380 military applicants for licences, forty R.A.F. and one Navy, plus a further one hundred applicants in Austria.

The R.A.V.C. in Italy was unable to disband any of its units at the end of the war because they were to be very fully employed for a long time organizing an orderly disposal of surplus British Army and surrendered animals. Also, five additional small units called "Equitation Training Units" were formed and staffed with R.A.V.C. to provide vocational training for interested officers and other ranks impatiently perhaps awaiting their turn for repatriation. The Army by now had recognized the value of transport animals in mountain warfare; it had become accustomed to working with them; it valued their steadfastness under fire, and a genuine bond of affection had in fact developed for the long-suffering mule who, with the infantry, had borne the brunt of two harsh winters in Italy. Now, however, it was to be the turn of the horse, hitherto utilized by the Army on a comparatively small scale as riders by the pack companies, and to a relatively small extent generally in the Italian campaign.

Contrary to expectation, very few mules—at the most a 1,000—were among the 65,000 or so animals surrendered in North Italy and Austria. There were, however, some fine quality chargers and riders of the German Cavalry Corps handed over in excellent condition at Spittal, in Carinthia. Headquarters, 78th Division, and its D.A.D.V.R.S. were not backward in selecting the best of these, which included a good many Trakheners and Hanoverians, as part of an official scheme for field sports for all ranks of the 8th Army during the period following hostilities. This was a wise idea which had the blessing of A.F.H.Q. and the enthusiastic backing of the last commander of the 8th Army, Lieutenant-General Sir Richard MacCreery—a cavalry-man and keen sportsman. His staff were instructed to apply their energies to issuing detailed instructions, based on the best local intelligence available, on a whole series of manly activities such as racing, shooting the chamoix and buck, fishing, sailing, mountaineering and winter sports. The hand-outs which emerged were a model of their kind and would have undoubtedly received the plaudits of the Editor of *The Field* or Mr. Baedeker. One staff officer was soon producing at his office in Trieste a beautiful printed four-page racing calendar for the Austrian and North Italy Racing Association with regular race meetings convened in places such as Acello and Treviso in Italy, and at Klagenfurt, Graz and Vienna in Austria. There were some 200 registered race-horses most of them captured German horses with a few Hungarians though there was to be one English horse of the 1st Cavalry Division that showed a clean pair of heels on the flat to all comers in Austria. "Ramle" was an English bay gelding (No. 1008) of about 16.2 hands who had not blossomed and shown his potential in the Middle East because of intermittent bouts of sand colic and debility. He had caught Colonel MacDonald's eye at No. 1 R.V.H., Ramle from where he was ultimately transferred to the less sandy location of the remount depot at Nathanya and he started to improve as most horses will when they receive individual attention. But it was not until the A.D.V.R.S., 8th Army, spotted him by chance once more in a veterinary hospital in Italy that his life became reorientated as a future equine V.I.P. He had by then been evacuated sick and unsuitable as a mountain-regiment rider. He was re-issued to H.Q. 8th Army and was subsequently handed over to the custody of the A.D.V.R.S. British Troops in Austria at Udine.

Soon afterwards he moved to the higher altitude of Klagenfurt in Austria where he continued to improve in bodily condition and spirit in the bracing Alpine surroundings. He was to race on four occasions in September and October 1945 on the flat carrying top weight on each occasion and ridden by Private Townsend, R.A.V.C.; each time he won his races with ease against the best possible opposition. He won the open race with a field of thirteen runners at the first meeting to be held in Vienna after the war, on the 20th October 1945. This was attended by an enormous crowd and was held in the presence of Lieutenant-General Sir Richard MacCreery, Marshal Koniev the Soviet C-in-C, General Bethouard the French C-in-C and other senior Allied officers. Under the conditions then prevailing in Vienna there were many administrative difficulties and some obstruction by the Russians in organizing the meeting and very special praise came to our D.A.D.V.R.S. in Vienna, Major B. C. M. Edmonds, who proved a most able Clerk of the Course and a humorous commentator. Although the lighter side of life was now more in evidence, there was still much work to be done by the Corps. The five equitation units at Persano, Passo Corese, Palmanova, Klagenfurt and Graz, were providing useful and enjoyable instruction on equitation and in the techniques for cross-country riding and racing together with the theory and practice of animal management. Officers and senior N.C.Os. with remount and riding experience were appointed to help; amongst them were Captain Bill Cliff, a former Weedon graduate, and Captain Alec Carter who some years before when serving as a N.C.O. with No. 5 Remount Squadron in the Lebanon, had had much to do with the restoration to health of the several hundred valuable French-bred draught horses of the Vichy forces which had suffered badly in the Syrian campaign of 1941.

In the early months after the war, there were about 3,000 riding horses attached to the many units of all arms dispersed throughout Italy and Austria, and the enthusiasm for recreational riding was a notable memory for those of us in the R.A.V.C. Never since the beginning of the war, had the Army been so horse-minded. The official emphasis was upon the enjoyment of life after a long war. A reasonably unrestricted use of army vehicles and petrol was allowed for recreation, sight-seeing and visits to the wonderfully staged Italian open-air operas at such places as Gradisca. One of the more common sights seen on the roads of Northern Italy and Austria were the large numbers of locally fitted three-ton lorries conveying horses to and from the races and other mounted competitions.

The officer who was most involved in making the administrative arrangements for the dispersion and handing over of the horses captured in Austria was Lieutenant-Colonel J. Rix the A.D.V.R.S. 5th Corps at Klagenfurt; he stressed how fortunate it was that an intact and functioning railway system had been the means of saving many thousands of horses by facilitating their rapid dispersion to Northern Italy and other depleted territories (see Chapter VIII).

Since horses provide the closing theme of this chapter it may be of interest to give some details of the Russian horses found in the large Cossack concentration near Lienz. They were small statured horses of about 13.0 to 14.0 hands, bred in the Don Valley. Some were stocky, strong-legged and very hardy looking ponies with typical Mongolian heads; quite a number were dun colour. There were others with a lot of quality which rode very well indeed: they were beautifully proportioned miniature thoroughbreds called Anglo-Donetz horses said to have derived from Russian stock crossed with English thoroughbreds imported into the Don Valley between the two world wars.

The Cossacks were genuine horse lovers and did the best they could, right up to the last moment before they left Lienz, to maintain their charges in good condition. These unhappy men had fought on the wrong side: with, instead of against, the Germans, and finally had to return to an uncertain and doubtless unenviable future in the country of their birth. Many threw themselves from the bridge at Lienz into the fast moving River Drau rather than be handed over to the Soviet Army. This handover of Russian Cossacks to the Soviet Army was a sad and unforgettable experience for the unfortunate British infantry unit which had to enforce the order at bayonet point.

It is fitting to end the chapter with a final reference to Nos. 1 and 4 C.M.V.Ss., both of which had travelled great distances through many countries in the course of their duties in the Middle East and in the Central Mediterranean. They had suffered their share of the discomforts when working in close support of the pack groups and their temporary premises had had their share of the enemy artillery attack. The "Kicking Mule" sign of No. 1 C.M.V.S. became one of the best known unit insignia in Italy.

CHAPTER VI

The India Base

THE amalgamation of the veterinary and remount services during 1941 in other commands was not copied in India where the two departments remained separate until after the war. The account of the Army Veterinary Services in India and Burma therefore omits all but an occasional reference to the remount question.

Until November 1944 the Director of Veterinary Services in India was also responsible for the veterinary administration of South-East Asia Command. Even after this date when S.E.A.C. was divorced from India control it made little difference as India remained the supply base for the Allied Land Forces South-East Asia Command. A chart of the administrative lay-out of the A.V.S. in India and Burma in 1944 is given at Appendix V.

During 1939 to 1942 the Veterinary Directorate consisting of a Director, Assistant Director and attached officer, controlled an establishment of fifty-nine officers who, by the end of this period, had been reduced to forty by War Office postings to the Middle East and East Africa. Then came the great expansion involving relatively huge increases in personnel and stores together with vastly increased responsibilities.

It was not until early 1945 when the strength of officers R.A.V.C. and I.A.V.C. had risen to 481 that sufficient officers became available to fill the establishment—twelve times the 1939–42 figure. The intervening period was obviously one of great strain for the Veterinary Directorate. By early 1945 it had increased to a Director (Brigadier), Deputy-Director (Colonel), two Deputy-Assistant-Directors, two staff captains, and an officer supervisor.

Brigadier H. C. Dibben, the D.V.S. at the outbreak of war, was succeeded, in 1940, by Brigadier J. M. Soutar who, with Brigadier E. S. W. Peatt, who took over in February 1944, shouldered the heavy burden of the expansion programme. Both these Directors had as their deputy Colonel J. J. Kane whose peace-time training in staff work together with his experience as the war progressed, was of the greatest value not only to his Directors but to the whole of the Army Veterinary Service. Colonel Kane himself officiated as Director for some three months in 1945 and from April 1947 until the handing over in August, 1947.

The reductions in establishment, mentioned in Chapter II, continued after the outbreak of war and were still in progress in 1941. By that time the officer establishment had been retrenched by 24 per cent., fourteen hospitals had been closed down, and no plans for mobilization of field veterinary units existed except those for the defence of the North-West Frontier. These reductions occurred without a corresponding decrease in the animal strength as large numbers of horses and mules from mechanized units were concentrated in remount depots. There was no suggestion that animals would be wanted on an extensive scale but the establishment in 1941 included 42,000 horses and mules, 3,800 camels and 17,500 cattle; and a five months reserve (for 78,000 animals) of imported veterinary supplies, together with a two months supply of indigenous items and a small reserve of naganol, had been accumulated in medical store depots; in addition the Base Depot Veterinary Stores held a six months reserve for 10,000 animals.

India had already contributed A.T. companies, mules and I.A.V.C. personnel for the operations in France, and later some 3,200 horses, mules and camels were sent to Aden, East Africa, Greece, Palestine and Iraq. Personnel of the I.A.V.C. on the establishment of Indian mule-transport companies and cattle stock sections were required for the Middle East and later on for the Central Mediterranean Force. By 1945 there were one Mountain Regiment R.A., nine animal-transport companies and seven cattle stock sections R.I.A.S.C. serving in these theatres and twenty veterinary assistant surgeons were carrying out their duties there under the administration of R.A.V.C. officers.

The fall of Singapore and Malaya made India re-orientate her defences to face the Japanese in the east and the lessons learnt in the retreat from Burma, where there were few roads suitable for motor transport, had shown that battalions needed to be organized completely on a pack basis if they were to have freedom of action in hill and jungle. So it was that in 1942 the necessity for the increased employment of animal transport brought home the fact that the Army Veterinary Services would have to be substantially increased.

By then, due to retrenchment, many experienced officers had left the Service, and base formations had to be denuded of their veterinary officers in order to keep mobilized units up to strength. The position, however, had improved by the end of 1944 when the officer strength had increased to 246, which included 150 emergency commissioned R.A.V.C. officers. By V.J. Day (15th August 1945) the establishment of veterinary officers had risen from fifty-seven in 1941 to 481. This number included 258 officers with British veterinary qualifications of whom 230 belonged to the R.A.V.C., and 223 licenciates of Indian veterinary colleges of whom 180 were originally veterinary assistant surgeons I.A.V.C.

The supply of veterinary assistant surgeons was an equally disturbing problem. In November 1943, a total deficiency of 145 was affecting the efficiency of many formations and field units could only with difficulty be kept up to establishment by withdrawal of V.A.Ss. from static units in India. Recruitment was handicapped at a crucial period during the Corps expansion plan, when owing to the formation of the Indian Army Medical Corps in April 1943, terms were given to medical licentiates which were markedly superior to those obtaining in the Indian Army Veterinary Corps. Until the position was equalized for both Corps in the following November, recruitment failed to improve. Gradually, however, the shortage on establishment for units already mobilized and those about to mobilize was reduced to about one hundred. A further stimulus to recruitment was provided later in 1943 by enabling suitable veterinary assistant surgeons with at least one year's service to obtain commissions in the I.A.V.C. Such V.A.Ss. were, however, required to pass through G.H.Q. India, Officers Selection Board in exactly the same manner as other applicants for commissions as combatant officers of the Indian Army.

On V.J. Day there were 329 veterinary assistant surgeons serving in the Army Veterinary Services.

Special difficulty was experienced in providing sufficient farriers. Prior to mechanization farriers were trained in the forges of cavalry and artillery regiments so the disappearance of horsed units meant that if animals were to be re-employed in large numbers there would be a serious shortage of trained farriers. This difficulty became apparent early in the war and to meet it a Farrier Wing was established at the Army Veterinary School, Ambala in 1941. This produced approximately fifty farriers per annum and was only sufficient to replace the trained farriers then wasting out in animal-holding units. The course was of five months duration and turned out farriers of all grades.

The increased demand for animals led to the expansion of the Farriery Wing; at the same time, to meet the urgent needs for farriers in units, the training period was reduced to two months for Grade III farriers.

By November 1943 the original instructional staff of one chief instructor and four assistant instructors had increased to a total of forty-three, eight of these being British farrier-quartermaster-sergeants. Eventually the wing consisted of five training teams each capable of providing practical instruction for thirty-six trainees at a time. Three of the teams were located at Ambala and the other two at Jullundur.

To keep abreast of expansion it was agreed that some thousands of I.A.V.C. other ranks would be required for the new veterinary field units to be mobilized to meet the increasing commitments of the Army Veterinary Services in operational theatres overseas, Burma and South-East Asia. It was also clear that the existing I.A.V.C. Depot could not possibly deal with recruitment and training on this scale. So, on 1st December 1942 an I.A.V.C. Centre was formed at Ambala—none too soon. In the first year of its existence the new Centre had to form and function simultaneously. During this period and for some time afterwards while matters were being corrected, the Centre was grievously handicapped by an establishment which was in the nature of an experiment, and which was later admitted to have been totally inadequate. For example, each Training Squadron held 400 recruits plus N.C.O. instructors; it was officered by one lieutenant! Ludicrous as this was on paper in practice it was even worse as the officers posted had no experience of command and often no knowledge of Urdu. The rest of the establishment was on a similar scale.

Eventually, however, a reasonable staff was authorized (see Appendix VI) and the Centre worked so efficiently that in October 1946 the General Officer Commanding Lahore District reported it as "An excellent Centre in every way. No special problems. Man-management of a very high order. In many respects a model for all."

For a considerable period the only R.A.V.C. officer was the Commandant, Colonel G. Barnett, the second in command being a retired officer of the Punjab Regiment, Lieutenant-Colonel H. Gell. This officer was later succeeded by Lieutenant-Colonel J. S. Kingston, R.A.V.C., and eventually a few I.A.V.C. officers were posted for administrative duty. The training these officers received in the Centre was to prove of great value to both India and Pakistan after the partition.

The composition of the Centre varied from time to time, some branches being added and others discarded according to circumstances. In general it consisted of:—

HEADQUARTERS — Overall administrative responsibility.

Training Regiment — For recruits, first divided into three squadrons each for 400 recruits, later reduced to two squadrons and still later to one squadron.

Depot — Through which all trained personnel passed on entering or leaving the Centre.

RECORD OFFICE — Controlled all postings of all ranks.

Officers' Training School — March 1944 to September 1945.

Army Veterinary School — Divorced from Centre in 1944 to function as separate instructional institution.

Demobilization Squadron — Formed in 1945 from a discarded training squadron.

Resettlement Training Wing — Formed 1945.

The normal five months recruits' training period comprised twelve weeks basic military training, three weeks riding instruction, two weeks elementary animal management, three weeks veterinary first aid.

Some idea of the activities of the Centre in so far as training and drafting of Indian other ranks were concerned may be obtained from the following brief statistics for the year 1944:

(a) Received 2,073 recruits including transfers from other arms.

(b) Received 1,195 I.O.Rs. into the depot from field service areas and other sources.

(c) Drafted 2,647 I.O.Rs. from depot to veterinary units.

(d) The average daily strength was 2,360—this included the training staff.

By V.J. Day the Indian other rank strength of the I.A.V.C., had increased to 6,385.

The expansion of the I.A.V.C. greatly increased the work undertaken by the Record Office and one of the complex problems with which it had to contend was to deal with I.A.V.C. personnel in over 300 different units, veterinary or otherwise, whereas its counterpart in an Infantry Centre had only to cater for the personnel of some eight to ten battalions. From the outset every effort was made to impress on the staff of the Record Office the importance of their work. To assist unit commanders who often, quite naturally, lacked administrative experience, a booklet was issued by the officer commanding the Centre entitled *I.A.V.C.—Pay at a Glance* which gave in simple language all necessary information regarding upwards of a dozen separate elements which made up men's pay and allowances under various conditions of service. In addition a representative from "Records" toured active service areas to explain the importance of accurate maintenance of pay books. The result of this far-sighted policy was that demobilization was carried out with exceptional smoothness, free from the difficulties created by inaccurate and incomplete documents.

As stated in an earlier chapter newly commissioned R.A.V.C. officers were urgently needed for service in India, Burma and S.E.A.C. They received a short period of basic military training at No. 1 R.V.H. Doncaster and then were sent to India. On arrival they were immediately posted to units, some of which were in operational areas. These officers had little or no time to acclimatize or to acquire knowledge of tropical diseases and eastern conditions, or to obtain sufficient military knowledge, particularly in relation to jungle warfare. Many officers were therefore ill-equipped in the military and technical sense for their work and, furthermore, often became casualties from the more common diseases of the East.

It had been generally agreed that an officers instructional branch at the I.A.V.C. Centre was an urgent necessity but the chief difficulty at the time was that training-officers with veterinary qualifications could not be spared for instructional work.

However, in March 1944 the Officers Training School was added to the I.A.V.C. Centre. Up to the cessation of hostilities approximately 200 veterinary officers, British and Indian, attended courses each of two-and-a-half months duration.

The course included basic military training and technical training. Basic military training included physical training, drill, weapon training (rifle, sten gun, pistol and grenade) fieldcraft, equitation, military law, map reading, M.T. driving and maintenance, administration, and Urdu for British officers. Technical training covered the varied problems with which veterinary officers were likely to be confronted in the field. For this reason the veterinary staff were selected on account of their recent experience under field service conditions. Prevalent diseases were given special attention. Particular emphasis was laid on certain aspects of animal management which had proved to be of vital importance in reducing animal wastage in the field. Saddle-fitting was dealt with in practical detail and the close proximity of the farriery wing proved ideal for instruction in the shoeing of army animals. Officer students were required to remove shoes and prepare the foot for shoeing. The more common surgical conditions encountered were covered by lectures and demonstrations whenever possible. Arrangements were made to visit representative units of other branches of the Army in India, especially those with which veterinary officers had to deal during their service.

Each course terminated with an examination and announcement of results, and an interview with each officer by the Director of Veterinary Services in India, who took the salute at the march past.

The value of these courses was inestimable and it was unfortunate that the facilities of the O.T.S. were not available to the first drafts of our emergency commissioned officers; however, as many as possible of these were selected for courses at a later date as and when the opportunity arose.

The following units, excluding those existing at the outbreak of war, were raised and trained for India Base and South-East Asia Command up to June 1945.

Indian Mobile Veterinary Sections	16
Indian Advanced Field Veterinary Hospitals	12
Indian Field Veterinary Hospitals	7
Indian Veterinary Reception Hospitals	3
Indian Veterinary Convalescent Depots	2
Indian Brigade Veterinary Sections	3
Indian Veterinary Detachments	2
Indian Field Veterinary Laboratories	3
Indian Mobile Anti-Surra Units	3
Indian Veterinary Conducting Sections	2
Indian Reserve Base Depot Veterinary Stores	3
Indian Base Depot Veterinary Stores	7
Indian Field Depot Veterinary Stores	5
I.A.V.C. Centre and Records	1
R.A.V.C., I.A.V.C., Officers Training School	1
Farriery Wing Army Veterinary School	1
Animal Clipping Teams I.A.V.C.	3

Pool of Veterinary Officers A.L.F.S.E.A.   I

Pool of Sowar Dressers I.A.V.C., A.L.F.S.E.A.   I

A total of 76 units. It is instructive to compare the multiplicity of units in a service which dealt only with the veterinary aspect of animals in operations and had no responsibility for the supply and retention of remounts, with the simplicity of the combined veterinary and remount organization of the Central Mediterranean Force.

The A.V.S. was, in 1939, dependent on the Director-General Indian Medical Service for veterinary stores, drugs and instruments. In 1941 provision of these was taken over by the Army Medical Service on estimates prepared by the Veterinary Directorate. Finally, in 1943, the A.V.S. undertook the issue of veterinary stores to all animal-holding units.

There were the usual war-time difficulties in obtaining supplies and the position was aggravated by unforeseen demands on stocks by the United States Army and by the Chinese forces. In 1944 the supply situation improved and a new method of provisioning was devised to speed-up the receipt and distribution of stores. All indigenous items were demanded from the Department of Supply (Medical Division) and received direct into veterinary store depots. Imported stores had still to be demanded through the Medical Directorate but I.A.V.C. personnel at the Army Medical Import Depot, Bombay, re-packed veterinary consignments on arrival and forwarded them to the veterinary stores depots.

The stores organization included three reserve base depots, located at Lahore, Avadi and Panagarh; seven base depots which were usually attached to field hospitals; and five field depots which were usually attached to advanced field hospitals. The system of attachment of small stores was adopted in order to use the motor transport possessed by the parent unit. In forward areas veterinary officers made their demands for stores and equipment, through their A.D.V.S. or D.A.D.V.S., to the nearest field or base depot. To ensure speed in delivery and to avoid breakages in transit, I.A.V.C. escorts and couriers were widely employed.

As to vaccines, sera and biologicals, during the war almost the entire supply came from the Izatnagar section of the Imperial Veterinary Research Institute.

Of all the early problems in connection with veterinary stores the supply of antrypol for treatment of surra undoubtedly surpassed all others in urgency. Pre-war planning in India had not visualized the possibility of great numbers of transport animals being required for a future war on the Assam-Burma front; in consequence no appreciable supplies of a specific drug for the treatment of surra had been assembled other than the 3,700 grammes of naganol sanctioned in 1939 as a mobilization reserve. This reserve was increased after the outbreak of war to 10,000 grammes consequent upon a further supply from German sources in India being made available by the Controller of Enemy Firms. Before the war the German firm of Bayers Ltd. provided the main supply to the world of a specific drug for the treatment of trypomosomiases in man and animals called Bayer 205 or naganol.

French chemists in 1928 succeeded in analysing Bayer 205 and subsequently marketed a substitute for it known as Fourneau 309.

Although by the outbreak of war Imperial Chemical Industries had also produced an analagous product which was marketed by British Drug Houses Ltd. under the trade name of antrypol, only small amounts were available and it had not been tried out by the Army in India. As a consequence, early in 1940, arrangements were made in consultation with the Imperial Veterinary Research Institute to test both the French and British substitute for naganol. These tests proved that both gave results as satis-factory as naganol. In 1940, and again in 1941, the Director of Veterinary Services represented to the D.G., I.M.S. the necessity for providing further supplies of antrypol in order to build up an adequate stock pile against future requirements. Another difficulty had arisen by May 1941 as the result of the British Drug Houses Ltd., being unable to produce this drug any longer, and from then onwards Imperial Chemical Industries (Pharmaceuticals) Ltd. assumed the provisioning responsibility. But it was not until January 1945 that stocks and reserves (which had by then risen to just over 500,000 grammes) were considered adequate for S.E.A.C. and India.

So important did antrypol become that between 1942/45 the stock positions of the drug were notified each month to the Quartermaster-General and the issues were controlled by the Veterinary Directorate G.H.Q. India. On occasions when arrivals of consignments from England were notified, officers were detailed to collect the drug personally from ships where they lay at anchor at Indian ports and to conduct it to forward areas where it was most urgently required. Several consignments of antrypol were lost in transit by enemy action thereby adding to the difficulties in the treatment and control of the great menace of surra.

It was discovered early in the Burma campaign that the field veterinary equipment (which was similar to that used by the R.A.V.C. in Europe) was quite unsuited to prolonged use in the monsoon weather of Burma. This was primarily due to the fact that the Indian pattern veterinary chests lacked resistance to rain and moisture thereby affecting certain hygroscopic drugs stored in the chests, such as chloral hydrate, perchloride of mercury, lead acetate and ammonium carbonate. This had a destructive effect on all metal containers and on other drugs and dressings.

The fault was, to some extent, overcome by local improvisation of sectioned chests made from metal mortar boxes and other forms of ammunition boxes. It was found necessary also to replace hygroscopic drugs by suitable substitutes free from chemical properties likely to cause deterioration of the contents of the chests.

In so far as "Special Force" requirements were concerned, the supply of essential veterinary stores to the Long Range Penetration Groups was effected, on many occasions, by air-drop. Mistakes occurred by including medical stores and veterinary stores in the same parachutes, the disadvantages of which were obvious. Packages were usually made up into what were termed "Fifteen day drops" which included drugs and dressings for the treatment of wounds and other stores as demanded. The most important item of all was the "Surra Drop Package" consisting of two-gramme ampules of antrypol. Under the conditions behind the enemy lines it was usually impracticable to weigh each dose of antrypol for individual animals hence the desirability of it being supplied in ampule form.

The protection of animals against gas had to be organized. The proposal to add a veterinary wing to the Chemical Defence Research Establishment at Rawalpindi in Northern India had been considered before the war but had been shelved for financial reasons. In 1940, however, the Chemical Defence Experimental Establishment, U.K., asked India to give priority to the development of a respirator and protective clothing for army animals. Largely as a consequence of this request, a veterinary wing was added to the C.D.R.E. (Rawalpindi) in January 1941. This establishment included two R.A.V.C. officers (the senior of whom, Major L. H. Poer, was designated "Veterinary Research Officer") one civil laboratory assistant and four I.O.R.s I.A.V.C. This wing, which operated until V.J. Day in close liaison with the veterinary wing C.D.E.E. (Porton) carried out much useful research work and was constantly called upon to devise new methods of protecting animals against gases under tropical conditions. Pamphlets and instructions were drafted and circulated for general information, chief of these being a pamphlet entitled *Defence of Animals against Gas*.

It was not until October 1944 that it was possible for the Indian Military Veterinary Laboratory, Lahore, to delegate some of its work to the first of the three mobile field veterinary laboratories raised for service in India and with 14th Army.

In the early years of the war veterinary officers and units were entirely dependent on the main laboratory situated in Northern India for the investigation of disease. Later the demands for the examination of morbid specimens and for the supply of certain biological products and vaccines could not always be satisfied in a reasonable time. Furthermore, pathological specimens sent for examination in many cases arrived in a useless, deteriorated, or putrid condition rendering proper examination an impossibility. When serious outbreaks of equine surra occurred in 1942/43 in Assam, and in Mona and Sargodha Remount Depots in India, it was necessary for one of the two officers on the establishment of the Lahore Laboratory to travel vast distances to investigate, during which time all routine work as well as research was left in the hands of the remaining officer. This intial problem of over-centralization was only solved when sufficient trained officers and Indian other ranks were available to operate the field veterinary laboratories. Three of these units were raised, the first in October 1941 and the remaining two in July 1945—all of which were designed and equipped primarily for diagnostic work. During the short period until V.J. Day in which they functioned, they proved immensely valuable, enabling rapid and accurate diagnosis to be made in the many outbreaks of contagious disease encountered at that time.

No. 1 Field Veterinary Laboratory was posted to Assam to investigate epizootic lymphangitis outbreaks that were the cause of considerable wastage in equine animals in the 14th Army between June 1944 and V.J. Day. The officer commanding this field laboratory, Captain J. J. Bullen, produced a promising biological diagnostic agent, cryptococcin. In 1946 and 1947 it was reported that cryptococcin was successfully employed as a diagnostic agent in at least two different outbreaks of epizootic lymphangitis in India.

No. 2 Field Veterinary Laboratory was posted to Tuticorin in Southern India to investigate epidemic anthrax and contagious pleuro-pneumonia in slaughter sheep and goats which were in transit from India to Ceylon.

No. 3 Field Veterinary Laboratory was held in readiness to leave with other veterinary units for S.E.A.C. but owing to the sudden ending of the war it was never dispatched.

The feature essential to all field veterinary laboratories was their mobility and one of the two lorries on the establishment was fitted with laboratory appliances and equipment to enable investigations to be carried out on the spot—an important factor in a tropical climate.

The main laboratory at Lahore operated throughout the war on an establishment of two officers, one veterinary assistant surgeon and seven Indian other ranks. At various periods small numbers of veterinary officers including three Italian army veterinary officers (prisoners-of-war) with research qualifications, were attached for work of a specialist nature. The functions of this laboratory continued as in pre-war days: research into diseases of army animals; investigation of certain outbreaks of disease; laboratory training of officers and other personnel; production of biological products for the Army Veterinary Services; and experiment with the latest therapeutic drugs and preparations.

On an average 5,000 pathological and bacteriological specimens were sent from all parts of India for examination each year from 1942 onwards with a peak of 13,000 specimens dealt with in 1944/45. Further details of the work of the laboratory are given in Chapter XI.

Various local production schemes were set in motion in 1944 so that the Army could produce a proportion of its needs in meat, poultry and eggs thereby relieving the heavy strain upon civil sources.

The schemes also aimed at an improvement in the quality of food stuffs. Production was initiated by the formation of "Intensive Production Units" specially equipped to carry out this work and organized by the R.I.A.S.C. Smaller schemes were also started, the aim of which was to enable static and semi-static units to be, to some extent, self-supporting in food. Inexperience, however, wrought a severe toll and heavy mortality occurred from time to time in these installations. This was attributable, in the main, to insufficient knowledge of animal husbandry (particularly in overcrowding small animals under the Indian climatic conditions) with the result that epidemic scourges such as pasteurellosis, salmonellosis, coccidiosis and Ranikhet disease inflicted huge losses.

Sheep and goats (5,000) were obtained by local purchase and were held mainly by local production units in Eastern Command. Production was not very successful because of the poor quality of stock initially purchased, inferior animal husbandry and heavy losses from contagious pleuro-pneumonia. The preliminary control measures introduced to combat losses from this disease did not meet with satisfactory results because of its extreme infectivity.

As regards pigs (10,500), owing to the varying quality of indigenous stock, breeding stock was imported from Australia and South Africa. The consignments from Australia suffered heavy losses en route and as there was no conducting veterinary staff, the cause of mortality was never determined. Pig production was carried out very successfully and except for one serious outbreak of swine paratyphoid losses from disease were negligible.

Poultry production (108,000) met with varying results: under unit schemes results were good, but in the large intensive production units losses resulting from contagious disease and faulty management were very high. Control of contagious diseases, particularly coccidiosis and Ranikhet disease was very difficult because of the system adopted of intensive production in too confined a space. Mismanagement of brooders by inexperienced personnel resulted in heavy losses amongst the young stock.

Consignments of rabbits (9,000) from Australia suffered very heavy losses because of unsatisfactory conditions of transportation and from coccidiosis. Rabbit production was hindered by further losses from this disease amongst consignments distributed throughout India.

On the Burma front the local supplies of fresh meat were exploited as far as possible but before long it was clear that the supply would have to be maintained from India. Tinned meat was unacceptable for religious reasons to most Indian troops, yet on medical advice a meat ration was regarded as essential for health and efficiency. It therefore became necessary for the Army to organize a constant supply as livestock on the hoof. There was no alternative to this method of meat supply in a tropical climate such as Burma's. To maintain the stream of livestock it was essential to export cattle, sheep and goats from distant parts of India to the fighting areas. The work devolving upon the Army Veterinary Service was very heavy as all animals were subjected to veterinary examination before purchase and hundreds of thousands had to be vaccinated against rinderpest and anthrax before dispatch by road, rail and sea to their ultimate destinations. The control of contagious disease proved difficult owing to the great distances animals had to travel by rail under congested conditions in the heat of Indian summers. Under adverse circumstances such as these, diseases normally controllable by careful segregation measures and prophylactic inoculations attained a very high virulence. Especially did this apply to contagious pleuro-pneumonia in goats and sheep, anthrax and rinderpest.

Livestock were involved in journeys sometimes as long as 1,500 miles to reception points. The Army Veterinary Service therefore, represented the necessity for establishing regularly-spaced staging centres where animals could be de-trained, rested and examined by veterinary officers. The utmost vigilance was required to reduce the mortality figures which to some extent resulted from the employment of inexperienced personnel during the transportation of livestock.

The following figures for the year 1944/45 alone illustrate in some measure the extent to which the resources of the Army Veterinary Services were called upon for this work:

Livestock on the hoof examined   770,726
Livestock on the hoof issued   676,887
Mortality (all causes) ..   ..   47,511 (over 7 per cent.)

Causes of mortality were roughly speaking: specific diseases 45 per cent. (contagious pleuro-pneumonia in goats and sheep 32 per cent.; anthrax 7 per cent.; rinderpest 5 per cent.; variola 1 per cent.), other causes (e.g., exhaustion, privation and starvation) 55 per cent.

India has always been notorious for animal plagues and epidemics. Perhaps nowhere else in the world has an Army Veterinary Service such a variety of diseases to combat. During peak periods of the war an average of sixty-five outbreaks of various disease per month were handled and epizootics of anthrax, glanders, strangles, surra, contagious abortion, contagious pleuro-pneumonia, rinderpest, foot-and-mouth disease, variola, encephalomyelitis, epizootic lymphangitis, salmonellosis, pasteurellosis, mange and coccidiosis, were of constant occurrence.

Rinderpest has probably existed for hundreds of centuries in India and is now thoroughly enzootic, but initial outbreaks can sweep a newly-invaded country from end to end. It is always liable to appear as one of the major animal scourges of war-time and it was feared, both in Britain and the U.S.A., that it might be used by the enemy in bacteriological warfare. It is to the great credit of the Army Veterinary Service that in India it was successfully controlled by regular immunization of all army and military dairy farm cattle. The most serious outbreaks occurred in slaughter stock during transit or at various staging centres. During the war two of the biggest staging centres for locally purchased cattle were at Allahabad (United Provinces) and at Katihar (Bihar), both of which were under veterinary surveillance. Mortality from this disease without the protection conferred by inoculation approximates 100 per cent. in European cattle in India and 50 per cent. in indigenous cattle. As a result of careful supervision and inoculation of Military Farm stock and slaughter animals mortality never exceeded 1 per cent.

CHAPTER X. Tracker Team. British and Iban handlers with V.O., Malaya, 1961.

CHAPTER X. Tracker dog, Malaya, 1960.

CHAPTER X. Tracker and patrol dogs, Malaya, 1960.

CHAPTER X. R.A.V.C. handler and guard dog, Singapore, 1954.

CHAPTER X. Tent-bag method of lowering a tracker dog from a helicopter, Malaya, 1953.

In 1944/45, 15,511 goats and sheep died of contagious pleuro-pneumonia, despite the many preventive and therapeutic measures which were tried. The main difficulty with this disease lies in the fact that no effective protective vaccine has yet been produced. Resistance to contagious pleuro-pneumonia was undoubtedly lowered by the transportation of sheep and goats (notoriously bad travellers) over great distances during hot weather.

Anthrax is normally an easy disease to control by vaccination under peace-time conditions, but it assumed epidemic proportions in Southern India and Ceylon as soon as it became necessary to step-up, in 1944/45, export of livestock to the island to 11,000 animals per month. Over a period of eight months 3,260 sheep and goats succumbed to the disease at staging centres, in transit by ship, and after arrival at Ceylon. Of this mortality 60 per cent. occurred actually in Ceylon after arrival, despite all possible measures having been taken to protect stock by inoculation as soon as they were purchased. A contributing factor to this high mortality was considered to be the heavy infection of lairages and pens when animals were concentrated at the ports of Tuticorin and Cochin (Madras Province) for shipment. As soon as it was found that normal inoculation procedure could not prevent the disease occurring in epidemic form the following procedure was adopted: veterinary staff was increased to supervise and sort animals at time of purchase; animals were concentrated at inland reception centres and as far as possible on free range; the time animals spent in lairages and pens at ports of embarkation was reduced to a minimum; the purchase of animals was restricted to areas in Southern India which were relatively free from anthrax.

These measures were successful in substantially decreasing the incidence of anthrax. As regards animals of the Military Farm Department, all stocks were inoculated bi-annually and the disease never at any time menaced the health of the troops or animals.

Foot-and-mouth disease was widespread in military farms throughout the war and although no appreciable mortality occurred in cattle considerable economic loss resulted, chiefly from reduction of the milk yield, and from secondary lesions of a septic nature involving the feet and joints. The disease was of frequent occurrence amongst livestock on the hoof, and in imported pigs, and mortality amongst these was somewhat higher than in Military Farm cattle. Measures taken by the Army Veterinary Service to limit the disease consisted chiefly of careful examination of all stock before purchase.

Glanders, that highly contagious and serious disease which in the past severely interfered with campaigns, never became a threat in World War II. This was due to the extensive use of mallein and to the careful inspection of all equine animals at the time of purchase. Some fifty cases were diagnosed in India during the war, the majority of which were detected during routine mallein tests. A serious outbreak involving most of the fifty cases quoted occurred in 1943 in units located at Babugahr and Meerut (United Provinces). All infected animals were immediately destroyed.

A consignment of remount horses and mules from Durban was landed at Karachi in May 1943. During the voyage two mules died from African horse sickness. The consignment was placed in quarantine as the disease does not occur in India and it was of vital importance that it should not be introduced. No further case occurred during quarantine or after restrictions had been removed. The South African authorities were requested to ensure that no animal recently recovered from horse sickness should be shipped to India.

In all, 35,500 mules and ponies and donkeys were imported from South Africa without introducing horse sickness into India. This lends support to the contention that, given suitable prophylactic precautions, it is safe to move equine animals from endemic areas to potentially endemic areas.

The major public health contribution of the Army Veterinary Service in India during the war occurred in December 1944 with its assumption of responsibility for the inspection of all fresh meat supplies to the services. Prior to this, meat inspection, as in force in Europe and America, was unknown in India, except for small scale inspection carried out by the United States Army Veterinary Corps for their own troops. From the outset the greatest problem was the acute shortage of veterinary personnel and this necessitated nearly every V.O. and veterinary assistant surgeon in India Command being prepared to carry out meat inspection duties if called upon. This was feasible in a small station where it was carried out by veterinary personnel as part of their duties, but in the larger stations full-time inspectors were provided, with the result that over 100 officers and veterinary assistant surgeons were engaged in such work. Early in 1945 an establishment of one officer (D.A.D.V.S.—Major) and thirty-two officers and Viceroy's commissioned officers I.A.V.C. was approved for this important work. As graduates or licentiates of Indian Veterinary Colleges had little knowledge of European standards of meat inspection a special training course was introduced at the Officers Training School, Ambala and about 150 officers and V.C.Os. received preliminary instruction there. In a short time the establishment of full-time meat inspectors, I.A.V.C. had accepted their new duties in the centres and army butcheries where they were so urgently required. Instructional pamphlets dealing with the correct routine of ante and post-mortem examination of slaughter animals were drafted and issued by the Army Veterinary Service. It was important that all concerned should be made to realize that meat from diseased animals might set up serious illness in man, the diseases of major importance in India being anthrax, and tapeworm disease resulting from cysticercosis in beef and pork.

Anthrax was common in certain parts of Southern India and its eventual appearance in army butcheries was considered inevitable. As a result of strict ante-mortem examinations only two serious outbreaks occurred, one of which resulted in the condemnation of 250 carcases. Enormous numbers of ante-mortem examinations of animals were carried out and in the last quarter of 1945, the figures recorded were well over half a million. Of that number 25 per cent. were rejected as unfit for slaughter and of the remainder the carcases of 341,000 sheep and goats, 14,500 cattle and 15,000 pigs were subjected to further post-mortem examination in 130 military butcheries operating at that time in India.

Tape worm infestation was known to be prevalent among British and Indian personnel of the Services and to have been the cause of some of the cases of epilepsy. Cysticercosis was found to affect no less than 10 per cent. of pigs and 1 per cent. of slaughter cattle.

The Army Veterinary Service, in collaboration with the Royal Indian Army Service Corps, was called upon to tackle a series of difficult meat inspection problems more or less simultaneously—these included:—

1. The buildings and hygienic arrangements were poor due to faulty construction, poor drainage, insufficient hot water supply and bad lighting. The equipment in many butcheries was quite inadequate for the handling of large quantities of meat and offal.

2. The transportation of meat in unhygienic conveyances. Slaughtermen were in many cases devoid of knowledge of the basic principles of hygienic handling of meat or indeed of simple public health rules. Rejected meat from military butcheries in the past often found its way into the bazaar vendors stalls and from there into officers messes and public restaurants.

3. Religious prejudice resulted in a proportion of the meat ration being issued to units "on the hoof" thereby evading veterinary examination and permitting slaughter under unhygienic conditions by untrained men in the unit lines.

All these difficulties had to be strongly represented to higher authority before any appreciable improvement resulted. It is fair to say that although meat inspection on hygienic lines fell far short of the standard prevailing in America and Europe the main object was achieved, and clean, disease-free meat was issued to the forces from the moment the Army Veterinary Service was in a position to supply the inspectors. At the same time the Army gave the lead to the civil administration by making the Veterinary Service responsible for this important aspect of public health.

The local purchase of animals in India by the Army Remount Department was on an increasing scale from 1940 onwards. Mules were required for units proceeding to France, East Africa, Iraq, Middle East and later for the Burma Campaign. Camels were required in 1940 for the Aden Garrison, destined for possible use in British Somaliland, and also for army units in India. This involved the veterinary examination of all animals before purchase, the malleining of all horses and mules, and the application of the mercuric chloride test to camels to eliminate those infected with surra. Transport bullocks after purchase were inoculated against rinderpest. The buying, which was conducted in widespread parts of India—including the North-West

Frontier Province, Punjab, Sind and the United Provinces—produced 41,500 horses, mules and donkeys, 3,600 camels and 8,800 transport bullocks.

The Military Farms Department was established in India many years before the war to provide fresh milk for the Army. It also provided a clean fodder supply thereby so reducing the incidence of anthrax that outbreaks of this disease became very infrequent amongst army animals, especially in cantonments. During the war this department was called upon to implement a very extensive programme of expansion to meet vastly increased demands for milk and other dairy products including canned butter, evaporated milk and cheese. During the peak years its holding increased to over 70,000 animals. To cope with this expansion the Director of Veterinary Services provided in April 1944 an organization for the exclusive use of the Military Farms Department which included an A.D.V.S. at Headquarters and ten Executive Veterinary Officers at Circle Headquarters in charge of groups of farms. Sixty-two veterinary assistant surgeons were allocated on the basis of one per farm of approximately 1,000 head of dairy cattle. Apart from the extra personnel, instruments, drugs, vaccines and hormone preparations, some of which were not previously held by the Army Veterinary Stores, were supplied on a large scale.

With the commissioning into the R.A.V.C. of a number of civil veterinary surgeons specialized in cattle problems it was found possible to provide a first-class veterinary staff to ensure the welfare of military farm animals during the latter part of the war. Commencing in 1944 vigorous measures were taken to investigate infertility in cattle which was causing a large number of uneconomic animals to be retained in dry stock farms. All such animals were categorized and if considered to be infertile were recommended for casting. Pregnancy examinations were carried out on an extensive scale and at the Lahore farms alone 10,000 such examinations were recorded during one year. As a result of these measures it was estimated that a large financial saving must have accrued. For example, on one farm of 4,500 cattle, 400 infertile dry stock were cast as "sterile" thereby saving the Military Farms Department approximately 600 rupees daily in feeding costs. It was considered as a result of extending this practice to other dry stock farms that approximately £540 per day may easily have been saved.

Hundreds of thousands of inoculations were given during the war years—the majority of which consisted of prophylactic inoculations against rinderpest, variola, haemorrhagic septicaemia and anthrax. In the last two years of the war, thirty Italian army veterinary officers (prisoners-of-war) were employed on military farms. This expedient worked well: not only did the Italians perform their duties satisfactorily but they became available when the maximum number of British and Indian V.O.s were needed on the Burma front.

This then is a brief account of the great part played by the Army Veterinary Service in the development of the India Base and the preparations to defeat the Japanese in

Burma. By 1945 the animal strength of army units, including those in S.E.A.C., rose to about 84,000 and, in addition, there were 194,000 animals on military farms and in livestock production units, and an annual turn-over of 770,000 slaughter stock.

The veterinary statistics for the animals of the units and remount depots of India Base (excluding farm and slaughter stock) for the period 31st March 1944 to 1st April 1945 give the following figures:

	Average Strength	Admitted for Treatment	Cured and Remaining under Treatment
Horses	11,632	14,340	13,673
Mules	21,191	11,883	11,352
Donkeys	5,600	5,332	5,105
Camels	5,029	6,471	5,703
Bullocks	8,564	2,882	2,640

CHAPTER VII

The Burma Campaign

Burma had become independent of India in 1937. It had its own army, with an element of British and Indian troops, and was not an administrative responsibility of India. It came under Far East Command in 1940. When the Japanese invaded Burma in the extreme south in January 1942, the defending forces were driven back and, after some resistance on the Sittang river line, Rangoon was lost on the 8th March 1942. Then the Burma Army began its 600 mile retreat to the Indian frontier which the rearmost elements crossed in late May 1942. For the next two years our forces on the Manipur and Arakan fronts were mainly on the defensive, while behind them the process went on of preparation for an ultimate offensive against the Japanese, of expansion of the Indian Army and of improvement of the long lines of communication from India. The operations during 1942/43 on these fronts were of a comparatively minor character, the most noteworthy being the campaign of Wingate's Long Range Penetration Group behind the enemy lines.

In the autumn of 1943 South-East Asia Command took over operational control from India. Towards the end of 1943 operations against the Japanese assumed a different aspect. Hitherto when the enemy employed his favourite tactics of cutting our communications, our troops had fallen back to restore them, and the process was then often repeated. Furthermore, both sides had been more or less inactive during the monsoon period. Now the policy was to stand firm and rely on air supply when land communications were severed and to fight on, march on, and fly on throughout the monsoon. How well this policy worked was seen in 1944 when the enemy took the offensive first in Arakan and then on the Manipur front. Although in both cases large elements of our forces were temporarily cut off, they held their ground and were supplied by air-lift.

In each case the enemy plans were thus completely frustrated, his forces practically annihilated and the scattered remains driven back. The defensive period was over.

By the end of 1944 our forces were on the offensive in all parts of the front. This was maintained and the virtual reconquest of Burma was complete when the unexpectedly sudden end of hostilities came with the final surrender on 15th August 1945.

When the Japanese invaded, the animal strength in Burma was at a low ebb. The arrival from India of the 17th Indian Division on a mixed scale of M.T. and animal transport did not cause any marked increase in veterinary duties, and when it was decided that battalions would have more freedom of action away from the roads if organized completely on a pack basis, the difficulty of implementing the decision lay in the shortage of mules, especially the large type of equipment mules.

In January 1942 the veterinary organization was confined to:—

H.Q. Burma Army	A.D.V.S.
1st Burma Division	D.A.D.V.S.
	No. 2 Mobile Veterinary Section
17th Indian Division	No. 4 Mobile Veterinary Section
Maymyo	No. 1 Military Veterinary Hospital
Moulmein	No. 2 Military Veterinary Hospital
Rangoon	Branch Veterinary Hospital

This organization was required for the mountain artillery, mule-transport companies and infantry pack animals. In addition to his administrative duties the A.D.V.S., Lieutenant-Colonel J. Southall, was O.C. No. 1 Military Veterinary Hospital at Maymyo, and in the absence of a representative of the Remount Department until December 1941 he had to act in that capacity also.

In the early stages of the campaign ineffective animals were evacuated by No. 2 Mobile Veterinary Section to the hospital at Maymyo. Later during the retreat, when rail and road communications became disrupted, casualties had to remain with the M.V.S. From Paungdi to Monywa the section never had less than 100 sick animals against the maximum of fifty for which it was designed. At Monywa all but eighteen animals were lost as the result of an air raid. Thereafter evacuation ceased until the unit was moved to Allanmyo when it dispatched the surviving casualties by rail from Taungdwinigyi, which involved a ninety-mile road journey first. Since there were no proper depots of veterinary stores, supplies had to be obtained from evacuated civil hospitals as the army withdrew. When Moulmein fell No. 4 mobile section was successfully extricated and all the drugs and equipment of No. 2 hospital were salvaged. Similarly, thanks to the initiative of an Indian veterinary assistant surgeon, the stores of the branch hospital at Rangoon were saved. The entire equipment of No. 1 Military Veterinary Hospital was lost when the Japanese captured Manya whither it had been recently transferred with the object of forming a field hospital. As the retreat speeded up both mobile sections could do very little as their lorries were commandeered to carry troops. They arrived in Imphal via Kalewa about the 13th May and combined to improvise a temporary hospital. Sickness among officers and other ranks reached high proportions and by early June 1942 the only veterinary personnel of the Burma Forces were one British officer (D.A.D.V.S.) one veterinary assistant surgeon and six Indian other ranks, I.A.V.C. to look after 225 sick animals in the improvised hospital, in addition to attending those still with the units.

The condition of the operational animals was well maintained during the retreat until the last month when long marches with little rest and uncertain forage supplies had their inevitable consequences. There were contributory factors also such as lack of experienced personnel and difficulty in obtaining saddlers tools and materials with which to readjust pack saddles as animals lost condition. The mortality from bombing was high, as were casualties from saddle galls, but the amount of foot lameness was not great. All records were lost so further details of this period cannot be given but it is known that approximately 1,500 animals were successfully withdrawn from Burma.

The organization of lines of communication from India to the Burma frontier started in February 1942 with the construction of a rail-head and advanced base at Dimapur (or Manipur Road) till then an unimportant station on a single track metre-gauge railway line from Gauhati on the Brahmaputra river. The country surrounding Dimapur was dense jungle and the narrow road to the forward areas, as far as some 200 miles away, wound along a hill side with a steep cliff up one side and down the other. From a height of 500 feet at Dimapur the road climbed to 5,000 at Kohima and then dropped into the Imphal plain at 2,500 feet.

In April 1942 No. 6 Indian Field Veterinary Hospital arrived from Lucknow to become the base hospital at Manipur Road and had the honour of being the first field veterinary unit in Assam. An area of seemingly impenetrable jungle inhabited by wild elephant had to be cleared before the tents could be put up. During April and May the unit personnel worked stripped to the waist building the hospital with improvised material; it was a struggle against time to get established before the monsoon broke. Mosquitoes swarmed in the shade of the jungle biting by day and night despite all anti-malarial precautions. In the meantime reinforcement units with animals started to pour into Assam and some thousands had arrived from Gauhati to Ledo and from Dimapur to Palel. The retiring forces from Burma were trekking back via Kalewa—Tamu—Palel—Imphal—Dimapur. A detachment of the base hospital was sent forward to Palel to form a branch hospital under the command of a R.A.V.C. officer where it rendered valuable assistance although hampered by lack of veterinary staff. The animals that survived the journey out of Burma were in very poor condition from lack of rations, and many were severely galled. Another R.A.V.C. officer remained with these units and did especially good work by treatment and advice in unit lines around Imphal.

The base hospital, depleted in numbers by malaria, served as a clearing house for veterinary personnel of other units going up or down the road. Animals requiring prolonged hospital treatment were dispatched by rail to the expansion hospitals at

Lucknow or Meerut. In June the monsoon was in full swing and the maintenance system was not helped by the washing away of about 100 yards of road between Kohima and Imphal, and later the breaking of a bridge between Imphal and Palel. These interruptions in the supply route resulted in a serious shortage of an already meagre ration for animals in the forward areas.

Conditions were now ideal for the occurrence of surra and the first case was detected towards the end of July. This outbreak was particularly grave, firstly because all the forward troops were dependent upon pack transport for their food, ammunition, and medical supplies, and secondly on account of our unpreparedness to deal with an outbreak of the disease for the reasons with which the reader is now familiar. It again became imperative to make demands on the endurance of the few but willing veterinary officers R.A.V.C./I.A.V.C. and men who, in their continual struggle to cure and control diseases, carried on splendidly, often in ill-health, and under the most trying climatic conditions, with the added handicap of inadequate transport. The monthly incidence of surra reached 17 per cent. of the total equine strength (about 21,000) in the area, and, but for the excellent work of the available veterinary staff, the figure would most certainly have been considerably higher. Headquarters 4th Corps with an A.D.V.S. on its staff had arrived but there was little hope of receiving veterinary reinforcements. The O.C. No. 6 Field Veterinary Hospital, Major J. S. Kingston, who had recently recovered from a severe attack of malaria, was sent back in September to Lucknow for a well-earned rest. During the "rest" he was called upon to organize the expansion of No. 2 Veterinary Hospital and also raise Nos. 23 and 24 Advanced Field Veterinary Hospitals as officers were not available at the time to command them; an example of some of the difficulties which beset the Army Veterinary Service during the expansion period. No. 1 Indian Base Depot Veterinary Stores was now also situated in the base hospital and supplied all animal-holding units in Assam with veterinary drugs and equipment. Reinforcements eventually arrived to fill the gaps caused by the ravages of malaria, jaundice and dysentery (about 50 per cent. of the original staff were casualties and after continuous hard work in this jungle setting the base hospital was completed by April 1943. It consisted of barracks for personnel, stores and forges, operating theatres, cookhouses, washhouses, latrines, recreation rooms, tradesmen's shops (barber, tailor, bootmaker), water pipelines to cement troughs, one-and-a-half miles of "pukha" roads, large vegetable garden and exercising paddock.

The base at Dimapur had been established by cutting wholesale into the jungle and although very strict anti-malarial measures were taken, it remained a most unpleasant and unhealthy spot for the whole of the war. Nevertheless No. 6 Veterinary Hospital played a most important rôle in the veterinary organization of the operations in Assam and especially in our struggle against surra.

In 4th Corps area by the end of 1942, 17th Indian Division was moving down the Tiddim road and 23rd Division had reached the Tamu area. There were continuous patrols in the hills overlooking the Chindwin and the provision of pack transport for these, and the maintenance of the forward troops kept fifteen mule-transport companies fully employed in very difficult conditions over long distances. The available veterinary organization was more than fully occupied in carrying out measures for the treatment and control of surra and saddle injuries. The monthly average of animals admitted to field veterinary hospitals during the surra season in 1943 was 1,200 of which 125 died or were destroyed, 220 were cured and 855 remained under treatment. During the whole of 1943 a total of 12,130 animal casualites occurred in 14th Army, of these 5,410 died of surra and other diseases or were killed in action.

While the monsoon was the main reason for the absence of large scale operations the heavy incidence of malaria was partly responsible.

The principal operations carried out on this front in 1943 were those of the Long Range Penetration Group under Brigadier O. C. Wingate, known as the "Chindits". This force, approximately of brigade strength, entered, in February 1943, enemy-occupied country through the front held in Assam by 4th Corps to cut the main railway line between Mandalay and Myitkyina and generally to sabotage their supply lines. They remained behind the enemy lines until June, being maintained throughout by air. The reserves and equipment accompanying the "Chindits" were carried by nearly 1,000 mules, supplemented by elephants each loaded with 800 lbs of heavy equipment including rubber boats for river crossings. A considerable number of mules were successfully transported in gliders, specially adapted for the purpose, from the training areas in the Central Provinces, India, to the operational or "jumping off" base in Assam. The R.A.V.C. officer, Captain A. W. Peyton, who accompanied the force was unfortunately reported missing believed killed on 30th March 1943 and no record is available of the number of casualties from enemy action, surra, and other diseases.

Wingate's own report on his mules is revealing: "The great bulk of the mules reached the Brigade early in November (1942) in a raw, untrained and unhardened condition. To receive them and train them was a training team from Jullundur. Otherwise we were woefully short of either officers or men who had any knowledge of animal management. The labours of Captain Carey-Foster of the Veterinary Corps, whom I unlawfully placed in command, accomplished wonders and the mule company certainly worked hard. I had hoped that the Gurkhas (muleteers) would be of the same stuff as the original 3/2nd Gurkha Rifles. Being as they were raw recruits from the Regimental Centres, they possessed only one martial quality—physical toughness. There is no doubt that the man leading the mule in Long Range Penetration must be as good or better a fighting man than his comrade in the infantry company. The physical effort of mule leading is such that double pay for muleteers is underpayment. I realize that many of the difficulties in raising the Mule Company were inevitable. But another time it will be possible and necessary to avoid these causes of inefficiency. The great difficulty in our army is to find the indispensable minimum of persons who

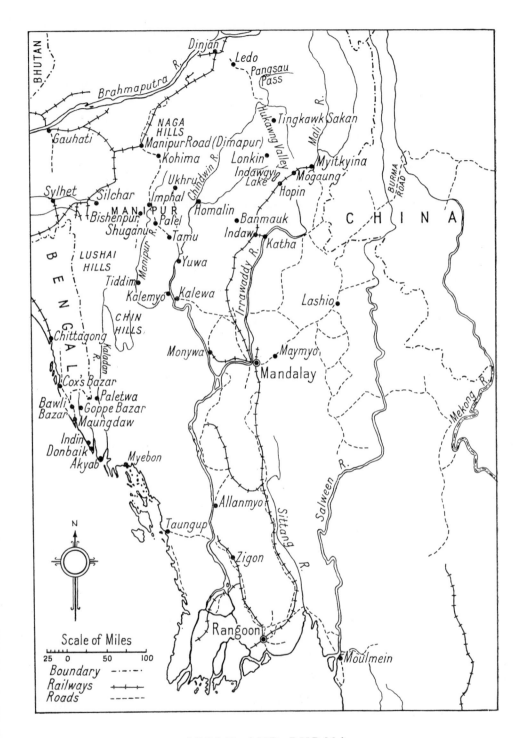

BHUTAN

Brahmaputra R.

Dinjan
Ledo
Pangsau
Pass

NAGA
HILLS
Gauhati
Manipur Road (Dimapur)
Tingkawk Sakan
Kohima
Lonkin
Myitkyina
Hukawng Valley
Sylhet
Ukhrul
Indawgyi
Lake
Mogaung
Silchar
Imphal
Homalin
Hopin
MANIPUR
Bishenpur
Palel
Banmauk
C H I N A
Shuganu
Tamu
Indaw
Yuwa
Katha
LUSHAI
HILLS
Tiddim
Kalemyo
Kalewa
Lashio
CHIN
HILLS
Chittagong
Monywa
Maymyo
Cox's Bazar
Mandalay
Paletwa
Bawli
Bazar
Goppe Bazar
Maungdaw
Indin
Donbaik
Myebon
Akyab

Allanmyo

N

Taungup

Zigon

Scale of Miles
25   0   50   100
Rangoon
Boundary -·-·-
Railways +—+—+
Roads - - - -
Moulmein

ASSAM AND BURMA

can tell one end of an animal from another. Here again, the answer is to centralize the available talent." He also emphasized the fact that mules can only be hardened by long and frequent marches under load.

In June 1943, Brigadier W. D. A. Lentaigne, who was commencing to raise the first brigade of troops destined for service with General Wingate's second expedition, asked the D.D.V.S. Central Command, Colonel C. M. Stewart (later to be D.V.S., A.L.F.S.E.A.C.) whether he could devise an operation for devoicing mules. In *The Journal of the Royal Army Veterinary Corps* of May 1946, Brigadier Stewart describes this meeting: "He commenced the conversation by telling me that, during the first expedition, it very soon became evident that neighing of ponies and braying of mules, the noise of which carried for great distances on a still day or night, were frequently responsible for advertising to the Japs the presence of a party of troops who might otherwise have been comparatively safe from discovery in jungle country. Later, when the physical and mental condition of all was greatly affected by hardship and lack of food, the noise made by the few remaining hungry and lonely animals caused considerable anxiety among men nearing the safety of their own lines.

"He explained that removal of the constant feeling that their presence might be advertised in this way was highly desirable, if not indeed essential. He went on to describe the enormous advantage to a commander and his men, carrying out a night operation or any similar approach towards the enemy, of the knowledge that their animals were unable to disclose their presence to the enemy.

"Brigadier Lentaigne had evidently discussed this question with others, probably doctors and veterinary surgeons, as he was able to suggest various methods by which the desired results might be obtained, but to all there were formidable objections. Before leaving, he impressed me with the urgency of finding a solution as quickly as possible, but I could only say I would do my best.

"It was clear that any solution decided on had to be capable of application to large numbers without throwing the animals out of work for more than a short period; also, it had to be permanent in its results and have no effects on the subsequent ability to perform normal work."

Numerous experiments were carried out and eventually a technique was perfected which included total excision of the vocal cords under a general anaesthetic. This technique was demonstrated to several R.A.V.C. officers and soon afterwards surgical operations were commenced on the animals of this brigade. With trained casting teams one surgeon dealt with as many as thirty animals in a day. The muting operation was also carried out at other centres, including a remount depot where reserve animals for this "Special Force" were located. Results on the whole were very good. Of the total of 5,563 animals subjected to the operation there were forty-three casualties, the majority of which occurred at an early stage when climatic conditions were unfavourable.

A small number of animals regained a varying amount of voice. An experienced observer later stated that if a mule remained mute for six weeks after the operation it was permanently incapable of making a noise. Animals were considered to be fit for exercise with pack saddles ten days after the operation, and to be capable of carrying full loads as soon as the external wounds had healed. The chief post-operative problem during the monsoon season was the infestation of operation wounds with maggots, but spraying with anti-fly solution was generally successful in controlling this complication.

During 1942 and the early part of 1943 the forward troops were operating at the end of a very tenuous L. of C. over 150 miles from railhead at Chittagong, a situation which presented considerable administrative difficulties. The maintenance system in Arakan at the beginning of 1943 was complex. Supplies were brought by lorries from Chittagong and by ponycart transport from Cox's Bazar to the head of the Naf estuary near Bawli Bazar, whence they went by water in sampans to Maungdaw. There the L. of C. divided. One road ran south down to Indin and from there the forward troops were maintained by M.T. and pack transport. The whole of the 14th Indian Division had pack first-line transport which was the cause of some difficulties as the formation had been trained on a mechanized basis. In mid-March, during a Japanese counter offensive, when our troops withdrew to avoid being cut-off, several pack companies were lost to the enemy. Eventually 14th Division occupied positions astride the Mayu Range from Bawli Bazar to Goppe Bazar in the Kalapanzin Valley but, when relieved by the 26th Indian Division, there was no rest for the three pack-transport companies working in the forward areas as there were no others yet ready to take their place. The maintenance of troops in the valley was particularly exacting as all supplies had to go over the Goppe Pass from Bawli Bazar. The pass was very steep and steps had to be cut to get the animals up. The journey was extremely tiring for them and many injuries and sore backs were caused by the difficulty of the climb, accentuated by saddles of inferior manufacture.

This sector was comparatively quiet during the monsoon but there was no respite for the pack-transport animals. Limited veterinary facilities, shortage of mules, and operational demands often made it necessary to work animals before their galls and other injuries had healed. The first case of surra in Arakan was detected in August 1943 and altogether ninety cases were treated. All cases were located between Cox's Bazar and Bawli.

A new phase in the history of the campaign on the Burma front began in November 1943 when South-East Asia Command was formed under a Supreme Allied Commander. The D.V.S., G.H.Q. India, Brigadier J. J. M. Soutar, however, continued to be responsible for the administration of the Army Veterinary Service with the 11th Army Group which comprised 14th Army and Ceylon Army Command. H.Q. 14th Army, situated at Comilla in East Bengal, had assumed control of

4th Corps consisting of 17th, 20th and 23rd Indian Divisions in Assam and North Burma and 15th Corps consisting of 5th, 7th and 26th Indian Divisions in the Arakan. These six divisions were on an animal and M.T. scale of transport. In addition certain other formations were assigned to S.E.A.C. for future operations but remained for the time being under India Command. Of these only the 3rd Indian Division—the cover name for Wingate's Special Force—concerned the Army Veterinary Service.

In November 1944, the title of 11th Army Group was changed to that of Allied Land Forces, South-East Asia Command (A.L.F.S.E.A.C.). The situation regarding the supply of veterinary officers and units improved and as more officers and trained personnel became available both administrative and executive appointments could be filled and newly raised field veterinary units dispatched to S.E.A.C.

In this campaign, against an enemy whose favourite tactics were to infiltrate behind the fighting troops, administrative units and installations in operational areas could not be left to the protection afforded by the dispositions of the forward troops and protective screens; for this reason particular measures were essential for their security. Briefly the basic principle adopted was that each formation should have a secure administrative base, or "Admin. Box" as it was popularly known. This was a relatively large area which had to be held by comparatively few troops and required a perimeter which also had to be held to deny the enemy close observation of the area. This was effected partly by the administrative units themselves, who were responsible for their own defence and for the defence of the sector of the perimeter within their area, and partly by additional troops specially allotted to the base. Throughout the Japanese offensives in 1944 in Arakan, Assam and North Burma, veterinary units in operational areas and on the L. of C. were called upon to defend their "boxes" from enemy attacks and it was repeatedly proved that every man fighting in enemy-infested jungle should be armed and competent to use his arms.

"Special Force" was a development, late in 1943, of Wingate's original Long Range Penetration Group. The Special Force or "Chindits" trained in the jungles of the Central Provinces, India, and was composed of three British, one West African and two Indian infantry brigades.

The animal strength of the force was 547 horses, 3,134 mules and about 250 bullocks, the latter being regarded as meat on the hoof. All the mules and horses, including reserves, were subjected to a muting operation whilst the brigades were in their training areas. The veterinary establishment of Special Force consisted of one A.D.V.S., two D.A.D.V.S., three executive veterinary officers, two brigade veterinary sections and one mobile veterinary section.

The three veterinary sections I.A.V.C. were commanded by R.A.V.C. officers.

During the training period the veterinary staff, realizing that the six brigades had only recently been converted from a mechanical to an animal basis of transport, devoted as much time as possible to improving the standard of animal management.

In operations such as were visualized by Special Force insufficient attention to this essential part of training could have proved costly. In early 1944 Special Force resumed operations against the Japanese lines of communications in the areas Indaw, Mogaung and Myitkyina. Movement to the forward area was by rail. I.A.V.C. personnel accompanied the animals. The journey which lasted eight days, and involved a change from broad to narrow gauge, was remarkably successful in that casualties and injuries were negligible. The mules travelled well and lost little or no condition but some of the ponies, and especially the bullocks, showed the effects of the long train journey.

From the forward areas 2,216 animals belonging to the 14th, 77th, 111th and 3rd (West African) brigades were flown in as three air-strips were established on the advanced strongholds of the Chindits deep in enemy occupied territory. These were known as "Aberdeen", "White City", and "Broadway", and were capable of taking Dakotas and, in some cases, gliders. This was found to be a most satisfactory method of transport and very few mules gave trouble en route. Four mules had to be destroyed while in flight as they had broken loose and were a danger to the others.

The 16th Brigade marched in via Ledo Road and Naga Hill tracks to "Aberdeen" stronghold, a distance of approximately 400 miles, and 23rd Brigade marched on north and east of Kohima to its area of operations. The A.D.V.S., Lieutenant-Colonel C. Holland, remained with rear headquarters, and one D.A.D.V.S., Major K. I. Barlow, went into the operational area with the headquarters of Special Force. A veterinary officer accompanied each brigade. I.A.V.C. personnel accompanied the two brigades that marched in as far as road head. The other D.A.D.V.S. superintended the emplaning of animals at the initial fly-in and the veterinary personnel allotted to airfields and assembly areas were available to give assistance with difficult animals to the loading parties. Chloral hydrate was held ready but seldom used. Reinforcement animals were held at No. 1 Air base, Sylhet, and later were flown in to comply with demands from columns under arrangements made by the D.A.D.V.S. as regards loading, selection of types, reception, and distribution in Burma. Three brigades took their veterinary officers with them on operations though there was some difference of opinion as to the usefulness of this policy. Although it was contended that the veterinary officer could accomplish more by staying at the air-base from where he could be flown in to any point at which concentration of animals occurred, it was generally agreed that he was more useful with the brigade during operations. Again, the Brigade Commanders, having relied on their V.O.s in the training phase were very reluctant to leave them at base while the veterinary officers were equally determined to accompany their brigades on operations. This latter policy was apparently fully justified but it must be remembered that the long range penetration type operations demand an "A.1 plus" medical category.

Small veterinary hospitals were set up in the three strongholds and some fifty casualties were evacuated by air to air-bases in Assam, and later cleared to L. of C.

hospitals. Evacuation of all animals by air was not practicable but it would have been ideal if the systems of evacuation and reinforcement could have been co-ordinated. A limited number of animals were flown out towards the end of the expedition.

The type of aircraft used by Special Force was mostly the Dakota (C.47), and to a lesser degree, W.A.C.O. gliders, modified for the carriage of animals by the addition of coconut matting on the floor and bamboo poles lashed to the interior of the aircraft in such a way as to provide a separate compartment for each animal carried. It was necessary both in the case of Dakotas and gliders to carry animals well forward. The usual load was four or five mules or ponies. If five were carried, the first three were placed as far forward as possible abreast and the other two behind the outside mules. When four were carried two were placed each side so as to leave a passage in the centre. During the flight animals were normally quiet. A nose-bag feed for each animal was often found useful in quietening potentially troublesome animals.

Later the staff of Special Force went into the matter of how, in the event of emergency, reinforcement mules could be provided for the small complement of animals normally held by columns of a long-range penetration brigade, when no landing strips could be provided. As a consequence of this, and largely on the initiative of Major K. I. Barlow, R.A.V.C., mule para-dropping trials were improvised and carried out at Chaklala (India) in 1945. To protect the animal from injury it was narcotized with chloral hydrate and secured to a wooden platform, $6\frac{1}{2}$ feet by 4 feet, padded to prevent injury to vital parts. To the total load of approximately 1,000 lbs. were secured the statichutes. Seven live drops took place. The mule loads were ejected at 600 feet and the landing was estimated at fifteen feet per second. The experiment showed that droppings in this way were operationally possible.

In 1944 Major K. I. Barlow, then D.A.D.V.S. Operational H.Q. Special Forces, wrote as follows:

"(i) The following V.O.s and I.A.V.C. personnel accompanied bdes, from training area:—

Bde.	Veterinary officer	I.A.V.C.	Remarks
16th	Capt. D. Cameron	1 V.O. 1 V.A.S. 4 I.O.R.s	Returned from MS. $82\frac{1}{2}$ Ledo Road.
77th	Capt. A. Fyfe	1 Ris. 2 N.C.O.s 3 I.O.R.s	V.O. flew in with bde. to Broadway. I.A.V.C. personnel remained in Lalaghat area.

CHAPTER X. Group of war dogs, No. 1 W.D.T.U., B.A.O.R. and, *below*, CHAPTER XI. Western Front, 1917. Pack horse with gas mask in rolled position on nose. *Imperial War Museum photo.*

CHAPTER XI. Western Front, 1917. Horses and driver wearing gas masks. *Imperial War Museum photo.*

Bde.	Veterinary officer	I.A.V.C.	Remarks
111th	Capt. D. H. Greeves	1 V.O. 1 V.A.S. 7 I.O.R.s.	Returned from Imphal.
3rd W.A.	Capt. D. W. P. Lake	1 Dfr. 6 I.O.R.s	Flew in with bde.
14th	Capt. D. H. Witherington	1 N.C.O. 5 I.O.R.s	Flew in with bde.
23rd	Capt. R. McCrea	1 N.C.O. 5 I.O.R.s	Through ops with bde.

"(ii) On airfield and in assembly areas valuable assistance was given to columns by small veterinary first aid posts and loading parties dealing with emplaning of difficult animals. Chloral hydrate was held ready, but seldom used.

"Diseases

(A) Non-specific

(i) Saddle injuries, considering the nature of the operations, were not unduly numerous but owing to the fact that there was a load which could not be left behind for every mule in a column, many injuries became aggravated or their healing retarded.

Towards keeping an animal under load and preventing worsening of the lesion a lot can be, and was done, by V.O.s in strongholds and elsewhere, by chambering of the panels and adjustment of saddles and loads.

The main causes of saddle injuries were:—

(a) Big hill country .. .. .. 16th and 23rd Bdes. and 14th to lesser extent.

(b) Difficult loads .. .. .. P.I.A.T.
Lifebuoy.
R.A.F. set and charging motor.

(c) Lack of spare animals .. .. Animals could rarely be allotted as 'spare'.

(d) Deterioration of saddlery .. Consequent on low standard of manufacture and resulting in decomposition of stitching and new type nummahs.

"(e) Long and continued marches .. Days of rest were rare and were dictated by the operational situation and not the necessity of reorganization.

(f) Overloading .. .. .. Rare and usually due to equipment of personnel casualties having to be carried till man could be 'flown out'. Became more common when animal casualties rose in July.

(ii) Injuries from shell, bomb, and grenade splinters, etc., were most common in the Henu Block, Broadway, and Blackpool (Hopin Block), and casualties from automatic and S.A. fire were suffered to a lesser extent in the various actions fought.

"Revetments and sunken standings were constructed in strongholds and saved many animal casualties.

(iii) Heat exhaustion.

(iv) Foot injuries and disease.

(v) Skin diseases.

(vi) Colic.

(vii) Bamboo and 'Panji' injuries were not uncommon, especially from the latter around Jap defended positions.

"(B) Specific

(i) Surra. Original planning had not made any provision for this disease. 14th Army had not been consulted.

"On instructions from D.D.V.S. (Col. S. O'Donel, M.C.) 14th Army, D.A.D.V.S. made arrangements for prophylactic treatment to be carried out in bdes. due to fly in from Lalaghat, antrypol being flown down from B.D.V.S. at Imphal, but animals of only three columns were protected as the 'D' Day for the bdes, was suddenly advanced.

"At this stage (early April) regular prophylaxis in columns already in Burma was planned for and surra 'drop packages' came forward from India, but on the results in animals of 14th Bde. and 23rd Bde. (100 per cent. prophylaxis carried out by 202 L. of C. Area in the latter) it was decided by 14th Army that the project was not practicable.

"No positive case was found from the 252 animals of 16th Inf. Bd. flown out to Comilla in May and examined in veterinary hospitals there, and they had marched through the worst surra areas of Burma, although in the cold weather months of February to April.

"The surra equipment was retained at air base against a possible recrudescence of the problem which did in fact occur in July, when surra was diagnosed clinically by V.O.s of 14th and 3rd W. A. Bdes, and antrypol and surra drop packs were supplied by S. D. aircraft, for therapeutic treatment.

"Infection occurred as flies became more numerous with the onset of the hot weather and rains, and where civilian and captured enemy animals were encountered south and east of Indawgyi Lake.

"Treatment was undertaken by V.O.s of 14th and 3rd W. A. Bdes. at Namun and Lakhren when they were halted there, and later at Pahok, on cases judged by them, on clinical signs, to be positive.

"As bdes. came out through C.A.I., D.A.D.V.S. saw 90 per cent. of the surviving animals of the Force and the opinion was formed by him that approximately 30 per cent. were infected with surra.

"The problems of surra in L.R.P. animals is a difficult one, but is considered not insoluble given the following adjuncts:—

(a) Light-weight microscopes, with magnification of 600, capable of being dropped from aircraft and not too heavy to be carried on with rest of V.O.s equipment.

(b) A British R.A.V.C. dresser in each column specially trained and reliable in carrying out intravenous injection if the V.O. cannot contact the column when either prophylactic or therapeutic treatment is indicated.

(c) A quicker method (50 c.c. syringes?) of administering the drug, than that offered by the i/v set.

"One of the lessons of the 1944 operations was that animal refitments more often than not depend upon the constructions of a strip (1,200 yds.) capable of taking a Dakota, and that columns must budget on keeping their animals going and it would appear that the risks of drug fastness and abscess formation attendant upon antrypol injection are better accepted than those of wastage resulting from uncontrolled surra.

"It is suggested, therefore, that planning should allow of an elastic use of antrypol during operations.

"Subsequent to the hand-over to 36th Div. animals were located at Pahok (near crossroads) under conditions which appeared to favour the spread of surra infection and it has been alleged by reports of 36th Div. that 100 per cent. were infected. This is not considered to represent the true surra picture when animals were operating with columns of this formation.

(ii) Tetanus
(iii) Piroplasmosis } Were reported in rare cases."

One of the column V.O.s of Special Force, Captain D. H. Witherington, has left on record his own experiences in these operations:—

"The Brigade landed by air at 'Aberdeen' (near Kalat in Kalat Forest). Moved southwards across the Banmauk Road. Here (a few miles east of Banmauk) 42 and 73 Columns established a road-block to protect our crossing and harass Jap supply columns moving west to the Imphal area.

"The main objective now was Bonchaung and bridges round about. In this area the Brigade's first serious casualties were sustained in men and animals; 59, 84 and 65 Columns lost approximately eleven mules. About 24th April 1944, the Brigade concentrated near Gahe for several days while operations on Indaw were taking place. Here 65, 84, 59, 16, 61, 42 and 73 Columns were visited and a large number of sit-fasts cut out (fifteen in 16 Column) and about ten bursitis withers dealt with.

"From Gahe seven columns moved north again, crossing the railway and damaging wherever possible. At Tongpila we concentrated for three days and I went to 'White City' (Henu road-block, formed by the 77th Brigade) to visit 47 and 74 Columns, which until this period I had not seen since 28th March.

"The risk of surra infection of these columns from other Brigade animals in the fort was considered. From Tongpila we moved in extended order to Honktonkski and thence along the range of hills to Meintheingyi. I commenced the journey with the first column and then dropped back a column a day so that I eventually reached Meintheingyi with the last column. This proved a very difficult and tiring march for men and animals—considered an impossible track by the villagers—and water was scarce. At Meintheingyi all columns halted to refit and collect stores dropped by parachute (S.D.) before heading for Namun, on the south edge of Indawgyi Lake, and the Chaungsali Pass. There was apparently no surra in the Brigade at this point.

"74 Column, followed later by 61 and 57, caught the Japs in a state of unpreparedness on the pass and shot all of them. They then sat and waited for the enemy's supporting troops to move up. These were similarly dealt with and a large amount of medical kit was captured. Here, too, a number of Jap ponies fell into our hands.

"Columns not concerned with the pass assisted with the evacuation of casualties of the 111th Brigade (and our own) from the Lake. 16 Column moved north, followed later by 61, and shot-up Japs escaping down the Indaw Chaung. They contacted Chinese forces here. All columns were inspected by me at Namun and surra prophylaxis begun. The pass (held from three to four weeks) was then evacuated after demolition by sappers. Monsoons had started, and from Namun onwards our time was spent mainly in a fight against the elements. We wanted to cross over the hill between Moxo-Sakan and the Mogaung Valley. Several tracks were tried and new ones cut, but only 47 Column succeeded by travelling several days ahead and so missing the monsoon downpour. The eight columns of the Brigade were close together for this month and this was ideal from the V.O.'s viewpoint. Losses in mules at this period were heavy owing chiefly to the bad going and surra.

"The hills were eventually crossed by the Lakhren-Padigatwng-Pahok route and operations proceeded at 'Hill 60' and Taungni prior to handing over to the 36th Division."

"PREPARATIONS IN INDIA
"Training

"The training of the mules was rushed and in many cases the muleteers had never touched a mule or pony before in their lives when they took over the animals. Muting operations, lack of saddlery and equipment, etc., also interfered with training. Some mules were saddled for the first time just a few days prior to the movement to forward areas.

"Transport by Rail

"Movement to forward areas was by rail; this was quite successful with no casualties. The only difficulty was experienced when the change-over from broad to narrow gauge took place. The narrow-gauge wagons were not properly adapted for carrying livestock and we were lucky to have no mishap here. The mules lost little or no condition during the rail move, which lasted eight days. Some ponies and bullocks, however, lost condition. There was no trouble whatsoever from thrush after the move. Lime was scattered about the floors of the trucks and some of the dung was disposed of daily en route in most wagons.

"Transport by Air

"Transport by air was simple. Loading was not difficult and very few animals objected to the roar of the engines. Restraint inside the planes was afforded by two rows of bamboo poles, dividing the standing into four. It was the general rule to tie the animals two before and two behind at the front of the plane. Bullocks travelled well three abreast. Any animals which caused trouble inside the plane were doped fifteen minutes before departure with chloral hydrate. Total casualties during the air move were two mules: these broke loose from their standing and became quite uncontrollable and had to be destroyed.

"BEHIND THE JAPANESE LINES
"Condition of Animals

"For the first six weeks mules put on condition and were remarkably fit. Ponies, in particular Indian-bred animals, lost condition, whereas South African ponies rarely did so. The light-legged Indian-bred ponies proved quite unsuitable in these campaigns.

Feed.—The grain situation was acute at times, often periods of five days elapsing without a grain feed. The supply of 30 lb. per animal per five days was sufficient for mules, but quite inadequate for ponies. Naturally the larger animals were given extra at the expense of A.T. mules. However, the mules survived very well on bamboo leaves.

"Once the monsoon started the grain was almost invariably damp and mouldy.

"The exclusion of bran, coupled with an increased grain ration, improved the situation.

"Ballast Sacks (U.S.A.A.F.) with zip fasteners made ideal grain containers for a top load.

"*Fodder.*—Packings of hay and bhoosa in supply containers proved quite useful if consumed on the spot. However, most of our animals preferred bamboo and wouldn't touch the hay!

"*Watering.*—Water was often a problem before the monsoon started. Small pools in the rocks of chaung-beds were the only supply for men and animals, so the latter went short. It was customary in some columns for each animal to carry its own two chaguls of water in case of emergency; these proved invaluable at times.

"*Feet.*—Mules' feet in most cases were hard and they were never shod. Ponies' hoofs were poor and cracked badly when shoes were cast. All animals carried a spare set of shoes, but once these were used, in the case of ponies, replacements were difficult to obtain.

"*Animals under Fire.*—Owing to the Japs' tactics the animals were often in the front line. The majority would stand quietly and very few were lost owing to bolting under fire.

"*Blinds.*—The use of blinds over the eyes seemed to worry the mules more than the noise of rifle or machine-gun fire. Also our blinds were an awful nuisance on the line of march, constantly falling down, no matter how securely tied up. In wet weather they became coated with mud and caused sores over the eyes. An improved pattern would be more useful.

"Saddlery

"Saddle fitting in the Brigade was carried out rather hurriedly and after a few days' march under full load the number of galls exposed a very high percentage of saddles which required refitting. This was done on the line of march. Stuffing pockets were found to contain anything from fishbones to wire nails! These pockets in many cases had been inadequately stuffed and judicious use of saddle blankets tided over the difficult period during the first three weeks until columns halted for a few days, when more drastic measures were taken. Girths and cruppers were a weak point and constantly giving way even in the good weather.

"*Top Loads.*—Top loads were a constant cause of trouble. They caused rubs along the back and loins and the saddles required constant attention. Top loads should be dispensed with as far as possible; they are particularly bad when travelling over hilly country, when the load tosses backwards and forwards over the back. Grain carried as a top load does not cause these undesirable effects to the same extent.

"*Bullock Saddles.*—As fitted these were not a success and quickly galled the hump. Bullocks soon lost condition on the march, and the back lost its shape completely so that it was impossible to fit the saddle to the back. Practically all bullock saddles were dumped, and two parachutes slung over the back, supported by groundsheet and blanket, worked well, though invariably they slipped back when going uphill. Bullocks were successfully used for carrying casualties in one column.

"*Saddlery in the Monsoon.*—Once the wet weather commenced saddlery was soon in a very bad state. In spite of covering with a waterproof sheet when offsaddled, the numnahs became soaked and remained so for several days before they could be dried out. Stitching broke and numnahs fell to pieces. Backs were rubbed badly in many cases. All blankets were equally soaked so that they gave little protection to the back under the saddle. Girths broke at the rate of twenty a day in a column in the wet weather and various improvisations had to be made to enable the column to move. New girths were unobtainable for some time and this rendered some columns completely immobile for a few days. Dubbin was used on the saddlery throughout the campaign.

"Boric powder was applied to wet backs before saddling in some cases and gave satisfactory results. Naturally it could not be used on the scale of a column.

"Veterinary Equipment

Field Veterinary Chest.—There was one field veterinary chest per column. This was inadequate for column requirements. The quantity of oily dressing, for instance, could be increased fourfold. Each column veterinary chest should contain the following articles:

"Oily dressing	Pot. permang.	Chloral hydrate balls
Lysol	Copper sulphate	Bandages
Mosquito ointment	Antrypol	Cotton-wool
Acriflavine cream	Tabs. lead acetate	Tow
Acriflavine powder	Tabs. zinc sulph.	Gauze
Sulphonamide powder	Aloes ball	Anti-tet. serum
Tabs. M &B sulphapyridine	Tabs. hyd. Perchlor	Sinus forceps
Boric powder	Probe	Ammon. carb. balls
Artery forceps	Suture needles	B.P. knife and blades
Dressing forceps	Bullet forceps	Anti-gas gangrene serum.

"*Veterinary Wallet.*—At least two veterinary wallets were required in each column, as frequently Commandos or reconnaissance parties were some distance from the main column and dressings were neglected in these groups. The contents of the wallet was considered satisfactory, but the substitution of a Bard Parker knife and blades for the folding knife would be better.

"*Veterinary Supplies by Air.*—It is essential that a more complete list on the lines of the medical ones should be compiled. Veterinary stores must have separate QQ numbers from the medical list.

"A great mistake in the operations was the dropping of veterinary stores in the same 'chute as the medical stores: the disadvantages of this procedure are obvious. The rush in collecting stores after a stores drop (S.D.) when a quick get-away is desired does not allow for sorting out the goods. Veterinary kit should be dropped in a separate container.

" '*Fifteen-day Drop*'.—This was quite inadequate: the contents (except for bandages) lasting only four days in the column. It was usually received in a very bad state, e.g., boric powder, zinc sulph., lead acetate, and hydarg. perchlor. packed in soft bags, arrived as a messy paste, owing to their hygroscopic nature on the one hand and to a leaking oily dressing container on the other! The bandages and cotton-wool were often soaked in oily dressing! Sulphapyridine tablets were usually in good order if the container had not burst open at the end. Thermometers were often broken—this is an unnecessary inclusion in the 'fifteen-day drop'.

"*Veterinary Officer's Kit*.—The veterinary officer requires an E.I. mule; the load weighing 200 to 220 lb. At least four weeks' supply of stores must be carried, for S.D.s cannot be relied on for stores when food naturally has the priority. As the veterinary officer fluctuates between columns it is sometimes difficult to get in the QQ at the right time. The mule load consisted of grain (30 lb. every five days), two blankets, two groundsheets, two chaguls of water and two veterinary officer's chests (80 lb. per side).

"Common Wounds and Injuries

"*Saddle Injuries*.—Although columns had a small reserve of mules without pre-scribed loads, invariably every mule was loaded at the outset with extra ammunition, etc., so that in actual fact there were no spare mules.

"Practically every animal carried a full load and if one fell out for any reason it meant overloading others. However, the bullocks came in useful for bringing on the spare equipment at the earliest stages of the campaign. Column personnel were by no means efficient at saddle fitting at first and had to learn by experience. Slight alteration in the stuffing pockets (or even reversing the panels so that they were on the correct side!) would have saved a large number of bad injuries. Troublesome loads were caused by the large number of packs to be carried for sick personnel. They were put on spare animals (if any) or else carried as top loads, e.g., on the wireless-battery mules. Naturally, this led to overloading and galling. Anything up to twenty packs were carried on column animals, each pack weighing 60 lb. or more.

"Types of Injuries

"*Buckle Galls*.—New girths stretched considerably and buckle galls resulted, but use of coiled loading ropes beneath the load eliminated the pressure over the offending area until the girths could be shortened to the correct length. Top loads—such as Piat and Lifebuoy—should be condemned. Right from the start they were a source of trouble, and the tossing movement (caused by the high load) resulted in serious galls over the back. Even the use of a blanket did not save the undesirable effects. In hilly country, and especially in the monsoon with wet saddlery, the conditions became worse.

"*Rib Galls*.—These were common on mules carrying the 22-inch wireless set. The leather panniers used lost their shape after three weeks' march, with 'bowing in' in the middle causing excessive pressure in one particular area. Here the use of groundsheets and blankets, and coiled loading ropes below the load, lessened the effects to a great extent.

"*Heel Galls*, caused by creepers, etc., were common. The usual treatment was the application of mosquito ointment, when they healed quickly.

"*Girth Galls* were worst in aged mules with poor circulation. Girths had to be incredibly tight to keep the saddle in place over the very rough country and steep hillsides traversed. Most trouble came with the rains, when girths were soaked and muddy. A piece of Mae West lifebelt over the girths often helped these cases.

"The use of two independent girths (American style) was useful to avoid girthing over the old sore.

"*Wither Galls.*—These were not common. A few cases of fistulous withers occurred as a result and were treated successfully with M &B soluble, and later mag. sulph and glycerine. A very convenient dressing in wither-gall cases, where it is difficult to keep on any covering as protection against flies, is to make a complete 'cast' with strips of bandage and mosquito ointment. The dressing keeps in position for long periods, and has also fly-repellent properties. Mules with old gall scars along their backs were a nuisance right from the start. They should be avoided for future campaigns if possible.

"Routine Treatment of Galls on Column

"White lotion was used for initial swellings and very superficial galls. Gentian violet worked wonderfully well in cases where the skin was rubbed badly, and in superficial sit-fasts. It was certainly the most effective agent used, for it produced a scab over the wound so that the animal could be saddled. The cause of the injury was naturally removed as well, in conjunction with treatment. In many cases the saddle numnah was cut out (or a blanket similarly treated) to eliminate pressure over the gall.

"Sulphonamide powder and acriflavine cream were used in deep sit-fasts to encourage granulation. Nearly every sit-fast (and some were very large and deep) was saddled, and the animal would carry a light load for a week until healed completely.

"Sit-fasts.—These were cut without hesitation as soon as reported and they healed remarkably well under load, provided that pressure over the affected area was removed.

"Owing to the large number of simple surgical cases, such as sit-fasts, it is essential to supply a Bard Parker handle and blades with each column veterinary chest. The knife issued loses its edge after one operation. In fact, all columns in the Brigade eventually equipped themselves with a Bard Parker knife.

"Battle Wounds (Bullet and Shrapnel)

"Owing to the fact that no lines of communication existed, many mules had to be destroyed with wounds which could have been treated successfully in hospital. The Jap seemed to go for the animals, as he realized that they were our only life-line on the move. Gangrene turning to gas gangrene resulted in some earlier casualties, but the use of anti-gas gangrene serum saved later ones. This is a most essential component for the column veterinary chests. One case of tetanus in the area of Indawgyi Lake resulted from a punctured wound, so that I consider anti-tetanic serum should also be supplied in chests.

"Treatment of shrapnel and bullet wounds was effected by surgical removal of all dead tissues and the piece of shrapnel or the bullet, then packing with sulphonamide powder. This was most successful. Drainage tubes were occasionally essential. A South African pony caught a burst of medium machine-gun bullets over his loins, two of them entering the abdominal cavity without noticeable ill-effects afterwards. He was carrying casualties again within a couple of weeks!

"Bamboo Wounds

"Caused by 'chopped-off bamboo sticks' these wounds were very common: they varied from superficial scratches to deep punctured wounds. If they were kept clean and free from fly-blows they healed very well, treated with sulphonamide powder and oily dressing. In cases of deep punctures anti-tetanic serum was given. Rotten bamboo which pierced the skin would often break off, leaving a piece of wood under the skin. These were not usually noticed until a huge abscess formed, unless, of course, the wound occurred in the fetlock or coronet to cause lameness.

"Poisonous Plants

"Along the Meza Valley we came across a plant of the order *Iridaceae* which was apparently attractive to some animals.

"Symptoms.—Within three minutes of consumption profuse salivation and swelling of the tongue and lips occurred. Submaxillary glands enlarged within an hour. Animals became dejected and off food and water for from eight to twenty-four hours. There was no systemic reaction.

"Treatment.—Pot. permang. mouth-wash. In some the swelling subsided quickly, whereas in others it persisted for twenty-four hours.

"Muted Animals

"It was generally agreed throughout the columns that it wasn't worth the risk to take in non-muted animals again. A small number of ponies were taken in non-muted and they caused much anxiety at times; they invariably greeted animals arriving into bivouac with loud whinnyings and were a particular nuisance when food was short. Whinnying at night brought about excellent attempts at neighing from the muted animals!

"On an average, about four mules per column regained their voices to varying degrees; this was naturally a source of danger to the column. On the whole, the Brigade was very successfully muted. My own pony was muted at the air base and flown 'in' three days later with a small, open wound. In less than a week of the operation she was on the march; in ten days she carried packs and within fourteen days a sick man! There was no loss of condition. In a very few cases the animal's wind was affected by the operation, presumably owing to some post-operative occlusion of the larynx. It was only on very heavy going that any distress was noticeable and most cases seemed to improve as time went on.

"CONTAGIOUS DISEASES

"Surra, biliary fever and rinderpest were the chief worries.

"Biliary Fever

"Two cases occurred in 16 Column at air base, but after this there were no more cases to my knowledge.

"Rinderpest

"This disease was rampant among native cattle and buffaloes. Our own bullocks were protected so that the risk of their infection was negligible and we lost none.

"Surra

"By far our most troublesome disease. Up to 20th July it is estimated that we lost (died or shot) between 120 and 150 animals from the disease. The incidence was highest among the Indian-bred ponies and lowest in Indian-bred mules.

"*Occurrence of Surra.*—For the first six weeks of the campaign the danger of surra was not great. There were few or no Tabanid flies in the area and we made no contact with local animals during this period. The first case of surra was diagnosed in 16 Column on 12th June at Namun in a poor Indian-bred pony.

"*Measures Adopted.*—Suspects were treated. The animals of the whole Brigade, except 47, 74 and 84 Columns, were given prophylactic doses of antrypol at the rate of 0.4 grm. per 100 lb. estimated weight, and injections were completed in two and a half days. The three columns not dosed moved out on operations before they could be done and the risk had to be taken. At intervals of three to four weeks prophylactic dosing was repeated in the columns, but in spite of this odd cases continued to occur. 16 Column Commando mules were not dosed at Namun and all succumbed to the disease within ten days, which would indicate to some degree the value of prophylactic measures.

"*Source of Disease.*—This might have been (1) from local native animals; (2) from Jap animals; (3) from White City; (4) from one surra-recovered animal issued from Remounts to 65 Column.

"(1) Native cattle roamed about in large numbers in the Namun area, and Tabanids abounded in myriads, being a nuisance to both men and animals. It was impossible to keep animals for more than two or three days up in the Chaungsa Pass near Namun, as they were in agony night and day from biting flies and would come down to Namun 'oozing' with spots of blood all over. They naturally lost condition rapidly. Smearing the animals over with oily dressing was a very effective counter-measure against the flies for a few hours. Without a doubt this area is a hot-bed of surra. Whether the local cattle are responsible as reservoirs is difficult to say. Tabanids and Hippoboscae were common in the marshes alongside the Indawgyi Lake, where our operations continued. Maybe the first infection occurred in the Meintheingyi area (a few days' march from Namun).

"(2) *From Jap Animals.*—61 and 47 Columns captured twenty-nine ponies from the Japanese at Chaungsa Pass. All these were examined by me, and none showed any symptoms of surra. At a later date some died of surra, but most likely contracted it from our own animals.

"(3) *From White City.*—A few mules were collected from White City (77th Brigade's animals) by 47 and 65 Columns. None of these were unhealthy at the time of taking over.

"*Symptoms.*—Very few cases occurred which showed the cardinal signs of the disease: they were usually acute; in fact, only two chronic cases were seen. There had been only one or two cases showing inco-ordination of hind-quarters up to 18th July. The usual story was a history of distressed respirations under load, temperature 101 to 104 degrees F., and injected mucous membranes. Rapidly (within two hours) the symptoms became worse and the animal refused to move even without load or saddle. It was customary on the line of march to dispose of these immediately.

"Some cases, when possible, were kept under observation for a few days, and in isolation, when petechiae invariably appeared in the ocular mucous membrane. A few mules died so suddenly that no definite symptoms of the disease could be found at all. The appetite in many cases was ravenous and desire for water pronounced, but in spite of this they quickly lost condition.

"*Reactions to Dosage (O.4G./100 lb.).*—If possible the animals were given forty-eight hours' rest after the injection, but often this was tactically unsound. The initial dosing of 59, 16 and 61 Columns in March gave fairly severe reactions.

"In June, when the weather was considerably cooler owing to rains, and maggots were not so troublesome, reactions to the injections were far less marked. However, they became more pronounced on each subsequent injection.

"*Surra Equipment.*—A completely useless intravenous outfit with a very small funnel was issued. It was a very slow and inefficient method of injecting antrypol and was dispensed with in the early stages. The number of assistants required for the intravenous method is a disadvantage. A 50-c.c. syringe is absolutely essential for efficient and quick injections. There isn't time on column for the use of apparatus such as the I/V set. A good supply of sharp needles with a sharpening stone is also essential. 10-c.c. syringes or a metal wound syringe (graduated) were used by me for all antrypol injections, averaging twenty mules per hour if stocks were used. Stocks were built of bamboo whenever columns halted for more than twenty-four hours, which enabled a thorough examination of all animals.

"*Surra-drop Packages.*—These were good. The small 2-gm. ampoules of antrypol were invaluable on the line of march whenever an animal showed signs of surra or when small numbers of animals were to be dosed, e.g., reconnaissance mules away from the main column."

We lost three officers on these operations. Captain A. M. Fyfe was drowned on the night of the 12th July 1944 while attempting to save a mule in the Mogaung river at Kainaing. Captain D. H. Greeves and Lieutenant Chatter Singh, I.A.V.C., were killed on 29th July when the two Dakotas in which they were flying from Sylhet to Tingkawk during the fly-out of the 77th Brigade animals were shot down by enemy aircraft over the Indawgyi Lake area.

The animal casualties incurred during the five months of jungle fighting behind the Japanese lines were 273 horses (50 per cent.) and 1,169 mules (37 per cent.).

The Japanese launched their offensive against the 4th Corps on the Imphal front in March 1944. They cut the Tiddim road, but not the Tamu road, and in early April they cut the Kohima-Imphal road and advanced on Kohima as a preliminary to the capture of Dimapur.

Our strategy was to fight in the Imphal plain and the 17th Division consequently began to withdraw from Tiddim reaching Imphal three weeks later after fighting all the way. The 20th Indian Division was also withdrawing from Tamu. The divisional veterinary staff, including the Indian mobile veterinary section and the Indian advanced field veterinary hospital, accompanied their formations.

On Imphal plain 4th Corps awaited the Japanese in a series of defended localities, organized like the administrative bases, in which veterinary units took their share of the defence in addition to their normal work. In 1944 Captain P. Wilson, then E.V.O. 63rd Brigade, wrote of his experiences during the move of his Brigade from Tiddim to Imphal during March and April.:

"When orders were received to move I was at Brigade H.Q. twelve miles south of Tiddim. The 9th Border Regiment, was already in Tiddim while 1/7 Gurkha Rifles and 2/5 Royal Gurkha Rifles were forward in the Kennedy Peak area. Orders to move were received at 0200 hours 14th March. I moved to Tiddim with Brigade H.Q. and attached animals, my veterinary equipment being carried on one of the mules. When leaving Tiddim this had to be scrapped as all mules were required to lift stores and ammunition. I carried what I could in the way of oily dressing and bandages and destroyed the remainder. My microscope was handed in to the divisional mobile veterinary section.

"The march from Tiddim started at 1800 hours. I marched at the tail of the column of the brigade (less 2/5 R.G.R. who were acting as rear-guard) complete with attached mules from A.T. companies. During the second day we camped at Tumla Lui where I had an opportunity of examining all animals. The second night was spent at Milestone 144 where considerable alarm was caused by a Japanese 'Jitter' party with a great deal of firing from small arms and automatic weapons. As a result of this six animals had to be destroyed next morning; these might have been saved in more normal circumstances.

"The following day we marched to the Manipur River (Milestone 127) where there was plenty of grain in a field supply depot and the animals had a welcome two days rest. There was no sickness among the mules and there appeared to be no biting flies. Saddle galls were surprisingly few and slight. The men appeared to be unaffected except that many of the B.O.R.s had sore feet. I expected to find several Chinese ponies with B.O.R.s riding them but only one was picked up. This was disposed of as transport officers were instructed not to collect these animals because of the danger of surra. From here onwards the Brigade took over an offensive role and I moved with the tactical H.Q. The entire Brigade was on a *pack* basis operating over most difficult country on Scale 'A' ration (very light scale). The animals did splendid work, evidence of their good hard condition. The Field Ambulance Troop came into its own and was used to carry casualties, on one occasion over seven miles of very rough country before reaching the main road. There was little loss of equipment which was confined to the loss of a wireless set when a mule fell over the khud side. There was a certain amount of trouble from mortar fire and sniping. During the actual fighting I could do little and had set up a dressing station in a village where the mules turned round. This was on the only route to and from the Japanese position and I found myself employed in helping to supply tea and field dressings to battle casualties. This was not without its touch of humour as at one time I tried to engage a Japanese casualty in conversation, having mistaken him for a Gurkha as his head was bandaged. At Milestone 109 there was a further welcome rest. Here I managed to 'win' a jeep from among some abandoned vehicles and took the opportunity to replenish the unit veterinary chests (obtained from No. 4 Mobile Veterinary Section at Milestone 127) and also to make up a chest for my own use, with a wound syringe, probes, etc.

"The only troubles among animals were minor injuries and some galls. The feet were in fairly good condition but some required attention and some re-shoeing. As all units except one, had discarded their farriery tools and spare shoes this was impossible, so all shoes were removed and the animals continued unshod.

"To the ordinary risks of war there was added that of parachute dropping of rations. In some cases these came loose and one mule received an abdominal wound from the resulting explosion where some milk and jam tins were dropped.

"At Milestone 82 we were again able to take stock of ourselves. The march from Milestone 109 to 82 took exactly twenty-four hours. Water could be found only once during the march. The going was very bad and the mules were under load for twelve hours and seven hours during that time. This, surprisingly, did not lead to any increase in the number of galls. I had anticipated some colic during a march of this nature but there were no cases during the whole march from Tiddim to Imphal. The animals had definitely lost condition which was not surprising as the work they had been doing was very severe. Rations while not at full scale were available up to 5 lbs. grain. I admired the way in which mule leaders, both infantry and mule companies, started to cut grass for their animals immediately after unloading, however long the march had been. Flies here were a nuisance but biting flies did not appear to be numerous. From Milestone 42 all the Brigade animals, including mountain artillery and attached mules, were loaded into lorries and taken back to Imphal. In spite of weak floor boards and in some cases a high wheel-box, there were no serious injuries. Here I managed to obtain a jeep for my own use and was able to see the animals into camp in Imphal, instead of arriving with the rear of the column, and on our next move to a rear position I was able to travel up and down the column during the march. When we arrived in Imphal there were twenty-two animals sick, the majority with galls a few of which had developed into sit-fasts. Ten mules were evacuated to hospital, nine with galls and one lame.

"The mules behaved very well under fire and on most occasions the leaders were excellent at keeping them under control. Shell fire does not appear to worry the mule but he shows a tendency to panic under small-arms fire. It was impossible due to the nature of the country to see units daily when operating off the road, and even when battalions could be reached by road it was not always possible to obtain transport although the brigade transport officer gave every possible help. The main difficulties occurred as a result of units discarding farriers' tools and veterinary equipment. There was only one unit which held on to these essentials and even my own had to be discarded in the early stages although later I was able to make up a chest which was carried in the brigade transport officer's jeep. Infantry N.C.O.s and mule leaders were very good in reporting injuries promptly but there was a tendency amongst animal-transport companies I.O.R.s to attempt to conceal injuries with a charcoal paste of some description rather than show them up. The general condition of animals at the finish of the march was good, taking into consideration the difficulties during the march, the hard work and nature of the country. The number of galls which occurred was not excessive and I consider this reflects credit on the transport officers and mule leaders particularly. The losses from small-arms fire and shell fire were three horses and nine mules.

"After arrival in Imphal the whole brigade was tested for surra and no positive case was found."

Kohima was invested in early April 1944 and relieved after sixteen days continuous fighting. At Imphal and Kohima our forces stood still and were supplied by air. In company with other administrative units the personnel of the mobile sections and veterinary hospitals took their share of the defence. Soon the Japanese began to withdraw under pressure of our troops. The Imphal road was opened in June and the pursuit of the enemy was maintained. During this period the forward troops were kept supplied by animal pack transport. The defensive period had ended and our offensive for the reconquest of Burma had begun.

Major J. D. Daly, then D.A.D.V.S. 4th Corps, has left on record an account of the work of the veterinary staff with an animal and M.T. division during active operations in May 1944:—

" '*A*' 48*th Ind. Bde.*—This brigade carried out two separate operations during the month. The first consisted of a move south of Imphal towards Palel where it came under the command of 20th Division from 7th to 11th May whilst clearing the enemy from that area. The second and major operation was carried out on an all-pack transport basis and consisted of moving south of Imphal to Shuganu and from there across country to the west to establish a road block at mile 33 on the Imphal–Tiddim road behind the 33rd Japanese Division.

"On the 13th May the brigade left harbour with a total of 1,300 pack animals. The march was carried out at night and took three nights over rough going in the shape of very steep hills and flooded paddy-fields. The force consisted of Brigade H.Q.s, two battalions of infantry and one mountain regiment of artillery. Having reached the road a block was established and held for eight days. The brigade then moved north and occupied the village of Moirang, stayed there a few days and then went on to capture the village of Thinunggen and afterwards rejoined the main body of the division. The whole operation lasted from the 13th to 31st May.

"*Veterinary Arrangements.*—It was not considered necessary to send a detachment from the Indian mobile veterinary section with the brigade as mule leaders could take animal casualties across country to road head at Shuganu from where they could be returned to harbour in empty supply lorries. D.A.D.V.S. was, whenever possible, informed of the number of animals to be evacuated so that their replacements were waiting at road head. As a result of heavy casualties, and to assist veterinary hospitals as much as possible, the mobile veterinary section was holding approximately fifty animal casualties.

"A R.A.V.C. officer as E.V.O. 48th Bde. and two veterinary assistant surgeons I.A.V.C. in charge of the mountain regiment of artillery and mule company accompanied the force.

"Battle casualties were heavy, particularly as animals had to be fairly concentrated in 'boxes', and were mostly caused by enemy shelling. There was no time or labour to spare for digging pits for animals and the best had to be made of whatever local protection was available. A fairly large number of casualties was also caused by rifles, machine-guns, grenades, mortar and on one occasion by machine-gunning from the air.

"The casualties were 145 killed or destroyed; sixty-two were evacuated through Shuganu where their replacements were picked up. Many more casualties were evacuated after the brigade made contact with the main body of the division. There was a large number of saddle galls, many of which must be considered unavoidable as conditions predisposing to these injuries were many including rough going over steep hills, flooded rice-fields, little or no opportunity to clean or repair saddlery, rain and mud and long hours under load imposed by tactical situations. There were few spare mules and in many cases mules which were already slightly galled had to be worked. Many of the casualties might have been saved under normal conditions but anything really serious had to be destroyed as it would have been a drag on the brigade. The executive veterinary officer suggested that sulphonamide powder be included in the V.O. chests as he considered it a most useful drug in dealing with wounds, from which it was not always possible to remove foreign bodies. He was of the opinion that it was of great value in preventing infection of wounds of this nature. As a result many were brought back to harbour which would otherwise have been destroyed.

"Animal rations were on the hard scale, i.e., no fodder. Sufficient for three days were carried and after that they were supplied by air. Supplies were well maintained until the last three days when no grain was delivered. A certain amount of 'paddy' was captured in Japanese lorries and fed to the animals. It was almost impossible to cut grass. Animals on the whole maintained condition fairly well.

" 'B' 63rd Bde. and 32nd Bde.—These brigades carried out operations from Bishenpur to the south and along the Silchar track to the west, as well as east and west of the Imphal-Tiddim road. During an attack on Bishenpur the Japanese occupied some bunkers in a 'box' held by part of the Mule Company. It was impossible to rescue all the animals and in the fighting, in which tanks were used, severe casualties to the animals resulted. In all, in the Bishenpur area 218 mules were killed and thirty-four wounded.

"The animals in these two brigades were widely dispersed throughout the area with companies and platoons occupying positions in the hills to the west of the Tiddim road. Engagements with enemy detachments occurred at the village of Irangbem and other smaller villages west of the road. There was also a battle around divisional headquarters 'administrative box'.

"The total casualties during the May operations from all causes were 550 killed or destroyed, fourteen missing, 376 evacuated to hospital, a total of 940. Shelling was found to account for most of the casualties; on one occasion one shell killed fourteen mountain artillery mules and four more had to be destroyed. The unit was just moving out of camp and for this reason the animals were concentrated.

"No cases of surra occurred during the month. Testing of animals was carried out as often as operations would permit.

"All veterinary officers and veterinary assistant surgeons had been warned to be on their guard against any tendency to slacken their efforts in combating the disease. The brigade veterinary officer and veterinary assistant surgeons all performed excellent work during the operations."

The pursuit of the enemy was carried on relentlessly and the chief obstacle was the weather. The last of the Japanese were driven from Indian soil by 20th August 1944. During the monsoon (i.e., between May and November) wheeled transport could not leave the roads, many bridges were down and landslides were numerous. Pack transport was indispensable and at a premium. Air supply was carried out with the greatest difficulty. A column of two brigades on a pack basis was detached from Kohima towards Ukhrul by way of a route over very difficult country, with tracks so bad that on one occasion it took four hours to advance 500 yards. The brigade veterinary officer accompanied the column which was supplied by air-drop. Not only were the atmospheric conditions during the monsoon very dangerous to aircraft but it was often impossible to find a gap in the clouds and to locate the dropping zones. No supply drop had been possible for some days owing to cloud and the brigades were enduring a serious shortage of rations for both troops and animals when, by a miracle, a gap in the clouds was found and under the gap was the dropping zone for the force. Later a serious situation arose once again in the Ukhrul column and although the troops suffered, the shortage was made up to some extent with mule meat. This commodity was an expedient which could be ill-afforded from the transport point of view owing to the shortage of this type of transport animal.

Tamu was captured by the 23rd Indian Division in early August and at the same time the 5th Indian Division continued to advance down the right bank of the Manipur river with one brigade on the left bank. All available mules were employed on an all-pack basis and when the road became impossible for M.T. they continued the lift forward to the advancing troops until December 1944 when both Kalemyo and Kalewa were captured.

Apart from the battle of the "administrative box" in February 1944 there were no large scale operations in Arakan. In November the 81st (West African) Division captured Paletwa and began to advance down the Kaladan Valley. A mountain battery and three troops of an animal-transport company involving 700 animals accompanied the division which was maintained entirely by air-drop until it was withdrawn in March 1945.

In the plan for clearing the Donbaik peninsula the 53rd Brigade moved down the Kalapanzin river. Mules and water transport were provided and supply was by air-drop every third day. The mules proved a hindrance in the repeated crossings of the numerous waterways while their food was a major air supply commitment and its carriage between air-drops a problem. They were all sent back and the column depended entirely on its water transport.

The 74th Brigade advanced down the coastal strip and was maintained by water transport which operated from Maungdaw to beach heads. Mules continued the lift from beach-heads to the troops.

During the operations which lasted from 15th December 1944 to 15th March 1945 over 2,300 animals were embarked and disembarked by naval and Inland Water

Transport craft under veterinary supervision. These operational landings were carried out between Foul Point and Akyab; Akyab and Myebon and Myebon and Ruywa. In addition a non-operational move was made from Ruywa back to Akyab. The Arakan campaign ended with the capture of Taungup in April 1945. It had attained its object—the capture of the airfields at Akyab and Ramree for the purpose of maintaining the 14th Army in Central Burma before Mandalay fell. It is doubtful if such administrative difficulties had to be faced in any other campaign as were experienced in Arakan. In addition to the uncompromising terrain the task was severely complicated by one of the worst climates in the world with a rainfall of 200 inches a year and by the lack of resources.

By early 1945 the Army Veterinary Service had developed and was carrying out its duties at a high level of efficiency. Sufficient veterinary officers, units, stores and equipment were now available to meet current and potential commitments. In addition to the divisional mobile veterinary sections, advanced field veterinary hospitals and field veterinary hospitals were located on the long and often disrupted lines of communication. Convalescent depots were established to relieve veterinary hospitals of cases which, though cured of diseases or major injuries, still required months of careful handling and good feeding before their return to remount depots as fit animals. One such depot situated in open country at an Assam hill station did particularly good work.

The newly-formed mobile anti-surra units and field veterinary laboratories proved most effective in dealing with the widespread outbreaks of surra and epizootic lymphangitis.

The standard of animal management in units showed considerable improvement evidenced by the reduced incidence of saddle and other preventable injuries. This improvement was chiefly due to the courses in animal management and veterinary first aid which were conducted at the Army Veterinary School, Ambala, and by veterinary officers in the field. These courses were attended by officers and men from units which had changed over from mechanized to animal transport and the results were excellent; students returned to their units with a tremendous respect for the pack animal which they had previously regarded as a vehicle. They soon realized that the mule is a stout-hearted and willing friend who will give of his best in return for considerate handling and the application of a few simple rules of animal management, feeding and kindness.

The incidence of surra had dropped from 17 per cent. of the total animal strength in 1942 to 2 per cent. of the animal strength in 1944-45. This decrease was made possible by the availability of mobile anti-surra units. These units with their batteries of microscopes were held centrally in the field ready for dispatch to any infected area where extensive blood testing and prophylactic treatment was required to be carried out. Frequently trypanosomes were detected in the blood of animals which appeared in perfect health with normal temperatures, a feature of the disease not previously recognized. Whenever possible infected animals were evacuated by M.T. to veterinary hospitals for skilled treatment. It was found that the use of prophylactic measures were often complicated by severe reactions of an unpredictable percentage of animals to inoculations with antrypol and commanders were naturally rather apprehensive of the results, particularly as repetition of the dose was necessary after an interval of three weeks. Nevertheless protective measures achieved great success. For example, 36th Division took over 800 animals in August 1944. These animals had just returned from operations behind the Japanese lines with Special Force and 80 per cent. were found to be infected with surra and in very poor condition. Owing to the shortage of mules and the tactical situation they were required to proceed on another expedition with 36th Division before there was time to subject them to a full course of treatment. They therefore received prophylactic treatment every three weeks up to the end of November when the biting flies had disappeared. Up to the following May only twelve cases of surra occurred among the animals of the division, which in the meantime received remounts to bring them up to a strength of 1,200 animals. Similar methods in a division operating over very difficult terrain with widely scattered animals in South Burma produced equally good results. Surra was, however, always present during the ensuing phases of the campaign and permitted no relaxation of continuous effort. Thousands of prophylactic inoculations were given to animals before setting out on operations.

The mortality due to surra in the Burma campaign can only be estimated very roughly—a conservative figure is 5,600 horses and mules.

It was subsequently found that our methods of control of surra were in all probability a great deal more effective than those used by the Japanese Army Veterinary Service, despite the fact that they were well supplied with miscroscopes, and never without a plentiful supply of naganol. This was borne out by our ability to maintain pickets beyond road-head throughout operations whereas the Japanese, particularly during the battle of Imphal, could not keep their pack animals alive in surra areas round the Imphal plain and were thus unable to supply their forward troops. During the follow-up after the Japanese had collapsed at Imphal, large numbers of their mules were found dead but uninjured, and it is a fair supposition that most of these died of surra.

The apparent puzzle of the Japanese inability to cope with surra was solved very largely by enquiries made by Colonel G. V. Short when he was A.D.V.S., A.L.F.S.E.A. in Indonesia.

"While there I was asked by S.E.A.C. to comb through the stores of (I think) the 15th Japanese Army Corps, with special reference to their veterinary equipment and drugs, and to send two samples of each item to S.E.A.C. for inspection and eventual consignment to India.

"I thought that the value of the notes made on the equipment would be more significant with comments by the Japanese veterinary officers who had used it. Accordingly from the prisoners' camp I got ten veterinary officers, of which nine had been trained in Japan and the other in Paris.

"The big surprise was in the answers on 'Naganol'. None of the Japanese-trained men knew how to administer it, though four of them knew that it was used against surra. The Paris-trained man knew that 'Naganol' was given intravenously but not the dose, though he did know that it was toxic if 'too much' was given. This would not have been so surprising had these men been without field experience. But four of them had been in charge of units equivalent to our mobile veterinary section, and three had commanded advanced veterinary hospitals."

What was particularly interesting was their firm conviction that equine surra was no more important than was the disease in cattle: a general nuisance but only occasionally of sufficient virulence to justify treatment. The high mortality among their mules and ponies were thought to be due mostly to anthrax or plant poisoning. The diagnosis was based on temperature recording, only when the typical oedema of the legs became marked was surra suspected. It would seem that the Japanese never realized that by the time oedema supervened even the correct treatment was usually too late.

All this may help to explain the seeming inconsistency of the plentiful supplies of naganol, together with the beautiful lightweight portable microscopes with which their forward units were equipped, and the hundreds of mules found dead in the Japanese supply areas around Imphal when our forces broke out. It also goes some way towards explaining the seeming anomaly of the Japs withdrawal from their battle stations around the Imphal Plain and Kohima while there was still plenty of food and ammunition in their road-head depots in the Upper Chindwin and Yu River areas: it seems that they were unable to supply their troops forward of these depots because they could not keep their pack transport animals alive in the surra zones.

The first case of epizootic lymphangitis was reported in Assam in June 1944 during the battles of Imphal and Kohima. The affected animals had been received from the Advanced Remount Depot at Dimapur, and since this was the key installation for operations it was not practicable to stop further issues. For the greater part of the year the jungle site of the depot was swarming with flies and animals were overcrowded. Consequently further cases soon occurred and all remounts issued had to be regarded with the greatest suspicion. The large number of animals turned out in paddocks were examined by driving them through narrow "crushes", but this system had dangers of its own for it was impossible to disinfect the "crush" after the passage of each animal. In addition more wounds and abrasions were often caused on which the flies immediately congregated. Branding of incontact animals was adopted in the early stages but it was soon discontinued owing to the danger of the brand wounds becoming infected.

The normal procedure of microscopically examining smears from wounds on animals exposed to infection was soon found to be insufficient and in disease areas all scars, abrasions and bruises were examined daily until the neighbourhood was declared free. Many wounds that could not be bandaged such as sore withers, were often found on examination to be infected. Thus the problem was no easy one. Of the fly-repellent dressings used B.I.P.P. proved the best, but D.D.T. was of the greatest assistance in controlling the spread. The effects of spraying the paddocks, stables, hospital buildings and surrounding jungle to a depth of fifty yards or more with D.D.T. 5 per cent. in kerosene were magical.

In the monsoon when animals were covered with mud the detection of the lesions was almost impossible. Also, animals in operational units were frequently split up into small detachments separated from the main body thus making constant veterinary supervision often impracticable. Again the supply of clipping machines was never in keeping with the demand which made detection of the lesions most difficult owing to the length of the coat. However, an improvement in the overall situation at the base and in the forward areas was effected by insisting that no remounts or unit animals should move from the Assam-North Burma area to the Arakan, which had a separate L. of C. As a result of this policy all animals from the Arakan were returned to India on the conclusion of operations without fear of introducing the disease. On the other hand animals from the northern line had to be segregated at various centres before dispersal.

Casualties were at times heavy during the epidemic following the hot weather in 1945, but reduction was effected with the introduction of D.D.T. and many units were declared entirely free though in others sporadic cases continued to occur. From June 1944 until V.J. Day about 730 cases were diagnosed. The main problem in connection with epizootic lymphangitis was to prevent its spread into India where it was considered to be non-existent among army animals. In Burma, however, the disease was believed to be relatively widespread amongst civilian animals.

Anthrax was highly endemic in Assam and Burma and the policy of prophylactic inoculations every six months for all army animals entering these regions from India was adopted. These measures proved very successful and mortality from this potentially dangerous disease was small, there being only thirty-nine case in 1942-43 and three cases in 1943-45.

Saddle injuries and sore backs constituted a serious problem throughout the war, especially in the early days, mainly due to the low standard of animal management prevailing in units, and to the adverse effect of the climate in Burma. It was obviously impossible to keep saddlery dry under conditions where a hundred inches of rain occur in six months. Added to this animals were exposed to extreme hardship often on short rations, with consequent loss of back muscle, while the continuous rain promoted softening of the scars covering back injuries sustained in the early part of the campaign.

The contribution of the Army Veterinary Services towards elimination of this cause of wastage was directed mainly to providing units and formations with veterinary staffs capable of advising and instructing personnel of units in animal management in general and the prevention, cure and treatment of saddle injuries in particular. Large-scale training facilities for officers and other ranks (British and Indian) were instituted at most veterinary installations including the Army Veterinary School, Ambala. To reduce the wastage in animals afflicted with severe saddle injuries and chronic scarred backs a plastic operation of the "Cherry" type was devised. A specialist conversant with the technique of this operation was appointed to instruct veterinary officers in hospitals. An appreciable reduction in this form of wastage resulted and many animals previously unserviceable were returned to duty, all scar tissues being removed leaving smooth pliable skin.

A factor which contributed in no small measure to this high incidence of saddle injuries was that in the efforts to meet demands animals were purchased by the Indian Remount Department from U.S.A., the Argentine Republic and South Africa. Whilst these purchases were being made the bazaars and hill roads of India were swept almost bare of any ponies and mules which might in an emergency carry a saddle for a few weeks. The standard of the Indian purchases was very low but they were bought in the hope that good feeding and care might improve them. Many had old lesions and the skin covering old healed saddle injuries was very thin and paper-like with the result that many were returned from operational areas as unserviceable. To minimize the problem the Director of Veterinary Services A.L.F.S.E.A. inspected collections of them and divided them into four classes: fit to work at base in carts; fit for pack work in dry season with specially folded blankets; likely to be fit for work after plastic operations; and totally unserviceable.

Towards the end of the campaign in Burma the standard of animal management showed much improvement and the incidence of preventable injuries such as saddle galls was reduced to a satisfactory level.

A major difficulty was the evacuation of animal casualties to and from base hospitals due to the lack of road and rail transport and to road blocks caused by landslides. To a large extent the problem was overcome in 1944 by taking full advantage of the decision to withdraw as many animals as possible from the forward areas before the onset of the rains. By this time hospital accommodation had increased on the lines of communication and between the forward areas and rail head.

Three-ton lorries, as employed in all other overseas theatres by the Army Veterinary Services, constituted the usual method of transportation of remounts and sick animals, and in some cases of all horses and mules of certain units. Fittings for the lorries were considered desirable, particularly for the evacuation of sick and to obviate accidents, but they were not regarded as essential where movement of animals on a large scale had to be organized at short notice. It was generally agreed that the United

States Army six-wheel lorry (as employed by the United States Army Veterinary Services and by the French Army Veterinary Services in Central Mediterranean Forces), with its four-wheel drive, was in many ways a better vehicle for conveyance of animals from the somewhat inaccessible places often occupied by units employing animal transport. More animals could be carried in this particular vehicle and they suffered less bumping during transit.

During the period of static warfare, the evacuation of casualties was fairly simple, the animal-carrying lorries of mobile veterinary sections being freely used. During the defensive period in 1944 when the Japanese launched their offensive on the Imphal front any three-ton lorry returning empty to railhead at Dimapur was used to convey animal casualties. During the rapid forward movement of our forces into Burma in 1945 it was necessary for divisions to retain their casualties, and mobile veterinary sections were employed in a rôle normally discharged by field veterinary hospitals— an improvisation which proved very valuable. It was, however, generally agreed that the veterinary and remount conducting sections, as used by the veterinary and remount services in Europe, would have simplified the evacuation and replacement of casualties, and would have proved a more efficient and economical system.

Live animals destined for the food of British and Indian troops were imported into S.E.A.C. during 1943-1944 at the average rate of 2,620 cattle and 15,790 sheep and goats per month. In December 1944 the peak figures were reached and consisted of 4,820 cattle and 34,655 sheep and goats. There was no greater financial loss in slaughter animals than that which occurred among the goats. They were purchased in the United Provinces for the most part and collected into depots after journeys from purchasing centres of frequently over 100 miles by road, followed by rail journeys of several hundred miles in tightly packed trucks often without water during the heat of the Indian summer. Exhaustion therefore played a big part in lowering the animals resistance to disease. The degree of exhaustion in the Indian depots was, however, of a minor order compared with that on the Burma front as a result of long rail journeys from India, unavoidable transhipment of animals at change of gauge and overcrowded depots. On one section it usually took forty-eight hours to do a journey of about 180 miles during which any food provided was generally trampled underfoot and watering facilities were inadequate. Although transportation was speeded up and conditions generally improved, the delivery of these animals to the troops in the field before they sickened and died or before exhaustion overcame them, remained difficult. The most common disease of the goats was a deadly and rapidly infective pleuro-pneumonia.

Casualties among sheep from this disease were comparatively light. They did, however, suffer from a contagious broncho-pneumonia and diarrhoea which was believed to be due to a parasitic infection. Rinderpest outbreaks were successfully controlled when protective serum was administered to all animals before dispatch from India, and subsequently at eight to ten days' interval. Foot-and-mouth disease, which was seldom absent, became particularly serious when cattle had to trek over rough stony roads. This trouble was met by transportation in lorries; the animals then arrived without undue fatigue or loss of condition.

Various schemes were started in A.L.F.S.E.A. to provide food from local resources. Pigs, goats and ducks were reared in large numbers but the only successful scheme proved to be that for breeding pigs, the necessary breeding stock being imported from Australia. The first two pig breeding units raised were placed in the charge of a warrant officer, R.A.V.C., specially transferred from the Middle East. These two units therefore started on sound lines and no serious losses were experienced.

The breeding of goats was a complete failure and the Chinese system of egg hatching also proved unsuccessful owing to "Keel" disease about which no local information was available before commencing the scheme.

After the capture of Kalemyo and Kalewa in December 1944 our troops crossed the Chindwin and established a bridge-head across the Irrawaddy about the middle of February 1945. Ever since its formation 14th Army had been operating in jungle-clad mountains where animal transport was indispensable. It was now entering flat open country where mechanization would have full scope and speed and mobility could replace the slow and cautious tactics hitherto necessary.

During this rapid forward movement divisional mobile veterinary sections retained casualties, treated them on the spot, and did excellent work in this manner. It was not possible to move hospitals forward for several months but in the meanwhile sections undertook hospitalization of the serious cases and the less important wounds and other ailments were treated in the animal-transport or unit lines.

The average strengths and sickness rates of the animals of South-East Asia Command for the period 31st March 1944 to 1st April 1945 were:

	Average Strength	Admitted for Treatment	Cured and Remaining under Treatment
Horses	6,758	6,931	5,834
Mules	23,595	12,988	10,926
Donkeys	739	997	937
Bullocks	815	221	209

Rangoon was captured on the 3rd May 1945 just before the monsoon broke. All resistance ceased with the final surrender of the Japanese Army on the 15th August 1945.

CHAPTER VIII

Civil Affairs and Control Commissions

WAR and its aftermath have always helped to spread animal plagues by the disruption of the veterinary services and the upset of the normal patterns of animal husbandry and livestock movement. During World War I the whole western region of Russia became infected with rinderpest which then spread to neighbouring countries and by 1921 had killed five to six million animals. In 1919 foot-and-mouth disease in a most malignant form swept West and Central Europe causing heavy losses. In 1944 only the most energetic control measures prevented African horse sickness from becoming established in the Middle East and spreading to other Mediterranean countries. It is impossible to describe adequately the chaos prevailing in a country which has been fought over by large armies—roads are blocked, bridges blown, towns and villages in ruins, refugees cover the countryside, administration is at a standstill and food is desperately scarce. Order must be restored quickly and the Army Veterinary Service has an essential part to play in the regeneration of the livestock industry and the prevention of epizootics until such time as the normal civilian organization can be resumed.

Our duties in Civil Affairs and Control Commissions include: the conservation of livestock by control of diseases and advice on husbandry, feeding and breeding; the preservation of a nucleus of breeding animals by control of slaughtering; the supply and distribution of essential veterinary stores and vaccines; assistance to the civilian veterinary service; and the control by systematic meat inspection of diseases transmissible to man.

These services were provided for nine countries. In the Middle East—Eritrea, Cyrenaica, Tripolitania and the Dodecanese Islands; in Europe—Germany, Austria and Greece; in Asia—Burma and Malaya. For Germany and Austria the veterinary staff was included in the Control Commissions and in other countries in the Civil Affairs organization.

In Europe the object was to control and help the existing machinery to function and this also applied in the case of the Italian colonies in the Middle East. In Burma and

Malaya it was necessary to start from scratch and to organize a complete veterinary service.

It required vigorous action at a high staff level to obtain authority to form a Civil Affairs veterinary service—few staff officers have any knowledge either of the basic importance of the livestock industry or of the potential dangers of epizootics and uncontrolled livestock movement. However, when useful results had been obtained by R.A.V.C. officers in Tripolitania and other former Italian colonies more notice was taken of our Service and this trend was reinforced by the acceptance of an excellent and most detailed veterinary plan for the Balkans which in its turn stimulated greater interest in the demands for North-West Europe and in the report of the Veterinary Panel of the Allied Post-War Requirements Bureau.

In 1943 the Panel had pointed out that in some countries, notably Poland, veterinary establishments and laboratories had been destroyed or robbed of their equipment and that both trained men and fresh supplies would be needed to re-establish the veterinary services. The Panel saw the main problem to be "The control of epizootic disease, especially cattle plague and pleuro-pneumonia which might enter Europe from the East and against which it may be necessary to set up frontier control. The Panel understands that before the war cattle plague had been stamped out in the Soviet Union but with war conditions its recurrence must be considered possible. The danger is that it may be introduced by returning refugees bringing with them domestic animals, the quarantine of which is involved with the control of the refugees themselves."

Information concerning the animal populations of enemy-occupied territories was scanty and little was known either of the veterinary surgeons available or of the incidence of contagious diseases. Furthermore, it was possible that the retreating enemy would adopt a "scorched earth" policy, in which case fodder would have to be imported for the survivors and additional animals would be needed to replenish the reduced herds. The scale of provision of veterinary assistance and stores was a matter of guess-work based on pre-war statistics and supplemented by recent intelligence reports.

The estimates for veterinary supplies were simplified, and packing and distribution facilitated, by the use of a "standard basic list" which gave an approved scale of supplies for a fixed number of animals (regardless of species) for a stated period—this comprised one "unit". For instance, the Middle East basic list appeared in units designed for 250,000 head of mixed livestock for one month, while Greece with an estimated animal population of 7,000,000 was shown as requiring twenty-eight units. The majority of these supplies were dispatched by the Army Veterinary Stores, Aldershot, which was expanded to meet the increased demand.

Besides taking measures to conserve and replenish the flocks and herds in the war areas, attention was given to the replacement of the vast numbers of draught and transport animals whose seizure for military purposes had crippled agriculture in many lands.

The success of the *blitzkrieg* has given the impression that the German Army was highly mechanized, but in reality it was organized largely on a horse-drawn basis with an animal establishment of over a million. An infantry division included some 5,000 horses on its strength and there were also mountain divisions and horsed cavalry brigades. The 3rd Panzer Army had about 80,000 horses when it fought on the Russian front. It was expected that the number of captured horses would greatly exceed our own military requirement and that thousands would be available for disposal to civilians.

In the *Journal of the Royal Army Veterinary Corps* of February 1946 Lieutenant-Colonel J. C. Rix gives a detailed account of the problem which faced him as A.D.V.R.S. 5th Corps on the surrender of the enemy forces in Austria in May 1945. These forces, which had retreated from Russia and Yugoslavia, included German, Croat, Cossack, Caucasian and Hungarian units with a total animal strength of about 58,000 horses. The German units, and in particular the German Cavalry Corps, kept their horses in good condition, as did the Cossacks; but most of the Croats deserted leaving theirs uncared for, and the Hungarian horses were in a most pitiable state of emaciation.

The main task of disposal fell on the D.A.D.V.R.S. 78th Division, Major B. C. M. Edmonds, with Nos. 1 and 817 C.M.V.S.s and Nos. 3 and 804 V.R.C.S.s. Within three months 44,476 animals had been sorted out, tested for disease, branded, and entrained to farmers in Italy, Germany, Austria, Russia and Yugoslavia. Unserviceable animals were used to feed the 200,000 surrendered troops and the thousands of displaced persons in the area. There is no doubt that the rapid distribution of these animals in time for work on that year's harvest was a most useful step towards the rehabilitation of agriculture in Europe. It was inevitable under the prevailing conditions that some animals should go astray. Lieutenant-Colonel Rix records: "Farmers in Italy, through Allied Military Government, were sent 12,606 horses. Animals were entrained at a rate of 400 a day over a period of five weeks by 804 Veterinary and Remount Conducting Section (O.C. Major D. C. Henderson) which did not only the collecting and branding but also the hand-over to representatives of the Military Government at Pontebba. From Pontebba they ceased to be our responsibility and were trekked across mountain passes down to the flat Po valley and across to the Bologna districts under arrangements by the Military Government. At first this was undertaken by bands of Italian partisans, but unfortunately very few of the animals that set off ever reached their destination: 75 per cent. were lost, some being auctioned on their way down and many ruined by bad treatment. However, most of them got to North Italy if not to that part of it which the Military Government had intended."

On the 30th June 1945 Colonel Glyn Lloyd was given the dual appointment of Chief of the Veterinary Section of the Allied Control Commission, Austria and D.D.V.R.S., Headquarters B.T.A. As well as dealing with captured animals, he and his staff of three officers arranged for the disposal of the surplus animals of the Allied Armies in Austria: 7,400 mules were allocated to U.N.R.R.A. and shipped to Greece while 4,600 mules were sent by train and air to Yugoslavia, for both countries were in urgent need of animals. At the same time they organized the control of a large foot-and-mouth disease outbreak which was thought to have been introduced from Hungary with the migration of refugees and livestock. The ubiquitous No. 1 C.M.V.S. assembled and distributed stocks of ex-*Wehrmacht* disinfectants but the D.D.V.R.S. reported that, although the outbreak had been checked, he had no further reserves of either disinfectants or vaccine.

Meanwhile in Germany the Veterinary and Remount Branch of the 21st Army Group had been busy with the disposal of surplus *Wehrmacht* horses to farmers, the control of German army veterinary units and the collection of captured stores. In addition, riding horses were issued to British units for recreational purposes; the Polish studs which had been dispersed throughout Germany were re-formed; and information was compiled concerning the functions, organization and general state of the German Civil Veterinary Service. It was found that this Service, headed by Dr. Frederich Weber, a close friend of Hitler, was one of the most pro-Nazi branches of public administration in Germany. The task of purging it and forming an equally efficient organization without loss of time fell to Brigadier S. L. Slocock with his Veterinary and Remount Branch of the British Control Commission for Germany.

Speaking at the N.V.M.A. Congress in 1945, Brigadier Slocock described the position thus: "The total area of the British Zone is some 43,000 square miles, divided into four provinces. To undertake this task some twenty-nine officers will be required; of this number it has only been possible to provide seventeen to date, so that the work is being carried out under difficulty. It is quite impossible to give an adequate picture of the actual physical difficulties which are encountered. The destruction has to be seen to be believed. Great cities like Cologne, Munster and Hanover have ceased to exist and in innumerable smaller towns no attempt has yet been made to clear streets long since blocked by bombing. The work now proceeding is the interrogation and screening of all officials to decide their fitness to hold office on political, professional and physical grounds. The production of foot-and-mouth vaccine is a matter of greatest urgency for the German centre of production was on the Island of Riems which is now in the zone occupied by the Russians."

Foot-and-mouth disease was prevalent throughout Germany at the time of the collapse and refugees with their animals were in danger of disseminating this and other diseases over a wide area. A livestock stand-still order was enforced by the Allies, who also agreed to treat Germany as an economic whole and to exchange statistics on the incidence of contagious diseases in their respective zones. However, it was almost impossible to control foot-and-mouth disease in the British Zone without vaccine and it was necessary to turn over part of the Behringwerke Institute at Eystrup from the preparation of swine fever serum to that of foot-and-mouth disease vaccine and to convert part of the Hanover abattoir into a laboratory for production of the virus.

Three years later the Veterinary Section of the Control Commission could report: "Excellent progress has been made in the control of foot-and-mouth disease. German veterinarians are very gratified at the recent extensive outbreak being brought under control in less than one year; they state that in former times this would have taken four or five years. Success is attributable to adequate supplies of vaccine which has permitted protective inoculation of all susceptible animals. The British Zone is in a position to produce bi-valent vaccine quickly should occasion arise—type A virus at Hanover, type B virus at Lübeck, with processing at Eystrup."

To meet the requirement for other biological products and medicines all captured veterinary stores were handed over to the German authorities and all possible assistance was given to manufacturing chemists and vaccine institutes to enable them to continue their output. If necessary essential material was imported by the Control Commission.

In addition to disease control, meat and milk production was supervised both to conserve supplies and to protect public health. Lieutenant-Colonel J. Hickman mentions in the *Journal of the Royal Army Veterinary Corps* of May 1947 that in most cases the directors of abattoirs were veterinary surgeons and, in consequence, the meat inspection was of a very high standard. Great emphasis was laid on the examination for trichinosis in pork though only one case had been detected in the British Zone since the occupation.

In April 1946 a committee of the leading German veterinary authorities in the Zone was established under the chairmanship of a R.A.V.C. officer to co-ordinate disease control and other veterinary matters. Gradually this form of supervision was relaxed and the Germans became responsible for their own veterinary administration and for the education of veterinary students at the Hanover Veterinary College which had suffered severely from bomb damage—for a while it was a college rule that students should spend two weeks in each term cleaning old bricks and helping in the rebuilding.

In the Middle East our Civil Affairs veterinary services were designed to run the existing machinery on a care and maintenance basis only but in practice it was usually necessary to reorganize the Italian services, to expand them to a limited extent and to make plans for livestock improvement.

Early in 1943 the D.D.V.R.S., Middle East Forces, Colonel E. S. W. Peatt, ran a series of lectures at the Civil Affairs Training School to give future administrators a background knowledge of livestock problems which would enable them to appreciate the value of a well-organized veterinary service.

Government by British Military Administration was established in Tripolitania, Cyrenaica, Eritrea and the Dodecanese Islands. The general standard of the Italian veterinary surgeons who now worked under R.A.V.C. supervision was low, although there were marked exceptions in Cyrenaica and Eritrea where large well-equipped laboratories had been founded, and in the Dodecanese where a competent Italian veterinarian carried on until imprisoned by the Germans, and when released by the British continued with his job without pay until eventually employed by the B.M.A.

In each territory the first step was to make a survey of the livestock and the prevalent diseases. Animal populations in Africa had not been greatly affected by the war but contagious diseases were on the increase and immediate measures had to be taken against rinderpest, bovine pleuro-pneumonia, blackquarter and swine fever.

In the Dodecanese the main task was to build up flocks and herds which had been reduced to less than half the pre-war level—horses and cattle could be numbered in hundreds only, pigs had nearly all been slaughtered, while even the dogs and cats had been eaten during the German occupation. To prevent further excessive slaughtering tinned meat was imported, abattoirs closed for five days in each week, and the slaughter of cows and ewes forbidden. Here, as elsewhere, the United Nations Relief and Rehabilitation Administration helped financially and imported livestock and poultry from the U.S.A. To provide immediate relief the B.M.A. imported pigs and other stock from Cyprus for distribution to the villages and for the establishment of a stud farm.

In addition to such special livestock development schemes and disease control, it was necessary to establish a strict portal inspection and quarantine of animals and to combat the activities of the blackmarketeers who hoped to reap quick profits by smuggling animals into meat-deficient areas. In all countries a constant watch had to be kept against rabies which had greatly increased amongst dogs and jackals during the war.

Shortage of transport, lack of trained staff and suspicion of the B.M.A.'s intentions were the greatest difficulties encountered—usually the taking of a livestock census was thought to be the first stage of a scheme for higher taxation—but there was a marked change in the readiness to co-operate when it was at last possible to convince the native population that we wished only to help them in their difficulties.

In the Balkans, U.N.R.R.A. undertook the bulk of the veterinary relief work though an R.A.V.C. advisory staff of five V.O.s was sent to Greece in October 1944 to organize the control of epidemics—particularly anthrax and swine fever—and to restore the Serum Institute in Athens to working order at the earliest possible moment.

During the fighting in Italy no one from the Corps could be spared for civil veterinary affairs and, in consequence, the work was undertaken by the United States Army Veterinary Service which provided representatives at Headquarters Allied Control Commission, Salerno, and on the mixed British and American staffs at the various provincial headquarters. Following the withdrawal of U.S. Forces from Northern Italy in 1945, civil veterinary affairs became a Corps concern.

South-East Asia presented a special problem as neither in Burma nor Malaya were many veterinary surgeons in private practice and the pre-war civil veterinary services ceased to exist when the Japanese invaded.

The veterinary section of the Civil Affairs Service in Burma commenced work in January 1945 and its activities spread with the progressive liberation of the country, finally terminating on the 1st January 1946 when the Civil Veterinary Department was resurrected. The head of the Civil Affairs veterinary section, Colonel G. Pfaff, had been a pre-war Burma civil veterinary officer who enlisted in the Corps for war service, and he stayed on in Burma with the new department. Most of his thirteen R.A.V.C. officers remained with him to carry on their work until officers of the Colonial Veterinary Service arrived to replace them.

Burma is a large country with few railways or all-weather roads and allied bombing and destruction of the Japanese lines of communication had been most effective. Railways and river steamers had ceased to function, roads were in very poor condition with scarcely a bridge still standing, and all this coupled with the heavy rainfall and lack of motor transport combined to make life difficult for veterinary officers carrying out widespread vaccination programmes. Of the thirty-three vehicles authorized for the department only thirteen were obtained but with great foresight all V.O.s had been trained in the care and maintenance of motor transport and the few vehicles were kept on the road.

Rinderpest was rampant in Burma in 1945. The failure of the Japanese to control outbreaks was probably due to poor communications. The vaccine is highly susceptible to heat and has to be travelled on ice and it would have been impossible under the conditions then prevailing to use it in an even moderately remote area. The general use of bullock transport also favoured the spread of the disease. By December 1945 the Civil Affairs veterinary department had produced a vaccine to suit existing conditions. Twenty-nine production centres were set up and 1,383,005 animals inoculated—five times more than the record number treated before the war. Vaccination against anthrax and haemorrhagic septicaemia was also carried out, and foot-and-mouth disease checked by the enforcement of control measures.

It should be mentioned that nearly all the veterinary stores and equipment needed for the rehabilitation of Burma were obtained on loan from the Army Veterinary Service in India, which also ensured that there was never any shortage of sera or vaccines.

When the time came to hand over to the Civil Veterinary Department, Burma was remarkably free of contagious diseases and the Director of Civil Affairs in his final report made special mention of the excellent work carried out by Colonel Pfaff and his officers.

In pre-war days Malaya remained free from rinderpest by strict quarantine measures despite cattle trade with the infected territories of Thailand and Burma. That Malaya was still clear of rinderpest after the Japanese defeat was due principally to the success of the R.A.F. offensive against coastal shipping from Burma and to the destruction of all the railway bridges across the main rivers of Thailand which sealed the comparatively disease-free southern part of that country from the heavily infected north. In fact, the whole problem of disease control proved far smaller than anticipated—a few outbreaks of haemorrhagic septicaemia in buffaloes, sporadic cases of rabies in dogs, minor outbreaks of glanders and epizootic lymphangitis originating from captured Japanese animals—which was most fortunate as it enabled the veterinary department to concentrate on the livestock census and bring to light a decrease of 50 per cent. in the numbers of pigs, sheep and goats. More serious still was a decrease of 55,000 buffaloes and oxen which were mostly used for work in the paddy fields and the shortage would have a disastrous effect on the rice crop which provided the staple diet of the country.

There was already a rice famine which increased the demand for meat. Lack of shipping precluded imports of livestock from Australia, Indonesia and Indo-China. Southern Thailand had plenty of rinderpest-free cattle for sale but, as an ex-enemy country, was only permitted to trade in rice. The temptation of Malayan cultivators to sell their remaining ploughing cattle for high black-market prices, the drain of the big towns on the countryside, the soaring price of meat and the under-nourishment of the people, all demanded immediate action.

The British Military Administration in Malaya included a Director of Veterinary Services, Colonel G. V. Short, and thirteen veterinary officers, of whom four were members of the Civil Malayan Veterinary Service before the war. To some extent their responsibilities concerning animal husbandry, abattoir supervision and meat inspection overlapped those of Food Control. In Singapore, one V.O., Major R. A. Wright, was seconded for four months to control all food, including rice, to the city. Another V.O., Major (His Highness) Tungku Abu Bakar, was appointed "Mayor" of Kuala Lumpur and exercised valuable control from the municipal side. In the *Journal of the Royal Army Veterinary Corps* of November 1946 Colonel Short writes: "It was a case not only of doing what one's hand found to do, but also of doing what was thrust into one's hands. That those hands were often those of veterinary officers is a high tribute to the profession, and an indication of the confidence felt in its ability and integrity."

Despite the embargo on trade with ex-enemy countries, Thai cattle were moved to Malaya, often by obscure jungle paths, and the veterinary department had some trouble in keeping track of them until later when the import of cattle was condoned and more regular routes could be used without fear. Soon the import of animals had been brought to a satisfactory level and the strangle-hold of profiteering butchers was broken by price controls and a system of deliberately glutting black-market areas. In response to a telephone call from the local veterinary officer a convoy of animals would be directed to a high-price area to swamp the market. Colonel Short recalls: "Two sharp lessons only were required in two different towns to spread the gospel of fair dealing throughout the country, and prices tumbled almost as quickly as deputations of butchers arrived at H.Q. to ask us to stop our persecution."

The final task was to prepare an establishment for the Civilian Veterinary Service which was to take over on the 1st April 1946. A comprehensive scheme was submitted for the development of the livestock industry backed by a first-class research laboratory and serviced by able veterinary and animal husbandry officers.

It is pleasant to relate that most of these proposals were put into effect and that in Malaya, as in many other lands, the Corps had helped to establish an efficient veterinary organization which would be of lasting benefit to the country.

CHAPTER IX

The Post-War Years 1945-1961

IN the final phase of the war and immediately after it the Corps undertook its customary duty of disposing of surplus animals swiftly and economically whilst maintaining a strict control upon the spread of contagious disease. The numbers involved were considerable. At one period the Army was employing over 120,000 animals with another 80,000 horses and mules taken from the enemy in Europe. Disposal measures overseas included liaison with military governments and U.N.R.R.A. to ensure that the needs of local agriculture for work animals were met as quickly as possible. The British horses of the 1st Cavalry Division which survived the war were found employment with the R.A.S.C. horse transport companies in the Middle East, and a few were returned to England or used for recreational purposes by the Army overseas. The greatest care was taken to ensure that none were sold locally and that unfit animals were destroyed humanely by a veterinary officer. Many of our officers remembered the pitiable condition of the old British Army horses left in Egypt and elsewhere after World War I and gave very loyal support to the promise made in Parliament by the Secretary of State for War in 1939 that all horses becoming surplus to military requirements whilst abroad would be brought back to the United Kingdom or painlessly destroyed.

In England several thousand horses, cobs and mules were sold by auction in small batches so as not to lower prices by flooding the market. In order to assist in meeting the enormous demand for sera by U.N.R.R.A. and other relief organizations, it was customary, prior to the sales, to send blood samples from the surplus horses to medical supply firms who paid excellent prices for those showing high antibody titres.

We had, in fact, been collaborating with the Wellcome Foundation for many years in the production of tetanus antitoxin. It is well-known that very few horses possess normal tetanus antibody unless they have been previously immunized. A preparatory period of six to nine months is necessary before immunization proper can be commenced: if started too soon the antitoxin produced tends to be non-avid and unsuitable for use. To obviate this delay and speed-up production of the much-needed serum, the

R.A.V.C. pre-immunized suitable horses which were coming to the end of their useful military life and later transferred them to the Wellcome Research Laboratories.

In 1943 this liaison was carried a stage further when the need for additional supplies of gas gangrene and tetanus antitoxins became most urgent. A stud of some 300 serum-producing horses was established at Glasgow Paddocks, Doncaster, under the management of No. 1 Reserve Veterinary Hospital. A scheme for training our officers at the Wellcome Research Laboratories for serum production work at Glasgow Paddocks met with only limited success as every able-bodied V.O. was needed for service overseas. In the end Mr. A. Thomas, M.R.C.V.S., of the Wellcome Research Laboratories became responsible for the technical veterinary control. We also had trouble in finding sufficient men to run the stables and used Italian and German prisoners-of-war to maintain the strength. In spite of the many difficulties this collective effort was most productive. High yields of valuable gas gangrene, tetanus and diphtheria antitoxins were regularly produced and by the end of 1945, when the scheme ceased, many thousands of litres of serum had been made available.

Concerning the final disposal of surplus army animals the Wellcome Foundation record: "Towards the end of the war, when stocks of diphtheria antitoxins were very low, we were fortunate in having the co-operation of the R.A.V.C. in permitting us to take blood samples from army horses which were due for disposal, so we were enabled to attend army sales and purchase horses which our tests showed to possess normal diphtheria antibody and to be suitable for the production of high value diphtheria anti-toxin. This co-operation enabled the Wellcome Research Laboratories to secure some 500 horses at a time when, in the ordinary way, horses with normal diphtheria antibody were hard to find. It is an interesting fact that quite a high proportion of R.A.V.C. horses possessed normal diphtheria antibody (as high as 30 per cent.), whereas very few horses from normal farm and town sources possessed the necessary basic immunity. The opportunity to acquire suitable army horses enabled the Wellcome Research Laboratories to build up, fairly rapidly, the depleted stocks of diphtheria antitoxin."

The disposal of surplus horses and mules involved much work and organization but nothing gave more trouble than the repatriation of dogs—both the pets of returning soldiers and the hundreds of dogs loaned by the public for war service.

Throughout the war the Director had reminded the Army authorities of the need to control the movements of soldiers' pets as they were a most likely source of rabies which, once introduced into this country, would become a real menace to the whole life of the community. It was remarkable that this did not occur as just under 1,000 dogs and cats are known to have been illegally imported after Dunkirk, and from 1940 onwards there were many Allied camps in the country to which foreign troops brought the usual train of pets. After V.E. Day British soldiers conveyed from overseas by unorthodox channels at least 200 dogs and cats, and would have brought more if the import procedure had not been simplified by the provision of a R.A.V.C. quarantine scheme. This was a most exasperating scheme to operate since few owners will act sensibly about their pets, but it was probably instrumental in preventing a repetition of a similar rabies outbreak to that of 1918 when dogs smuggled in by servicemen were responsible for an epidemic in which 328 dogs died and 358 people were bitten.

No. 1 Military Quarantine Station R.A.V.C. at Chilbolton Down in Hampshire began to receive dogs early in 1945. They were examined at their overseas stations by our officers and if free from disease shipped in W.D. transports to the United Kingdom where they were met by Corps men and taken to Chilbolton. The total charge for the examination, transport, and six months quarantine varied from £5 to £20 according to the rank of the owner. The actual costs were, of course, higher but as the Director, Brigadier G. A. Kelly, said at the time: "It is better that the country should be asked to bear the expense of quarantining soldiers' dogs rather than the much greater expense and added anxiety of dealing with outbreaks of rabies over a period of years. The cost to the State of anti-rabic treatment of persons and anti-rabies measures from 1918-1922 far exceeded the total cost of quarantine."

By 1948 most of the war-time Army had returned home and civilian kennels had re-opened so No. 1 Military Quarantine Station was disbanded after three years of useful work.

By 1946 the animal establishment was reduced to 27,000 and the number of veterinary surgeons in the Army fell to 348, of whom fifty-three were Regular officers. A good deal of political pressure was exerted at this time to secure the early release of veterinary surgeons from the Forces as certain government schemes for livestock improvement and disease control awaited an adequate veterinary staff before they could operate effectively. There were only about 2,000 members of the profession in practice in Britain and reinforcements were badly needed. The Parliamentary Under-Secretary of State for War, Lord Nathan, speaking in the House of Lords on this subject and the related one of the need for a larger professional establishment, said: "It is the desire, the aim and the intention of the Government that veterinary surgery shall be a profession worth while, and that that profession shall be improved in standards and in standing, so that it takes its place in its own sphere on the same basis in the same public esteem and with the same usefulness as the medical profession does in its sphere." Unfortunately he did not mention that it would also be equitable to give the veterinary surgeon the same emoluments as his medical confrere.

Amongst the many field units disbanded after the war No. 1 Cavalry Mobile Veterinary Section deserves mention. This section embarked for Palestine in 1938 to give veterinary attention to the two horsed cavalry regiments, the Greys and the Royals, which were there on active service. In 1940 the section moved to Egypt to look after the Polish Carpathian Brigade and the mule companies which were being formed for the Greek campaign. In 1941 it was posted to Syria with long treks across the desert to Iraq. In 1943 it again returned to Egypt to embark for the Sicily operations, and then served throughout the Italian campaign with the 8th Army as an advanced veterinary unit for the many mule companies operating in the line. After the break-through in Italy the unit moved into Austria. So No. 1 C.M.V.S., which started off as an ancillary unit to cavalry engaged in anti-terrorist operations in Palestine, finally ended its adventurous career in Austria coping with captured horses and a foot-and-mouth disease epidemic. On 29th September 1949, Major A. V. Franklin, who commanded the unit from 1940 to 1943, formally handed the flag of No. 1 C.M.V.S. to Sir Thomas Dalling, at a meeting of Council, for safe keeping by the Royal College of Veterinary Surgeons.

In February 1946 No. 1 Reserve Veterinary Hospital, Depot and Training Establishment was renamed "Veterinary and Remount Centre" and merged with the remount depot at Melton Mowbray. No. 1 R.V.H. first occupied the Doncaster racecourse in October 1939, and during the war 460 officers and 4,000 men passed through it for training, equipment, and posting to all parts of the world. The unit became an accepted part of the Doncaster community and to this day the town has a flourishing branch of the Old Comrades' Association. A plaque, commemorating the use of the racecourse as the home of the R.A.V.C. from 1939 to 1946, was unveiled at Doncaster by the Colonel Commandant, Brigadier C. A. Murray, on 22nd July 1950.

On 7th July 1951 the Colonel Commandant, Brigadier G. A. Kelly, unveiled at Melton Mowbray a memorial to the officers, non-commissioned officers and men of the Corps who lost their lives during the war. The memorial, which is in the form of a bronze plaque mounted on a stone plinth, was dedicated by the Chaplain-General to the Forces in the presence of the President of the Royal College of Veterinary Surgeons, the President of the National Veterinary Medical Association and many other dignitaries. The names of our veterinary officers who died on active service are also inscribed on the war memorial of the Royal College of Veterinary Surgeons.

In Palestine, at the end of 1945, No. 1 Veterinary Hospital was moved from Ramle to merge with No. 4 Base Remount Depot, Nathanya, which carried on as our Middle East depot until it was disbanded in 1948 prior to the evacuation of Palestine. "Ramle" had been an outstandingly happy and useful unit throughout its life and owed much of its character to its first commanding officer, "Mouse" Townsend, who made No. 1 V.H. the Mecca of all horsemen in the Middle East. He took over the Ramle Vale Hounds, giving them a new lease of life, and many officers, amongst them Major-General Jock Campbell, v.c., came direct from the battles in the Desert for a few days' leave at Ramle where they could ride a horse once more and live in the comparative comfort of a well-run mess. Major J. Bell, who commanded the hospital from 1941-1943, maintained the tradition and made added improvements.

In India and Burma the demobilization of some 14,000 men and the disbandment of 150 field units of the still separate veterinary and remount services was followed by the amalgamation of the Indian Army Remount Department and the Indian Army Veterinary Corps to form the Indian Remount and Veterinary Corps. As a first step the

Director of Veterinary Services, Brigadier E. S. W. Peatt, became responsible as D.R.V.S. for the administration of both services and the final amalgamation was completed in April 1947.

The newly-formed Corps had only been in existence a few weeks when the momentous decision was made to partition India and to split the Indian Army in two. This entailed the division of personnel, animals, stores and units of the I.R.V.C. between the new armies of India and Pakistan and the retirement or transfer to the British Army of all the seconded R.A.V.C. officers. Close and friendly relations with our sister Corps in India and Pakistan have, however, remained and we take great pride in being allied to the Pakistan Remount, Veterinary and Farms Corps to whom the responsibility for the Military Farms Department was added after the partition. In 1961, thanks to the good offices of Brigadier Mohammed Zafar Khan, Director, P.R.V.F.C., a replica of the badge of the R.A.V.C. was set in the rock of the Khyber Pass to commemorate our alliance and the many R.A.V.C. officers who served on the Frontier.

By 1948 the cumulative effects of demobilization and reduction of overseas duties had shrunk the Corps to a total of about 500 all ranks and the whole question of its future place in the Army had to be considered.

Contrary to general expectation the Veterinary and Remount Services had found plenty of scope for their activities in a war fought by an army based upon complete mechanization. Their chief rôle had been the traditional one of maintaining the mobility of the field forces by the provision of suitable and disease-free animals and the recovery and replacement of casualties. The Army still keeps a small training cadre of pack transport which could be expanded in an emergency, and the horses of the ceremonial units also need attention; but during peacetime, at any rate, the war dog is now the most important military animal and the most satisfactory method of employing dogs is to place the whole business of their provision and care, as well as the training of their handlers in the hands of the A.V.R.S.

During 1948-1958 the Corps establishment rose to over 1,000 to form war dog training schools and guard dog units and with our tracker and guard dogs we became enthusiastic bandit hunters and policemen. This does not imply that the normal veterinary duties, which include meat inspection, were neglected nor that the remount commitments were negligible—in 1948, 1,000 mules were purchased for the Greek National Army—but that our main effort was directed to developing the use of war dogs at a time when there were a vast number of military dumps and installations to be guarded with the greatest possible economy of manpower, and to supplying the demand for dogs for tracking bandits, spotting ambushes, and detecting arms caches in the various anti-terrorist operations in Malaya, Kenya and Cyprus. An account of these activities is given in the chapter concerning war dogs. Probably at no other period in its history has the Corps had so large a proportion of its strength employed on active operational duties.

It is worth recording that the first George Medal ever won by a member of the Corps was awarded in January 1955 to a dog-handler, Corporal P. J. Randall, for his bravery in East Africa when the lorry in which he was travelling overturned and caught fire. The citation reads: "The gallantry displayed by Corporal Randall in getting the driver out of the blazing cab before himself is of the highest order. Also his devotion to duty in checking all the men out of the vehicle, rescuing his guard dog, and in summoning aid, in spite of the great pain from his extensive burns, is exemplary." The R.S.P.C.A. presented Corporal Randall with its highest award, the Margaret Wheatley Cross.

For the veterinary officer there is a special fascination attached to work with operational dogs. He must use all his skill to maintain his animals at the peak of their performance and ensure that those below par for any reason are given immediate attention. An infantry patrol relying on an unfit dog to guide it safely through the jungle may easily be wiped out in ambush, and the lack of a vigorous well-trained tracker dog at a critical moment may allow a terrorist to escape to commit murder another day. The V.O. has to be more than a physician, though in the tropics particularly disease is always a problem; he must make himself familiar with the training and management of dogs and with their reactions to what is often an unsuitable environment.

The maintenance of health and the working of dogs in excessively trying climates where temperatures sometimes rise to 120°F. pose special problems. Colonel D. F. G. Smith recalls that when he was A.D.V.R.S., M.E.L.F., he had a section of thirty dogs stationed for two years at the port of Akaba on the Red Sea. They only worked at night and during the day remained in kennels which had extra thick walls and a double roof cooled by dampened khus-khus matting. Even so, on one exceptionally hot sticky day with a shade temperature of 118°F. six dogs showed symptoms of heat exhaustion and needed an hour in an empty refrigerated meat van before they recovered.

The class of dog most likely to become a heat casualty is, however, not the night-working guard dog but the specialist dog operating with infantry during the day on anti-terrorist duties. In the Far East some dogs may be infested with heart-worm which predisposes them to heat exhaustion, possibly by interference with the panting mechanism thus preventing loss of heat; and there are many other factors which may reduce the efficiency of dogs on active service. Operational dogs must be healthy, well acclimatized, physically fit, properly trained, and handled by men who have a sympathetic understanding of their job—it is our duty to see that these conditions are fulfilled.

In 1958 the Army Guard Dog Units R.A.V.C. in Cyprus, Singapore and Hong Kong were transferred to the control of the Royal Military Police, which while relieving us of the monotonous chore of nightly security patrols in these territories reduced our small establishment to a bare cadre. There was no change in other duties and the method of employing guard dogs in the United Kingdom and B.A.O.R. remained unaffected by the new policy. At the time of writing No. 1 War Dog Training Unit R.A.V.C. in

Germany is quite possibly the largest guard-dog organization in the world. The War Dog Training School at Melton Mowbray maintains a considerable guard-dog establishment in the United Kingdom and supplies animals for the R.M.P. and other security organizations in the Near East, East Africa, the Caribbean and the Far East. No. 2 War Dog Training Unit, Malaya, and No. 3 War Dog Training Unit, Cyprus, arrange for the local training of guard dogs and handlers, provide operational dogs, and give a veterinary service for the animals of both the Army and the R.A.F.

At the start of this period when the Corps was re-orientating its organization on a canine basis, the Director, Brigadier J. J. Plunkett, kept a shrewd balance between the effort to be expended on dogs and that still required for horses and mules. It was essential to retain a cadre which, in an emergency, could expand in order to provide a field veterinary and remount service for pack transport. In 1949 he obtained approval for a basic Corps peace establishment of some fifty officers and 350 other ranks, together with improved career prospects. Although the Corps offered a full and useful life in the Army the profession showed little interest and resort had to be made to the conscription of veterinary surgeons.

The National Service officers usually accepted the position cheerfully and several have taken Regular commissions. They did us well

Brigadier A. G. Heveningham, who took over as Director in 1951, repaired our tendency to drift apart from our civilian colleagues by forming a R.A.V.C. Division of the British Veterinary Association, thus enabling both serving and retired officers to participate in the counsels of the B.V.A. and to keep in touch with new developments in veterinary science. It was Dr. George Fleming of the Army Veterinary Department, who had been instrumental in founding the Association in 1882 so that it seemed that the wheel had turned full circle. At the inaugural meeting of the Division held at the Royal Veterinary College, London, on 16th January 1952, the President said: "The Association has, in the past, received good support from many individual members of the Corps, but we have felt for a long time that the R.A.V.C. was, as it were, outside the family circle. We will welcome you as a division and are confident that nothing but benefit to you, the Association and the profession can result from its formation." This address was followed by one from Sir Thomas Dalling, a former R.A.V.C. officer, who aptly dealt with the major changes occurring in veterinary education and practice, he said: "We must realise that with changes in the times our work must also change and we must not live in the past and forget the future. Our job now is the preservation of animal health rather than the cure of ill-health." He concluded by observing that we must meet our colleagues, discuss mutual problems, hear results of work done and obtain advice and criticism of our own work from other members. It was as well that we had these contacts and the goodwill of both the Royal College and the B.V.A. for, during the 1950s, the small National Service intake of the Corps engendered a disproportionate amount of irritation in the profession which was below strength and starved of new graduates.

Towards the end of 1952 the approaching Coronation of Queen Elizabeth II brought the ceremonial horse into sudden prominence. The Household Cavalry and the King's Troop, Royal Horse Artillery, were remounted soon after the war, partly with their old horses which had worked with horse transport during hostilities and partly with new intakes. Besides horses for these units, mounts were now needed for the senior officers of the three fighting services, the Prime Minister's escort and the processional marshals. The most exacting standards of quietness and deportment had to be instilled into the eighty additional animals brought to Melton Mowbray from all parts of Britain and from the Army of Occupation in Germany, as they would be subjected to great stress on the day and some of those taking part had not ridden for many years. Special care was taken to accustom the horses to noise. At a previous Coronation when everything had gone off perfectly until the procession reached the Abbey, the bells suddenly pealed out to the great alarm of the unprepared horses. So our animals got a daily dose of bells, as well as bands, cheers and the tramp of marching men relayed to them through loudspeakers; by this and other means they were made familiar to every sound and sight which might startle them on the day.

On 1st April 1953, the officer-in-charge, Captain (Q.M.) W. Richey, moved his training team to a well-equipped camp in Hyde Park where the preparation of the horses continued under city conditions and riders could get acquainted with their mounts and refresh their knowledge of equitation.

On Coronation Day the Corps manned veterinary first-aid posts along the processional route but the well-trained horses gave no trouble. In the procession itself we were represented by a small foot detachment under Captain G. Hamilton-Dick while Captain Richey acted as a mounted marshal—he later received a silver salver from the Sea Lords as a mark of their gratitude for a safe passage. The Quartermaster-General fully understood the amount of veterinary and remount preparation needed to achieve an incident-free mounted procession and wrote to Brigadier Heveningham: "Will you please convey to all members of the Royal Army Veterinary Corps who helped in the Coronation my personal and very real appreciation both of the hard work they have put in and of their enthusiasm and determination not to fail in the minutest degree. Each one of them has played his part in making the Coronation a tremendous success, acclaimed by all both in this country and overseas."

On 2nd October 1953, at the Royal College of Veterinary Surgeons, a plaque, presented by the officers of the R.A.V.C., on the occasion of the Golden Jubilee of the Corps was unveiled and dedicated in the Council Chamber in memory of James Ferguson Simpson, F.R.C.V.S., to whose courage and determination we owe the formation of the Army Veterinary Corps.

Between 1956 to 1958 the Army carried out one of its periodical reorganizations and the present and future usefulness of every one of its units was critically examined. Our Director, Brigadier A. G. Ralston and his assistant, Lieutenant-Colonel E. H. Lewis-Bowen, had the laborious task of justifying every minute detail of our activities to numerous committees and sub-committees, many of whose members were doubtful as to the utility of a veterinary service in a nuclear age. However, as the Army still intended to employ animals such a service was essential both on economic and humanitarian grounds. The advent of nuclear warfare and the dangers of fallout might call for a veterinary service to salvage food animals and ensure a safe supply of meat and milk. The problems of the Civil Affairs veterinary sections would be vastly increased under conditions of nuclear warfare and, in addition to the normal methods of replenishing breeding stock, a wide use might be made of artificial insemination using semen from areas unaffected by radiation or fallout. The lack of a field veterinary and remount organization had caused a slight fiasco in the Oman operations of 1958. In response to a demand for pack transport to operate on the approaches to the high plateau of the Jebel Akhdar, a number of donkeys were hurriedly purchased in Somaliland without veterinary examination. About 30 per cent. were soon found to be unfit for service for one reason or another. Then there were delays in transportation and the animals arrived too late to be used. If a trained R.A.V.C. team had been on call, fit trained animals could have been delivered without delay at the site of operations. As it was we could not have provided even normal veterinary coverage for these animals had it not been for the generous help of Mr. T. G. E. Gibson, Principal Veterinary Officer, Somaliland Protectorate.

As has been mentioned previously, it was decided to reduce the size of the Corps by transferring the administration of three Army Guard Dog Units to the Royal Military Police. The home of the Corps was to remain at Melton Mowbray.

The R.A.V.C. Training Centre and Depot is on the old site of No. 3 Army Remount Depot which was formed in 1903 for maturing young cavalry remounts and to rehabilitate convalescent horses. Prior to mechanization as many as 2,000 horses were sometimes held by the Melton depot—most of them out at grass in neighbouring farms—when cavalry regiments went overseas and left their horses with the Remount Department to await the arrival of their reliefs. Such great characters as Lieutenant-Colonel "Priest" Alexander and Major J. Orr Ewing were at the depot in those days. They will long be remembered in the district.

As mechanization of the pre-war Army progressed so the number of horses at Melton became fewer and by 1939 the depot was a mere detachment of the Equitation School—an interesting point as we still carry on some of the former functions of Weedon. In the first winter of the war the horse establishment rose to 1,200 and the Commandant of the Equitation School (Colonel P. E. Bowden-Smith), with Major G. A. Cattley and Captain J. F. Hart, took up duties at Melton. Two hundred R.A.V.C. men were posted from Doncaster for temporary duty until civilian staff could be engaged and the place was busy again. The first R.A.V.C. Commandant, Major J. J. Plunkett, was appointed in Autumn 1940 and the depot became a R.A.V.C. unit on January 1st 1941. Remount duties continued to be very strenuous up to the end of the war and for some time after whilst dealing with the demobilization and disposal of surplus animals. A squadron of Household Cavalry horses was trained for transport work and hundreds of cobs were bought and broken in for pack duties with the mountain division then being prepared for the invasion of Norway. Brigadier J. J. Plunkett in the *Journal of the Royal Army Veterinary Corps*, 1961, writes: "I had the task of finding these animals. Touring England and Northern Ireland in war-time was an experience. There were no signposts and a blackout at night. Most hotels were booked and one had to make careful plans about accommodation before starting out. The prices paid for ponies were good and the dealers played up very well. Early on I was accompanied by Lieutenant-Colonel Frankie Hill and later by Major Kearsley. I think our best week was in N. Ireland when we bought 250 pack animals from three dealers. I think they had a lot of friends and associates helping them from Eire where we were not allowed to go as it was neutral."

The excellent grazing at Melton still enables us to improve and make into valuable animals young horses which have been bought at a reasonable price because of their backwardness; and many horses of the Household Cavalry and King's Troop R.H.A. come to Melton to recover the bloom they have lost under the artificial conditions of life in London. But remount requirements are, of course, smaller now. About eighty horses a year pass through the remount section of the Training Centre; mostly troop horses for the Household Cavalry and gun-teams for the King's Troop R.H.A. Purchasing, which includes a very careful examination of each horse for soundness, takes place mainly in Eire and England. The animals are tested with mallein—more to keep the technique alive than because of any danger of glanders—and isolated for a period. Catarrh, strangles, and ringworm are the main troubles at this stage. Immunization with tetanus toxoid follows and the animals may then be issued to units or retained for training.

Much of the schooling of young remounts is done at the Equitation School under Major W. Richey, who is himself a Weedon graduate, where they and the future riding instructors of the British Army are trained together by the traditional Weedon methods. The students—officers and men from the Household Cavalry, Brigade of Guards, Royal Horse Artillery, Royal Army Service Corps and Royal Corps of Military Police—are each given three horses to look after. One of these horses is trained, one half trained and the third unbroken. By the end of the course the half-trained horses have become fully trained and the young remounts brought to the half-trained stage by an unhurried process of schooling which includes longeing, long-reining and learning to associate the spoken word of command with each movement and then to obey the pressure of the reins alone. For the students the course is a strenuous affair during which they acquire proficiency in equitation, dressage, the training of horses, veterinary first-aid and the art of instructing others. It is important that students should be capable of passing on what they have learnt at Melton thus ensuring that a high standard of animal management is maintained in the Army.

Closely associated with the remount and equitation sections is the School of Farriery which, besides providing for our own needs, is responsible for the advanced training of all army farriers. There is also a Saddlers' School.

The horses share the Melton training areas with the young war dogs of the War Dog Training School where Major (Q.M.) L. J. Radford has been the chief instructor for many years. These dogs are mostly bought at about eighteen months old—Alsatians for guard and general purposes; Labradors for tracking and arms-search. On arrival they are isolated, subjected to a veterinary examination and immunized against the major canine diseases. Then follows a thorough training in basic obedience, using a system based on patience, understanding and sympathy, before the dogs are taught their specialist duties such as guard, tracker, infantry patrol and so forth. When fully trained the dogs are married-up to their handlers who come from the various units to which the dogs are to be issued. Each trained dog is allotted one, two, or at the most, three handlers who work with it during the whole of their course and accompany it back to their unit. There must be a real partnership between handler and dog and care is taken to discard unsuitable men. A bad handler will quickly ruin the best-trained animal, and a dog will only work for a man he likes and trusts.

The sick horses and dogs of the depot are cared for at an up-to-date hospital equipped with modern methods of diagnosis and treatment. This is the only military veterinary hospital in the United Kingdom and the veterinary officers of other units send in their more serious cases for specialist treatment.

The depot, with its several schools and sections set in the heart of Leicestershire and its long-standing association with remounts and Weedon is a fitting home for the Royal Army Veterinary Corps. When the present programme of modernization of the barracks and the technical buildings has been completed it will be a show place of which the Army, the Corps, and the profession may well be proud.

CHAPTER X

War Dogs

IN March 1942 a meeting of representatives from interested War Office Branches, the Ministry of Aircraft-Production and the R.S.P.C.A. was held at the War Office under the chairmanship of the Director Army Veterinary and Remount Services. Its object was to discuss the ways and means of obtaining, training and feeding the large and increasing number of dogs required for guarding vulnerable War Department establishments. The meeting decided that 2,500 dogs were required immediately for training. As guard dogs were already being trained and employed it cannot be said that the decisions of this meeting marked the re-introduction of dogs as an integral part of the armed forces following the disbandment of the only military school that existed in World War I. It did, however, point to the importance being placed on the expanding demand for trained dogs; a demand which continued unabated until the end of the war and into the uneasy peace which followed.

Historically, accounts of the use of dogs for military purposes appear periodically in literature. The Romans, we know, used large ferocious specimens in close combat not infrequently completely protected by armour. In 1544 Henry VIII is said to have sent four hundred dogs "garnished with good yron collars" to the assistance of Charles V of Spain in his war against France. Again, during the Middle Ages big, strong dogs of marked ferocity were equipped with spiked collars and when loosed against the opposing cavalry caused considerable havoc. Reference is also made to the use of tracker dogs by Essex during his campaigns in Scotland and Ireland.

It seems not improbable that gentlemen of the Middle Ages, when going to war, were accompanied by their hunting dogs which fulfilled the dual rôles of assisting in their masters' pleasure and protecting their person and property. However, factual evidence of the operational employment of dogs is relatively sparse. It would seem that except for the occasional use of hounds as trackers and a wider employment of the large aggressive breeds as guards and sometimes in actual combat there appears to have been little effort made to exploit their talents for military purposes.

Even though many leading European countries, and in particular Germany and France, had set up military dog training schools, Britain was without one at the beginning of World War I and, in fact, one was not established until 1916. Its foundation was due primarily to the foresight and perseverance of Lieutenant-Colonel E. H. Richardson, a well-known breeder and trainer, who successfully persuaded the War Office of the potential value of properly trained dogs. The school was first located at Shoeburyness but as the number of dogs increased it was transferred to Natley Ridge in the New Forest where more extensive training areas existed.

The first demand was for messenger dogs and many trained dogs were sent across the Channel where they performed their vital and often dangerous missions over many a cratered battle field. Their arrival at the front was not however without opposition from certain commanding officers who, for one reason or another, were unwilling to employ them. Generally speaking opposition stemmed from ignorance and once convinced of their ability, commanding officers usually became their enthusiastic supporters. An official report on the Messenger Dog Service noted that "Whenever the General Officer Commanding a Corps took interest in the kennels good work was obtained from the dogs." Opposition to their employment was not confined to World War I and we find it appearing again especially during the terrorist operations which followed World War II. With well-trained dogs, expertly handled, suspicion and apathy can usually be quickly overcome. Unfortunately, particularly biased and antagonistic commanding officers have been known to set tasks under conditions where success was well-nigh impossible. These officers present a problem difficult to solve.

With increasing shortage of manpower guard dogs became more and more in demand. As these demands grew fresh sources of supply for recruit dogs had to be tapped. Although the various Dogs' Homes proved fruitful sources of supply the greatest number were obtained from private owners who willingly loaned their pets for the duration of hostilities. This latter source again proved the most profitable during World War II.

With the armistice the demand for trained dogs ceased and most of them were either returned to their owners or were found good homes. Some were taken across to Ireland as guards during the Sinn Fein operations, but all were finally disposed of when the Treaty was signed in December 1921.

Despite the proven worth of trained dogs no attempt was made to keep alive the techniques learnt during the war, and the inter-war years saw the Army without a dog training school. This unsatisfactory state of affairs continued until sometime after the outbreak of World War II when an experimental establishment of four dogs was opened at Aldershot. By 1942, forty dogs were in training at Swakleys Farm near Ruislip and Captain D. C. E. Danby was placed in veterinary charge. Much of the effort of this unit was directed towards devising methods of baffling tracker dogs once they had identified a track. The reason behind the experiments was that the Germans were making successful use of highly-trained dogs to locate allied agents parachuted into occupied territory.

As previously, once introduced the demand for trained dogs grew and the school establishment was raised to 250 dogs. To cope with the increased numbers fresh premises were found at the Greyhound Racing Association Kennels, Potters Bar, which remained the headquarters of war dog training until April 1945. In addition to meeting the large guard dog demand the War Dog Training School, as it then became, continued its experiments into the possible employment of specially trained dogs under conditions of modern warfare. One outstanding type which emerged was the mine dog which became a valuable asset in the struggle to overcome the menace of the land mine.

Potters Bar was well-equipped with a pharmacy, operating theatre and X-ray facilities and provided excellent opportunities for veterinary work. It was found that when dogs were sent to the school, from owners in all parts of England, Scotland and Wales, in numbers exceeding ten per day, they were liable to become ill within a fortnight. This was possibly due to the fact that they were unable to receive the essential attention. Generally speaking, however, few cases of illness were found in dogs on their arrival at the school. Some older dogs which were obviously unsuitable and showing signs of physical defects were returned immediately. When there was any overcrowding, through excess of "intake", throat infections soon developed, much of this may have been due to fretting and constant barking. Owing to the fact that it was a routine measure for daily temperatures to be taken for the first fortnight, many cases of acute tonsillitis were arrested before the infection was spread. All suspicious cases were immediately isolated and faeces and swabs were sent to the R.A.V.C. Laboratory. Few dogs passed through the school without having at least one attack of diarrhoea or dysentery. In almost all cases faeces tests revealed the presence of bowel parasites (predominantly coccidia).

Rejections of good, sound and healthy dogs, due to not passing their early gun testing with thunder flashes was at the rate of 65 per cent. Dogs acquired from a Dogs' Home were responsible for introducing an outbreak of kennel cough. Skin diseases were common in the months of May to October and were mostly due to the presence of lice and fleas. This was attributed to the use of straw as bedding. When the use of straw was stopped the incidence of skin complaints fell rapidly. Sarcoptic and follicular mange were rare.

When numbers of dogs exceeded the available accommodation, kennelling in barrels was very effective and dogs living in these seldom appeared on sick parade, even during the most treacherous months of January to March. In fact it was found that the sick rate dropped during the colder months of the year.

Distemper was never established in spite of one outbreak of disease clinically similar to distemper which lasted four to five weeks, involved eighty or more dogs and had a mortality rate of 45 per cent. All dogs within a fortnight of arrival at the school were protected with anti-distemper serum.

From records kept, it is clear that intestinal infections were responsible for over 75 per cent. of the overall sick rate. Owing to the fact that bowel parasitism was proved conclusively to be the cause of varying degrees of ill health, the paddocks were cleaned daily and at intervals of not less than six months were limed and left vacant.

Two outbreaks of hysteria following soon after each other and involving 30 to 40 per cent. of the dogs in the school were due to a change in diet or a combination of bowel parasites and streptococci infections. Eighty-eight per cent. of all dogs so affected were found to be harbouring bowel parasites and swabs indicated a streptococcal infection. Only one death was recorded and the rest recovered following treatment on specific lines for the two above-named infections.

The surgical side except for the repair of wounds and dental surgery was virtually non-existent. Most of the work of the V.O. and his dressers was in connection with prevention of disease rather than in the cure. Great vigilance was necessary in an establishment of over 300 to 400 dogs which were constantly coming and going. It seemed to Captain Danby that a marked saving in staff overheads could be achieved by making the school a R.A.V.C. unit. He repeatedly put forward the view that a great deal of duplication of duties could be avoided by this process. In early 1945 he was sent to reconnoitre a site for the War Dog Training School in Brussels. Before he left Belgium he had successfully indoctrinated Lieutenant-Colonel R. H. Stalker, A.D.V.R.S. 21st Army Group and, when the school joined 21st Army Group, Colonel Stalker lost no time in making it a unit of the Royal Army Veterinary Corps. The first R.A.V.C. commanding officer, Major G. D. Young, was appointed in November 1945.

The unit remained in Belgium a few months and in November 1945 it moved into Germany to prepared accommodation in Sennelager. The move caused a certain amount of amusement and a great deal of interest at the various stations at which the train halted. In addition to 150 soldiers and some 200 dogs, the party included fifty members of the A.T.S. and fourteen horses.

It might be appropriate here to pay tribute to the excellent work done by the A.T.S. personnel who formed part of the school. Posted in as kennel maids they did a first-class job and were most devoted to their charges. They were of particular value in the hospital where they were indefatigable in their ministrations to sick dogs. Although their duties were primarily concerned with kennel management some became expert trainers. Not a few refused the opportunity of being commissioned simply because it would necessitate leaving the school and the dogs.

With the post-war run down of the Army the World War I mistake of disbanding the war dog training organization was not repeated. This was fortunate as it will be seen later that trained specialist dogs were able to render valuable assistance in the Colonial insurrections which were to become a feature of the post-war era. Guard dogs too continued to make an invaluable contribution to the security of vulnerable installations in every military theatre. In 1947 a war dog training school was embodied in the establishment of the Veterinary and Remount Centre at Melton Mowbray. From then on all trainees, including officers, entering the Corps were given instruction in the basic principles of dog training, kennel management and the handling of trained dogs.

The wisdom of retaining war dog training establishments as an integral part of the Army, so keeping alive the various techniques of training, became apparent as one theatre after another was urgent in its demand for trained specialist dogs. To meet these demands schools were established in Malaya, Kenya and Cyprus. All played their part enthusiastically, not only in producing trained dogs but also inculcating the art of their employment and supplying skilled advisers to user units. In addition to their duties as trainers, personnel of the Corps were to be found as tireless handlers in the forefront of operations and not a few had the satisfaction of being personally responsible for eliminating some active terrorist.

There can be few breeds of dogs which have not been tried by the Army in its search for dogs of the right size and temperament for military work.

Until gunpowder started to dominate the battlefield in about the 17th Century the requirement was a big, bold, aggressive dog capable of being pitted against armed men and it is highly probable that the mastiff and its larger crosses were the species most sought after. However, the discovery of gunpowder completely changed the concept of war and with this change the dog lost its value as an attacking force.

In World War I both the Airedale and Collie were popular breeds. The former was trained successfully for both guard and messenger duties while the fleetness, agility and sagacity of the small variety of the Collie made it an excellent subject for messenger training. With the advent of World War II the Airedale was no longer the fashionable dog it once had been and it also fell into disfavour as a military animal although a few were enlisted and served faithfully as guards. The breed which did more than any other to supplant the Airedale in the eyes of the Army and, to a lesser degree the public, was the Alsatian. This is the one breed which most nearly fulfils all the requirements necessary for the various types of training practised in modern military schools. Endowed with a fine physique and impressive appearance it possesses a high degree of intelligence and responds quickly to training. It is very adaptable and is capable of withstanding wide variations of climate. As a guard dog it is without equal. It has also excelled as a tracker, infantry patrol dog and messenger, and to a lesser extent as a casualty-detection dog.

Another breed which has distinguished itself is the Labrador. No other breed has produced such a high percentage of reliable trackers. Although both varieties have been outstanding in this sphere the black has shown more all round superiority. There is a streak of softness not infrequently apparent in the yellow which, when present, appears to sap the determination to finish a difficult track. The Labrador has also exhibited a natural aptitude for casualty-detection work, and crosses with smaller breeds, especially the terrier type, have made excellent mine dogs.

Other breeds which have been used include the boxer, which, trained as a guard dog, was very popular in the Middle East, but because of its short coat is not universally suitable. The dobermann pinscher, popular in police circles, has not been very successful as a military animal and a nervous disposition has led to the rejection of many presented for acceptance. Again, being thin coated it does not stand up to really cold weather. A few did train up and several served with distinction in the Far East as patrol and guard dogs. It seems not unlikely that the best specimens of the breed have not been available to the Army as it would appear most improbable that the faith placed in their ability by the Palestine police, during the British Mandate of Palestine, was not without good reason. The bull terrier was rejected partly because of its thin coat but chiefly because its wilful nature made it difficult to train. A story is told that during a particularly wet and inclement night a bull terrier guard dog deserted its handler for the comforts of the guard room where it firmly refused all persuasion to resume its duties.

When discussing suitable breeds the claims of the mongrel must not be ignored. Many a first-class mine dog would encounter great difficulty in trying to trace its ancestry. Provided the candidate is active and inquisitive of ground scent and it is within the size range its breed is immaterial.

Mention too must be made of those two classic breeds the St. Bernard and bloodhound. Unfortunately, in neither breed has the supply position been sufficient to test their value as war dogs. Only one St. Bernard is known to have entered a training school and this was trained as a guard dog. Its size coupled with a very uncertain temper made it a difficult dog to handle and it was destroyed without ever being issued. Several bloodhounds have been trained as trackers in the United Kingdom but none saw operational service. So here again it is not possible to comment upon their value for this purpose.

While breed is important in selecting a dog for some particular form of training, age, temperament and conformation must also be given consideration.

Six basic types of training have been developed: guard, messenger, casualty detection (Red Cross), tracker, infantry patrol and mine detection. Each type involves a special training technique. It is not and never has been the policy to teach an individual dog more than one skill. Each dog must be a specialist in its own sphere. Any departure from this policy only results in lowering the performance of the dog for the task for which it was trained and it becomes "a Jack of all trades and a master of none". It has, however, been found expedient to modify or introduce slight variations to individual techniques to meet special requirements. For instance, messenger dogs may be trained to carry loads, casualty-detection dogs to search bomb-blasted buildings, mine-detection dogs to locate buried caches of arms and patrol dogs to act as silent sentries in jungle bivouacs or isolated outposts.

The training of war dogs is based on the reward system. The dog, through its natural desire to please, is trained to respond willingly to certain words of command and is rewarded when the command is properly executed. The reward may take the form of verbal praise, an encouraging pat or some titbit usually a piece of meat. Failure to obey must never result in physical chastisement which, if applied, will only cow or completely antagonise the dog.

Whatever the type of training there must be a complete absence of nervousness and gunshyness. It is therefore customary to test all dogs at purchase, or prior to being accepted into military kennels, for these unwanted characteristics. Those dogs required to work in or near the fighting zone must be so inured by continuation training that they can carry out their allotted tasks quite impervious to any battle noises.

The foundation of all specialized training is basic obedience without which a dog must never be launched on to the more difficult exercises of specialized training. It entails instant obedience to the five words of command—heel, sit, down, come and stay. It not only conditions a dog to respond more readily to the complicated demands of advanced training but it ensures, which is of equal importance, that the dog can be kept under the absolute control of its handler. Unruly, disobedient dogs have no place in the Army.

In modern times the first types to be introduced were the casualty-detection dog, messenger dog and guard dog. Only the latter two were used to any extent during World War I.

The casualty-detection dog is trained to quarter in front of its handler and, on discovering a casualty, to return to its handler and sit. The handler applies the lead and the dog then guides him to the casualty. In the early stages casualties are placed in fairly obvious positions but as training advances they are spread out and more or less concealed. A fully-trained dog should be capable of ranging up to seventy-five yards on either side of its handler and to discover every casualty within these limits.

Originally the messenger dog was a "one way dog" that is, it was only trained to run from an outpost back to its keeper at base. However, improvements were made to the technique of training until, in World War II, a trained dog would not only shuttle between outpost and base, but would also locate the outpost from which it was originally released should it have moved its position. The increased scope of the dog is accomplished by the introduction of two handlers both equally responsible for the dog's care and employment. In this way both share its affections and when released by one handler the dog willingly runs to the second. It is important to ensure the equal division of affection and that one handler does not gain ascendency over the other.

Guard dog training is probably the oldest of all specialized training. From the earliest times man has taken advantage of the alert and aggressive qualities of certain breeds to train them to protect his property or to act as sentries. With a suitable dog, training time is comparatively short. During its training the dog is taught to indicate to its handler the presence of a hidden intruder in a patrolled area; alert his handler to anyone's approach; protect him should he be attacked and, when ordered, attack and hold a man. The dog is always encouraged to go for the right arm as the average man being right handed it is more than probable that an intruder or assailant, if armed, would carry the weapon in his right hand.

A recent variation of the guard dog is the "Security dog". Here a bold rather than aggressive type is wanted. While being trained to corner or pursue and detain an intruder it must neither bite nor maul. Compared with guard dog training the general approach is light-hearted and boisterous. Even the pursuit must be treated as a game and when the "criminal" falls or is brought down he must wrestle playfully with the dog.

Of the six basic types the tracker dog requires the longest training, and, in consequence, it is usual to commence at a younger age than is the case with the remainder. It might take anything up to two years to produce a reliable animal. Although the British system, unlike that of the German, does not demand a dog to attack its quarry at the end of a successful track, a trace of aggressiveness in the temperament is an asset. Dogs so endowed show greater determination to overcome all obstacles and so complete a track successfully, whereas their softer and more docile brethren tend to give up easily in the face of adversity. The most important attribute of a good tracker is the ability to hold contact with the original track ignoring all diversionary tracks, even when these are fresher and foil the original. It is the attainment of this discriminating skill that necessitates the lengthy training period. Dogs without it are at the best merely "direction givers" and at the worst dangerous impediments. Much of the criticism which has been aimed at tracker dogs has stemmed from the failure of a poorly-trained or inferior dog to ignore the attraction of a hotter secondary scent. In training, the original track is often purposely crossed by a secondary one. At first this is only done once, but with greater frequency as the dog becomes more experienced. The points where the original and diversionary tracks intersect are always marked for the benefit of the trainer who, knowing where the dog has been at fault, is able to correct it. This, however, he must not do until he has given the dog every opportunity to realize its error and by casting back regain contact with the original line.

With the extensive use of mines in World War II much effort was spent on devising means of detecting and neutralizing them. The mechanical detector was, at first, a most useful instrument for this purpose. Unfortunately, in the game of plot and counter-plot the enemy cunningly produced mines manufactured of glass, wood and plastic and being completely without metal components they were beyond the scope of the detector. However, research soon discovered that intelligent dogs could detect these non-metallic mines and a technique of training was devised. At first many people were understandably sceptical of their ability. To prove their worth a training field was sown with some seventy-five mines which included glass and wooden varieties. The dogs detected all but one and this mine, unlike the remainder contained no explosive. As the dogs were trained on unfuzed mines filled with explosive this apparent failure gave, in fact, strong evidence of their ability to cope successfully with this dangerous and highly specialized task.

The infantry patrol dog was originally trained to work on an eighteen-feet line but this method was found to be impracticable when patrolling through closed country such as jungle. A technique was therefore devised whereby the dog was required to work loose in front of the patrol never ranging more than twenty-five to thirty yards ahead. In both methods the dog is trained to point on hidden humans once it has become aware of their presence in the vicinity. This presence is revealed to the dog by scent being carried to it by air currents; or by noise, inaudible to the human ear, but nevertheless detectable by the dog. Under the most favourable conditions points of up to 500 yards have been made. Patrol dogs must work in complete silence and must show no desire to investigate what they detect. Complete obedience is of prime importance as any loss of control by the handler can easily result in disaster to the patrol.

We have seen how as the pattern of war changed a new era in the employment of dogs for military purposes dawned. From the large, powerful over-aggressive animal whose worth lay in its ability to fight and kill, a more specialized type was required to meet the demands of modern war. Much thought and ingenuity were applied to devising new techniques, and it is not without some satisfaction that one surveys the various types of dogs which have been perfected and the manner in which they have been employed. Who, at the birth of the century, would have foreseen that fleet-footed dogs would zealously and courageously carry messages in battle; that dogs trained to detect buried mines would be included in the order of battle of a highly-mechanized invasion army; that skilled tracker dogs would hunt down many a terrorist in his jungle refuge, and that patrol dogs would fearlessly bring small bodies of men unscathed through enemy-infested country. However, subject as they are to outside influences their performance cannot be expected to be, and indeed is not, constant. This must be appreciated by those responsible for using them. When it is and when they have been carefully trained for their particular task their employment is rewarding in its success.

The messenger dog was one of the forerunners of modern training methods and not a few of these dogs took the field during World War I. Their ability to negotiate, at speed, all types of country by memory made them useful in the quick transmission of messages. In those days communications were more primitive than they are now, and often the only means of maintaining contact was by runner. This method was uncertain as a man, offering as he did, a good target frequently became a casualty. His replacement by a well-trained experienced dog not only speeded up the delivery of a message but also reduced the number of casualties sustained. An idea of their speed can be gathered from the following report:—

"The journey he did, used to take a man seventy minutes to walk and Jim did it in twenty-two minutes through barbed wire entanglements and a large number of batteries."

Many outstanding performances are credited to these nimble and courageous dogs. The certainty with which they carried out their duties under difficult conditions led one

British signals officer to issue instructions that, as far as possible, all important messages were to be sent by dogs. Their devotion to duty and their stoicism too were beyond praise. This is exemplified by messenger dog Dick, who, while carrying a message was severely wounded in the back and shoulder. Obviously in pain he nevertheless completed his run successfully. Following treatment the wounds appeared to heal and he was soon at work again. Unfortunately, he was later seen to be suffering and had to be destroyed. Post-mortem examination revealed a bullet embedded behind the shoulder and a piece of shrapnel lodged near the spine.

As mentioned earlier messenger dogs were at this time "one way" dogs. The procedure was for a keeper, as he was called, to be in charge of several dogs and both he and his dogs were located at a headquarters. When the services of a dog were required, a member of the patrol would collect one from the keeper and lead it forward on a strong lead. The person selected for this job had to be a stranger to the dog and was instructed not to pet or make much of it. In this way the strong and impatient desire of the dog to return to its keeper remained. With improved technique these dogs were later trained to shuttle to and fro between two fixed points, or, if necessary, between one fixed point and one movable point provided an aniseed drag was laid when the second point moved. Each dog had two handlers, one located at each point between which it was required to run. The perfection of the new technique greatly increased the scope of their employment. Their ability to shuttle between two fixed points led to some being trained to carry loads. Being able to carry up to one third of their body weight they proved very useful in the supply of forward positions with food and small-arms ammunition.

The distances messenger dogs can cover by memory is quite remarkable, and up to four to five miles is well within their ability. Perhaps what is even more remarkable is the length of time they are able to remember a "run". Experiments have demonstrated the ability of one dog to memorize a "run" for some three weeks when he covered it at speed and without hesitation.

There is little evidence of the use of casualty-detection dogs in war. The reason for this is due chiefly to the fact that their value lies mainly in a war of movement when they can sweep a battlefield once the conflict has moved on. They were nevertheless used by the Russians in both the Russo-Japanese and the 1914-1918 wars. Some were employed during the London blitz to search bomb-devastated buildings for casualties and here perhaps their greatest value lies. Their size and agility enables them to reach parts of a bombed building with safety more easily and quickly than can be done by a rescue worker. The Swiss have perfected this type of dog for mountain rescue and especially for locating buried casualties following an avalanche.

In Cyprus, during the troubled era which preceded the proclamation of independence, a modification of the casualty-detection dog called a hide-search dog was used effectively in the search and detection of terrorist hide-outs. Many of these were so cunningly constructed and camouflaged that even when suspicion centred on a particular building or area the hide-out itself could not be located. Relying on its sense of smell the dog could detect the occupants and in that way disclose where they were hiding.

"N9 Simmi (Boxer) Guard Dog Simmi joined the Section on 16th July 1942 and died on 18th September 1944. During his service Simmi had to his credit eighty-six arrests, most of these being outstanding in the whole-hearted manner in which he carried out his duties."

So ran the epitaph of one of the many thousands of guard dogs which have spent their lives in the protection of government property entrusted to their care.

The guard dog is by far the largest group used for military purposes and representatives may be found in all parts of the world playing their part in the fight against the depredations of thieves and saboteurs. Without their assistance the effective security of countless military installations and vulnerable points would present an insoluble man-power problem. Their employment not only gives increased security, but usually does so with a manpower-saving. Except in the case of the most determined their mere presence is often sufficient to deter a would-be transgressor. The guard dog was widely used in both world wars and many instances have been recorded of their excellent work. In the Middle East, especially, where dumps covered a very wide area and the native population have a proclivity for robbery their services were invaluable not only in the protection of property but also of their handlers, as the following report on Akeela, an Alsatian, vividly illustrates.

"One outstanding arrest and devotion to duty being when Akeela picked up eight thieves, some being armed with loaded sticks. The thieves seeing only one dog and its handler attacked with their sticks. Corporal Wigly, the handler, was struck to the ground but was able to draw his pistol and kill one of the thieves. During this battle Akeela was attacking and, drawing off the other thieves, finally secured the capture of one more. By this time assistance arrived and much W.D. property was saved and recovered."

Lance-Corporal Ball the handler of Blackie, another Alsatian, had cause to be grateful for its loyal protection in a very tight corner.

"Lance-Corporal Ball with his dog entered a warehouse and surprised a number of native civilians in the act of filling sacks with W.D. clothing. When the civilians saw they were being challenged by only one man and a dog they attacked. Blackie was released and knocked one man over and kept him down. At the same time he rendered valuable assistance to his handler by taking random bites at the other attackers. Finally Lance-Corporal Ball and Blackie managed to arrest five. The remainder were arrested as they left the warehouse by another policeman who was brought to the scene by the noise."

Guard dogs may be used in one of several different ways: as a patrolling or static sentry, on a running wire or allowed to roam loose in an enclosed building or compound. Of these methods the patrolling sentry is the one most commonly adopted. Here the dog, either on a lead or loose, patrols a given beat along with its handler. It is more usual to keep the dog on a lead as, by so doing, the risk of an innocent person being attacked is avoided. Should however the handler wish to release his dog on to a suspect he can easily do so by means of a quick release attachment on the lead. Where several patrols are employed on the same installation their routes must be carefully plotted to avoid picking each other up. It is customary also to introduce some means of supervision either by telephones or tell-tale clocks, the handler being required to check in at certain points on his beat at specific times. The length of any beat varies with the type of installation. Where buildings or dumps are well spaced out longer beats may be introduced than where their proximity to each other provides plenty of cover for any one breaking in.

In the rôle of static sentry a guard dog may be employed to protect some particularly vulnerable or important point. It is able to give its handler advance warning of anyone's approach and, if called upon, defend him should he be attacked. Because of the frequency with which guard dogs were used for the protection of vulnerable points during World War II they were commonly referred to as V.P. dogs, a term which later fell into disuse.

The running-wire method is particularly valuable where the site to be protected is limited, for example, the end of a building or an especially important stretch of a perimeter fence. The wire, which must be firmly fixed to the ground and permit the free running of the tether chain to which the dog is attached, should not exceed 100 yards in length. The dog is free to range along the whole length of the wire and attack anyone sufficiently rash to come within its reach.

Compound dogs have proved most valuable when the area is not too large, is completely enclosed and the perimeter fence proof against the dog breaking out. These dogs have been employed with marked success in Singapore. Here at one installation a handler deposited dogs at three different sites where they remained during the night, each being periodically visited by the handler to ensure all was well. The saving of manpower was thus very considerable.

A vociferous dog is normally selected when choosing an animal for duty in a building. As the handler should be within easy call so that he can investigate any alarm raised, the dog is not wanted so much for its aggressiveness as for its alertness and once alerted its natural reaction should be to bark and bark loudly.

The security dog referred to when discussing training is proving most popular in the United Kingdom. Being non-aggressive they can be worked loose with impunity. Again, in the absence of their own handler a second or third person encounters no difficulty in handling them. In larger installations with their handler on a bicycle they often run alongside. Their training teaches them to range over the area patrolled and to indicate their discovery of anyone by barking. If ordered they will also chase a fugitive and trip him or otherwise impede his escape until the handler can effect his arrest.

The mine dog was a brain child of World War II when the land-mine menace resulted in much thought and time being given to devising means of combating it. Once a technique had been perfected of teaching dogs to indicate the presence of buried mines four platoons of dogs were trained and saw service in N.W. Europe. subsequent to the 1944 invasion. Although the platoons were primarily for employment in rear areas one platoon did take part in the Rhine crossings. It was the commanding officer of this platoon who, when asked "Did mine dogs really find mines effectively?" replied that for six months the platoon worked nearly every day and never had a casualty on a mine-field. Neither was there ever any complaint received that a mine had been found in an area cleared by the platoon.

Commanded by an officer each platoon had an establishment of twenty-two other ranks (including one R.A.V.C. sergeant) and twenty-nine mine dogs, divided into a headquarters and three sections. They were chiefly used for clearing road verges, tracks and railway and tram lines and for this purpose were highly successful as the following excerpts from reports show:—

"An R.E. detachment of a dog platoon consisting of one lance-corporal, six handlers and eighteen dogs cleared six and a half miles of tracks between 11th and 16th February 1945 finding some sixty-eight mines."

And again:—

"We were working hard at this time, and as it was often the continental custom to have railway or tram lines running along the side of their main roads normal mine detectors could not be used and the dogs came into their own."

In some respects mine dogs are superior to the electronic detector. They are not defeated by the completely non-metallic glass, plastic or wooden mine; their speed of working is faster; they ignore surface metal fragments and on railway tracks are not affected by the lines. Against these points in their favour, they ignore trip wires; they may be distracted by shell fire and they react unfavourably to extremes of weather. They also have off days when they show little interest in their work. Because of this they must be carefully tested to ensure that they are at their peak before being worked over a suspected field. There is a tendency too for individual dogs to lose interest if worked for fairly long periods without discovering a mine. Again, although they are capable of discovering mines some considerable time after burial the time factor does affect their performance.

It is of interest to note that, by contrast, our platoons met with considerably more success than their American counterparts. The reason it would appear could be traced to the different training system.

Following World War II the next occasion mine dogs were operationally used was during the Korean War when twelve dogs arrived in the theatre in November 1951. Once again they were employed in rear areas chiefly in the proving and clearing of derelict mine-fields.

Having discovered that dogs could be trained to locate buried mines it was not unnatural that their skill was tested against buried caches of arms. Experimentally they gave some very heartening performances. In one test quantities of weapons were buried, at various points, to a depth of five feet in ploughed sandy soil. Although the surface was carefully harrowed to erase any signs of earth disturbances the test dogs located all buried sites with ease. An electronic mine detector failed the test. Although basically mine dogs, they were, because of their altered rôle redesignated arms-recovery dogs and, as such, ten dogs were sent to Palestine in 1946 to assist in the anti-terrorist operations. As not infrequently happens when dogs are first introduced to a theatre of operations they were met by faint amusement and very little faith in their ability. How they vindicated themselves and those responsible for their training and silenced their critics is fully contained in the following report.

"The following morning the dogs made finds in each of the settlements. Their 'modus operandi' was very simple. They scented keenly the ground over which they were cast and if they scented or sensed metal they sat down on the spot and were ultimately rewarded with a lump of meat. In two cases where the dogs 'sat' the ground had previously been covered by the Sappers with their mine detectors. At . . . it was a hen house with a floor of concrete slabs in which a cross-bred Labrador 'sat' before unbelieving eyes. The concrete was raised with the aid of a compressor drill and the earth below was dug out to a depth of four-and-a-half feet before the lid of a seven feet deep cache was reached. In it were stored some fifty assorted weapons including heavy mortars and machine guns together with many thousands of rounds of ammunition. They had been there for some considerable length of time and how they were detected at such a depth remained a mystery to all but the dog. In . . . there was a similar discovery, alongside the site of a new building a large pile of gravel concealed the entrance to a deeply buried cache. At this the dog pointed, and after it had been removed it indicated the exact position of a circular steel drum which was eventually found buried under five feet of earth. It contained a large selection of weapon parts, magazines, mines, explosives and military equipment."

Operationally tracker dogs were not used to any extent until the terrorist activities occurred in Malaya, Kenya and Cyprus. It was unfortunate that in the early days a sufficient pool of trained and experienced dogs was not available to meet demands as they arose. This deficiency led to dogs being flung into operations before they were properly trained and this, not surprisingly, led to failures. Those who opposed the employment of dogs were quick to regard these failures as supporting evidence in their arguments against the use of dogs. However this opposition was soon stifled as dogs became more experienced and techniques of employment improved.

In all these operations the enemy was a phantom figure rarely seen in the open but lurking rather in his jungle camp, mountain cave or safely hidden by fellow sympathisers in some well-secluded or camouflaged refuge. He only came out into the open to commit an act of terrorism and, having accomplished it, retreated rapidly to the protection of a prearranged hide-out. A speedy follow-up of an incident was therefore one of the few ways by which the security forces could get to grips with him. It was here that the tracker dog was so invaluable. Speed was the essence of successs as was shown when on the 7th September 1958 a patrol of the 3rd Royal Malay Regiment contacted two terrorists. One was killed immediately while the second escaped. In the subsequent follow-up tracker dog Scott II was used. On a hot scent Scott worked sure and fast over 4,000 yards of jungle, rubber and open country when the terrorist was cornered and dragged from his hiding place. Without Scott it is most doubtful whether the terrorist would have been caught, and even if he had, his capture would not have been effected so speedily.

The value of a dog in a night follow-up was proved by this incident which occurred in Kenya. A party of Mau Mau were seen raiding a smallholding but dispersed and fled into the forest when fired upon. It was 2 a.m. before a security patrol arrived on the scene. Fortunately, tracker dog Able and its handler were members of the patrol. Despite the darkness Able successfully located a track leading to the forest and it soon became obvious that the gang had joined up again. Following a track of some four miles through the forest, seven Mau Mau were caught by surprise, roasting potatoes around a fire.

It is normal practice to work a tracker dog on an eighteen feet line. In this way while contact between handler and dog is maintained, as little restriction as possible is placed on its movements. An instance when a handler lost contact occurred in Malaya when a dog was allowed to cast loose on a terraced hillside. It picked up a scent and before the handler could do anything it disappeared up the hill and into a hidden terrorist camp. In the following mêlée the dog was shot, fortunately not fatally and the terrorists escaped. Had the dog been on a lead it is fairly certain the terrorists would have been surprised.

As the value of tracking became apparent more emphasis was placed upon it as a means of ferreting out terrorists. Visual trackers and dogs were married up into teams. The visual trackers, most of whom are natives (Ibans) with an inbred ability to track, can give information about the nature of the track; for example, its age, how many people were in the party, whether they were carrying loads and if any member was wounded. They are also often able to follow older tracks than a dog. On its credit side the dog can usually track faster, can track at night, and usually gives a very definite indication when nearing the end of the track, a most useful and important piece of information. Worked together visual trackers and dogs form a most formidable team as the following operational report illustrates.

" On 18th August 1958 at approximately 0930 hours the tracker team 1st Loyals found a communist terrorist camp evacuated approximately five hours previously. The camp was examined by the Ibans and the escape route found. Due to cover-up tactics by the terrorists the tracker dogs were cast on to the track and Rufus and Rock worked alternatively for the rest of the day until 1800 hours. During this time it rained heavily and the only visual sign found was a resting place en route. At last light it was estimated the terrorists were about fifteen to thirty minutes in front. Distance covered on 18th August was about 3,000 yards in primary jungle. At first light on the 19th tracking continued. By this time the terrorists were apparently confident they had evaded pursuit and were careless leaving an easy visual track. Ibans were used all day on the 19th without difficulty. On the 20th Ibans continued and after about three hours tracking an occupied camp was found. In the ensuing attack four out of seven terrorists were killed."

The signs given by a dog when nearing the end of a track can be of the utmost value to a patrol. Not only will they prevent the patrol blundering upon its quarry but the element of surprise, so important in these conditions, is retained. The signs vary between individual dogs. Tail wagging, excitement, raising the head and increased speed have all been noted. It is one of the responsibilities of an experienced handler to read these signs in his own dog with confidence. The consequences could have been tragic when the handler of Lew failed to do just this. When Lew showed signs of nearing the end of the track, some fifty yards from where the quarry (a wounded terrorist) lay hidden, the handler who could see clearly for a distance of 200 yards and, thinking it to be at fault, forced Lew to continue. It was not until they were nearly on top of him that the handler spotted the terrorist lying in a depression. Although the latter was shot and killed, Lew was also wounded but luckily not seriously. Had the terrorist not been wounded, or had there been more than one, the patrol might have suffered severe casualties simply because the handler did not act on the information given by his dog.

A firm indication of the direction of an escape route is sometimes all that is required to effect a capture. This indication tracker dog Len was able to give following an ambush on 6th February 1956. Realizing the route lay in the direction of security forces already in ambush positions these were alerted by wireless. The outcome was that when two terrorists approached the positions the security forces were prepared and one terrorist was killed and a shot-gun recovered.

It is not always the terrorist who has been the target of the tracker dog. Many a common thief has been given cause to regret its ability to follow unerringly his track from the scene of the crime. Little did those thieves who broke into a R.A.S.C. depot think that within a very short space of time they would be arrested through the effort of a dog. But this is what exactly happened when tracker dog Query tracked some one and a half miles from the depot to a house where the stolen property was found and the occupants arrested. Example after example can be quoted of the wonderful work done by these dogs. Undeterred by the tropical forests of Malaya, the equatorial highlands of Kenya and the arid mountains of Cyprus they have won through and crowned success with success.

The class of war dog in the present-day army which is of particular interest to the infantry is the patrol dog. The success of a patrol depends a great deal upon the ability to locate the enemy without itself being detected. The patrol dog, trained to use its highly-developed senses of smell and hearing to indicate the presence of an individual or group of people in a patrolled area, renders valuable aid to the patrol in accomplishing this. During the Korean campaign patrol dogs were used extensively by units of the Commonwealth Division. The degree of success they achieved can be gauged from the fact that at one period 120 patrols were carried out by three patrol dogs without a single case of a patrol being surprised by the enemy. This was done, too, at a time when the enemy was also very active in patrolling and had proved himself a master of technique and at laying ambushes. The accuracy with which the dogs pointed was such that on one occasion artillery fire was brought down on the area pointed out by the handler and at least three of the enemy were killed. Most units that employed them became their enthusiastic supporters and considered them an essential part of the patrol. With the increased security provided by a dog, greater speed was possible and confidence boosted. In one unit the success achieved by dogs raised the morale of the dog troop so high that the only complaints heard were when one handler managed to get more patrols than his mates. The results were calamitous when one Commonwealth Division patrol (not British) ignored two successive points given by a dog. Except for two men the patrol including the dog, which was particularly tragic after the warning it had given, were killed.

Further evidence of the value of patrol dogs in Korea is contained in the following two extracts from official reports.

"The patrol dogs accompanied both reconnaissance and fighting patrols and were quite invaluable. When a patrol approached its objective without giving its presence away, the dogs invariably were able to indicate just where the enemy were and quite a number of prisoners were the result. In addition when moving towards their objective the patrol was able to avoid enemy parties, contact with which would have upset our plans.

It is the opinion of all N.C.O.s and officers who worked with the dogs that they are a valuable addition to the Battalion's strength. I myself agree with them and should like to feel that I could take on a number of these dogs in situations where they could be of value."

"A patrol was sent out to capture a prisoner and report if a certain wood over a mile in front was held by the enemy. The dog and the handler went five yards ahead of the patrol at a steady pace. Whenever the dog smelt anything it stopped and 'pointed'. The patrol was thus able to go right along the edge of the only main road into the enemy lines with perfect confidence. A lot of time was saved, an easy route could be kept the whole way and there was no danger of running into an ambush or enemy position without warning. Once the dog did stop and 'point' and the patrol hid by the side of the road and a minute later a strong enemy patrol went right past along the road. The dog did not bark or give the patrol away. It had smelt the enemy about 300 yards away. Except for a false alarm when the dog 'pointed' at some cows in a field the patrol reached its objective in half the time it would have taken without a dog and with much greater safety."

There are a number of factors which affect the performance of a patrol dog and the distance at which warning is given may vary from as much as 500 yards to as little as ten yards or less. Wind-direction and speed, volume or concentration of human scent, humidity, density of the vegetation all have their effect on the strength and certainty with which the point is given. The classic point, which is more usually seen when the dog is worked on a long lead, is when it freezes with head and body pointing firmly in the direction of the target. However, in many instances nothing quite so definite is given and the dog, especially when worked loose, may merely evince a momentary tensing of the body and interest in a particular direction. The handler therefore must be expert in "reading" his dog under all conditions and having become so he should be able to give, with confidence, a reasonably accurate assessment of the distance away of the target. The skill of some handlers in this respect can become quite uncanny in its accuracy.

It was in the Malayan operations that the patrol dog was first worked off the lead. This technique was introduced to offset the inability of the dog in dense jungle to point on the target from long distances. By working loose ahead of the patrol (usually not more than twenty yeards ahead) earlier points could be made and the possibility of the patrol being given insufficient warning to escape ambush greatly minimised.

In addition to the conventional method of employment patrol dogs may be used as silent sentries to prevent infiltration past an outpost position, or surprise attack. In this rôle patrol dog Michell did a first-class job. On the night of 11th April it was lying beside its handler on the perimeter of a jungle camp. At approximately 8.15 p.m. it rose and pointed on a bearing of 270°. During the following five to ten minutes it pointed twice on bearings of 290° and 225°. As a result of these warnings the camp stood to, and the attack when it came at 8.35 p.m. was from the angle expected.

So long as patrols are called upon to probe deeply into enemy territory; so long as the terrorist is poised in some well-prepared ambush, so long will the patrol dog play its vital and dangerous rôle.

No account on the subject of war dogs would be complete without reference to the men who handle them. However well trained a dog may be it cannot give of its best unless in the charge of an equally well-trained handler. Who are these men? Except when required to handle mine dogs they may come from any arm of the service or they may even be civilians in the case of some guard dogs. As the handling of mine dogs also calls for a knowledge of mines the handlers of these very specialized animals are drawn solely from Royal Engineer units. Nationals other than British have been instructed in our methods. In Germany since the war Germans, Jugoslavs, Poles and Balts have all been trained as guard-dog handlers. The Malayan anti-terrorist operations saw a number of Gurkha and Chinese soldiers trained to handle both tracker and patrol dogs. One of these was Lance-Corporal Thor Cheng Kim of the 4th Malay Regiment. With his dog Rusty he showed great determination in tracking down a terrorist band under the most difficult conditions which entailed several river crossings. In other theatres Cypriots and Hong Kong Chinese have given loyal service as guard-dog handlers. The main qualities of a good handler are without any doubt a sympathetic understanding of dogs, devotion to duty and an intelligence above the average. It is little good selecting a man who does not like dogs. Any dog will quickly sense dislike and as quickly reciprocate it. Selection must always be from volunteers. How true were the words of the commanding officer who wrote during the Korean War "I am also of the opinion that it is not only a waste of time but a serious mistake to accept any but keen and carefully selected volunteers as dog handlers." Being a specialist a handler is usually required to work with little supervision. It is therefore essential that he can be relied upon to apply himself devotedly to the job of promoting both himself and his dog to the highest possible standard of efficiency. Without considerable intelligence a handler will be incapable of interpreting with any certainty the dog's mute signs. This is especially so in those dogs trained for patrol, tracker and mine-detection rôles.

Showing a sturdy independence and the countryman's natural flair for working with animals many excellent handlers were, during the war, recruited from the ranks of farm hands, stalkers, gamekeepers and, when they divulged their means of livelihood, poachers. An amusing incident involved two men of this latter calling. Both, members of a mine platoon engaged in the Reichwald battle, asked their commanding officer, during a break in operations, for permission to stroll up the road to see some friends they had noticed. In a short time they returned with one of the "friends"—a deer, slung safely across one of their shoulders!

Where does the war dog stand today? It is not unreasonable to say that it is probably more firmly established as a part of the armed forces than ever before. Despite the breathtaking advances in modern armaments there will always be scope for the talents of trained dogs, no matter where the Army is called upon to operate. Nothing that man has invented, or is likely to invent in the foreseeable future, can replace those qualities which have made the dog such an outstanding member of the animal kingdom and the devoted servant of man.

CHAPTER XI

Contributions to Research

In November 1921 an Advisory Committee was set up by the Government to "report on the facilities now available for the scientific study of the diseases of animals, to indicate what extension of those facilities is desirable in the immediate future in order to advance the study of diseases whether in animals or man, and to advise as to the steps which should be taken to secure the aid of competent scientific workers in investigating diseases in animals."

The final recommendations of this committee included six paragraphs. The fifth paragraph read as follows:

"Suitable facilities for research should be placed at the disposal of the Royal Army Veterinary Corps."

Let us remember that in fact the general terms of reference of this committee were to recommend conditions for improving veterinary research in this country. It is obvious that the R.A.V.C. was considered to be a vigorous force in this connection to warrant a separate paragraph: This is reinforced later on in the committee's report: "It is suggested that facilities should be given to members of the Royal Army Veterinary Corps for training in research and for study leave. Closer collaboration between officers in the Royal Army Medical Corps and the Royal Army Veterinary Corps is desirable."

It is interesting to reflect that the total amount given by the State in 1920-1921 for veterinary research in the United Kingdom amounted to £3,696. Most of this was absorbed by salaries and wages leaving precious little for new apparatus. It was Major-General Sir John Moore, of the Army Veterinary Service, who in 1923 helped to stimulate the profession by officially proposing the formation of an Animals Research Council, to be similar in scope to the Medical Research Council. Since 1909, veterinary research had merely received the crumbs from the table of the Development and Roads Improvement Fund, which had other more vociferous babies to look after: this was to be the beginning of a more beneficent official approach to the "Cinderella of the Sciences".

The Army Veterinary Service was created on 24th May 1796, some 165 years ago. The title "Veterinary Surgeon" was coined by the Army at this time to distinguish between the surgeon of men and the surgeon of horses. This appellation subsequently became applied to the entire profession. An impressive number, perhaps the majority, of the inquiring minds of the veterinary profession since that date have belonged to the Army Veterinary Service: certainly veterinary knowledge would be a good deal less advanced in the world today had it not been for the past efforts of this Service.

It is difficult to plan for the future without an intelligent knowledge of the past. This is as true for veterinary medicine and science as any other discipline. It therefore behoves us periodically to review in tabloid form what frontiers of knowledge have been penetrated in recent years. It is, however, important to bear in mind the incredible advances made in these disciplines during the past fifty-odd years, which lessens to some extent the value of the earlier knowledge. Many diseases and pathological conditions which have beset mankind and his domesticated animals for centuries have been brought under control during this vigorous period. The Army Veterinary Service in its own specialized field has contributed its quota in pushing the fringe of human knowledge out a little further. The dethronement of the horse has been perhaps the greatest single factor in removing the Army from the forefront of research in veterinary matters. Nevertheless, the veterinary art embraces all species of domesticated animals and the successful elevation of farm stock and small animals as the prime interest of the civilian element of the profession has had its counterpart, albeit small, in the military sphere, too.

Three wars in the past sixty years, and many small "local" campaigns in between, have all stimulated the army veterinary surgeon to add considerably to our knowledge. On the whole it has been an effort of the individual rather than a result of officially sponsored schemes. Certainly, Leclainche's cynical remarks about bureaucracy cannot apply to the more enlightened chiefs of the Army Veterinary Service: he wrote "Bureaucracy under all systems of government and at every period of history, discourages and suppresses all possible rise of first-class professional or scientific talent and ability which is not docilely amenable to its authority." (Lechlainche, Hist. de la Med. Vet. 1936.)

It is very difficult to draw the line when it comes down to concrete contributions of the Army Veterinary Service to research. Although the R.A.V.C. has always, except in wartime, been small compared with other regiments and corps yet it is surprising how many veterinary surgeons have in fact served in a non-regular capacity at some time of their lives.

A line has nevertheless had to be drawn: as far as possible, for the purposes of this chapter, only contributions of an original nature made by veterinary officers whilst serving on the active list are included. Again, although the period covered is supposed to be from 1919 to 1961 yet where it is considered relevant, and this is often, it is not rigidly adhered to.

Prior to 1878 the teaching of the systematic care and management of animals in the British Army was carried out by Regimental Veterinary Surgeons, who happened to be keen on the subject. Its usefulness depended on their ability, on their own individual efforts plus the goodwill and co-operation of their commanding officers.

Mr. James Collins, the Principal Veterinary Surgeon to the Forces at the time, thought that the whole system needed some kind of co-ordination. He therefore projected the idea of the formation of an army school to bring this idea into effect. With the active help of a professional colleague, who fortunately happened to be the General Officer Commanding the Cavalry at Aldershot (Major-General Sir Frederick FitzWygram, Bart., F.R.C.V.S.) the Army Veterinary School came into existence on 1st June 1880.

The functions of the School were to be as follows:

1. (i) the care and management of army animals under all conditions;
   (ii) the selection and purchase of remounts;
   (iii) first aid.
2. Training of probationary veterinary officers in
   (i) military duties;
   (ii) care, management and diseases of army animals under all conditions.
3. Training of regimental farriers and shoeing-smiths as hospital assistants.
4. Be a centre for veterinary research.

It is worthy of note that the School, which became one of the most valuable institutions of the Army and remained so for over fifty years, did not cost the State one farthing piece during the first twenty-five years of its existence: various subtle methods were employed in achieving this astounding result. For example, a veterinary staff appointment in the Curragh had to be abolished in order to secure an extra £150 per annum for the Instructor at the School. When a second officer was needed, owing to the increasing activities of the establishment, this was contrived by reducing the senior instructor's extra-duty pay to £100 and giving the new officer £50 (Todd 1927). It was not until six years after its foundation, in 1886, that the School became, as its founder had hoped, a "centre of research".

The selection of Frederick Smith (afterwards Major-General Sir Frederick Smith) to be the first "Professor" was indeed a fortunate one. He was a fluent speaker, an enthusiastic seeker after knowledge which he could impart to others, and a loyal member of his profession which he loved. It may be said with truth that the Army Veterinary *laboratory* at Aldershot sprang into existence when he was appointed to the School. During his tenure of office from March 1886 to December 1892 forty-nine original articles were published in scientific and professional journals; in addition, three text-books came out under his name. He tackled research problems in pathology, physiology, hygiene, and chemistry with the utmost enthusiasm. The greater part of his research work was carried out under very trying conditions and with no official backing. Notwithstanding, his contributions on these subjects coupled with his efforts later as a penetrating veterinary historian benefited not only the army but the whole profession.

An important expansion of the School occurred in 1888 when an Army Vaccine Institute was created as an annexe. Lymph for vaccination against smallpox was produced at this institute for the Army, Royal Navy and the civil population. The institute remained in operation for twenty-two years until 1910 when the Board (now Ministry) of Health, owing to the great decline in public vaccination in this country, was able to take over the work. During these years lymph for over two million people had been issued.

The production of sera and vaccines always proved to be a major responsibility of the laboratory of the School. From 1908 to 1910 an anti-strangles serum was produced and extensive observations made on its efficacy. The production of the serum was continued up to the outbreak of World War I, discontinued during the war and commenced again in 1922. Other vaccines produced since the earliest days included those for pustular dermatitis and catarrh; in addition, mallein (see later) and spleen extract were manufactured in large quantities.

On the outbreak of war in August 1914, the Army Veterinary School, in common with all other Army schools, was closed. However, in 1915, Captain F. C. Minett was instructed to take over the laboratory at the School in order to commence the production of mallein, which up to then had been supplied by the Royal Veterinary College of London.

When it was realized that the war was going to be a prolonged one, steps were taken to include veterinary laboratories in the war establishments of the field forces. India happily still relied on the Imperial Institute of Veterinary Research, Mukteswar, but there were expeditionary forces in various parts of the world to be catered for. However, in spite of good intentions, the first official army veterinary laboratory was not established until February 1917—some two and half years after the beginning of the war. This laboratory was set up at Rouen for the B.E.F. in France and Belgium. Subsequently, similar laboratories were established with the expeditionary forces in Italy and Mesopotamia. In addition, each group of military veterinary hospitals were provided with a small diagnostic laboratory. The value of the latter was doubtful as they tended to increase unproductive work and to interfere with more useful duties. It is a maxim that laboratory work should be concentrated in one spot and fed by trained clinical and scientific personnel in the field—assuming, that is, that communications are good and there is no undue delay in the transmission of material to the laboratory.

Although the United Kingdom dealt with the great majority of animals to the various British Expeditionary Forces all over the world, there was no permanently established military veterinary laboratory in the country until 1918. Research work had in fact been carried out during the years of the war at various unofficial centres:

(1) At Swaythling, by Lieutenant-Colonel H. Watkins-Pitchford in a small laboratory temporarily established for the specific purpose of investigating pneumonia, influenza and other equine respiratory diseases.

(2) At Aldershot, Captain Minett at the laboratory in the erstwhile Army Veterinary School inquired into glanders in addition to his main job of producing mallein.

(3) At Woolwich, various officers of the A.V.C. carried out practical investigations into parasitology.

(4) At the numerous military veterinary hospitals up and down the country much new information on veterinary hygiene and animal husbandry was being collected.

In 1918, the Director-General Army Veterinary Services, Major-General Sir Layton Blenkinsop, co-ordinated the whole of this work and had it concentrated at the old Army Veterinary School at Aldershot. The School was given the grandiose name of the Central Veterinary Research Institute, with an establishment of five research officers.

The end of the war cut short the scope of this really wonderful conception. In 1921, it reverted from its wartime rôle to its pre-war status and became known as the Royal Army Veterinary School. Nevertheless, its functions included a modicum of research and throughout the next twenty years of peace a considerable amount of original work, especially in radiology, was carried out. Between 1919 and 1939 the one consistent thread of continuity was the meticulous production of mallein in the School's laboratory. The strain of *P. mallei* used by Captain Minett in 1915 did service until 1922 when a further strain was introduced, and although three further strains were obtained from Egypt in 1931 and successfully sub-cultured, they proved to have a very low virulence and were consequently discarded. It is of interest to note that the 1922 strain is still (1960) being used and appears not to have lost any if its virulence! Nearly a half-million doses of I.D.P. and subcutaneous mallein were issued between 1919 and 1939.

It will be convenient to divide the twenty years between the wars into four equal periods of five years apiece and to sketch briefly the activities of the Royal Army Veterinary School in other fields during each period.

The post-war period was an active one during which much work was done, and some of it published by serving R.A.V.C. officers. In some instances certain lines of research, begun in overseas theatres as a result of military necessity, were subsequently found to be of general value and were then continued or finished off at the Royal Army Veterinary School. For example, Knowles (1919) carried out some observations on recurrent (specific) ophthalmia at the bacteriological laboratory attached to No. 1 Veterinary Hospital at Cremona in Italy and completed the work on his posting to Aldershot. This particular piece of research work was a neat negation of Dalling's (1919) contention that his so-called "nerve-bacillus" played any rôle in the aetiology of recurrent (specific) ophthalmia. In continuing his studies of this disease Knowles (1920) compared the bacterial flora of the conjunctival sacs of normal horses with that of a series of horses suffering from recurrent (specific) ophthalmia. The chief difference in the cultural findings occurred in the case of "diphtheroids". These were the most numerous organisms in the normal eyes and they also showed the greatest increase in number during an attack of the disease. Meanwhile, Minett (1920) investigated the occurrence of bacilli identical with human diphtheria bacilli in horses and mules suffering from skin lesions resembling ulcerative lymphangitis. He also (1922) pursued some immunological studies with the Preisz-Nocard bacillus with special reference to ulcerative lymphangitis in horses. He discovered that, following the injection of the bacillus into horses and rabbits, immune substances of an anti-bacterial nature as well as anti-toxins appear. Before being demobilized Minett (1923) also carried out some work on the rinderpest virus.

The Commandant of the Royal Army Veterinary School (Lieutenant-Colonel Watkins-Pitchford) published the results of his own most painstaking and brilliant research into pustular dermatitis in the horse (1923). It is a controversial point whether Watkins-Pitchford has been given his proper due for some of his prodigious original work. The authorities leaned heavily on him whenever a particularly tricky problem reared itself. It is perhaps well to recall that in the domain of preventive medicine he devised the means of bringing under control some of the most deadly of animal diseases in the earlier days in South Africa, viz.: horse sickness, east coast fever and rinderpest. Considerable work on animal nutrition was carried on during this period; there were inquiries into the presence of vitamins in horse feeds, the nutritive value of hay-seeds by Linton (1919) and the feeding of military horses by Watkins-Pitchford (1920). The latter also interested himself in the pathology of bone changes in the limbs of the horse and in radiology (1923).

The period 1924-1929 is not very outstanding from the point of view of original research. It saw, however, intense clinical activity concerning various treatments of well-known conditions. Although little was published work on the following subjects was undertaken:

(a) Comparison of melioidosis and glanders;

(b) The part played by *Clostridium botulinum* in the causation of "grass-sickness";

(c) Further work on recurrent (specific) ophthalmia and pustular dermatitis;

(d) A detailed study of sclerostomiasis and the cultivation of strongyle eggs from faeces.

The period 1929-1934 may appropriately be called the "radiological" period of the School. It was during these halcyon days, when no one really believed the writing on the wall of the approaching disappearance in a few years of the mounted arm of the British Army, that some of the most useful contributions of the R.A.V.C. were made.

One had in mind the work of Majors Pryer and Oxspring in elucidating some of the problems connected with osteo-arthritic conditions of the limbs of the horse, which had puzzled generations of army (and civil) veterinary surgeons. In this restricted field, where the "art" often has not much use nor time for the "science", they were able to shed some light on a lot of amorphous thinking by careful work on the radiological aspects. This subject is given a little more attention in a separate section.

Owing to the limited laboratory staff, a drawback which has dogged the work of the School almost since its inception, routine work took up most of the time of its professional members. However, some research was undertaken into equine influenza, equine "enzootic spinal paralysis" and pustular dermatitis.

Most ambitious army veterinary officers felt a trifle uncertain, and rather unhappy, over the threat of the impending mechanization of the British Army during the period 1934-1939. Their careers appeared to be in some jeopardy: no horses meant no need for veterinary officers. It is no surprise, therefore, that there was a slight sense of apathy in the air as far as research was concerned. Nevertheless, there were sporadic bursts of energy when investigations into the flora of the respiratory passages of the horse, or the part the parathyroid played in the causation of lameness in the horse, were undertaken. The main long-term meandering research, however, during those darkening days was tied up with Professor W. M. Mitchell's theory of osteo-arthritic diseases in the horse. Experiments were carried out on osteodystrophia fibrosa using diets low in calcium but having a high calcium/phosphorus ratio. Acute symptoms of the disease were produced and the changes in the bones observed by regular weekly radiological examinations. In conjunction with these experiments the influence of vitamins, especially vitamin D on calcium metabolism, was observed.

The Royal Army Veterinary School closed down in 1938. In its place was established the "R.A.V.C. Laboratory" whose function was to be the following (note well the official order of precedence):

(*a*) Research;

(*b*) Radiology;

(*c*) Production of mallein, vaccines and biological products;

(*d*) Supply to the R.A.M.C. of blood and serum.

Lieutenant-Colonel R. H. Knowles, who became Officer-in-Charge R.A.V.C. Laboratory when it was formed, remained as such until 1943. He was succeeded by Major A. V. Franklin who was recalled from the Middle East. Most of the work of the Laboratory during the war years consisted of routine diagnostic procedures and the production of mallein. However, some research continued on the treatment of strongylosis in horses by Knowles (1940), and Knowles and Blount (1941) did useful work in perfecting a satisfactory method of counting worm eggs in faeces. Blount (1941) modified the Gordon Whitlock egg-counting chamber with a capacity four times that of the original, which is still (1960) used as the "R.A.V.C. Modification" and is specially manufactured.

A neat piece of research work by Bennison (1943) on "Demodicosis of Horses" gained him his F.R.C.V.S. A variety of demodex, affecting the Meibomian glands and the muzzles in horses was thoroughly investigated.

Perhaps it was inevitable that the scope for research in India, where the Army had for so long been so well organized, was to be so much more abundant than in the United Kingdom during the inter-war years. These were the halcyon days for service in India. The animal population of the Army consisted of horses, mules, donkeys, camels, cattle, and elephants and totalled nearly 100,000. Certain background geographical, historical and political influences had a direct or indirect bearing on the work of the Army Veterinary Service which was often reflected in the kind of research undertaken. Chief among these were:

(a) The vast frontiers;

(b) The probable active participation of India in other theatres of war if called upon;

(c) The differing sub-races, customs and religions of this enormous country.

When war broke out in 1914 the administration of the Army Veterinary Service was rather antediluvian: there was a distinct Victorian aroma permeating the Principal Veterinary Officer's office in Simla. With a captain as Assistant P.V.O., and three Inspecting Veterinary Officers, whose appointments were never "quite" official, his job was indeed a difficult one. The "circle" system of administration, each controlling three to four divisions, was abolished during the war and for the first time in the history of the Army in India the Veterinary Service was put on a satisfactory administrative base by attaching administrative veterinary officers to the newly-inaugurated Headquarters of Commands. After the war the Army Veterinary Services, for the first time, assumed the responsibility for the care and supervision of all military animals in India. In 1920, sanction was granted to the formation of an Army Veterinary Corps (India) and this commitment could thereby be undertaken and fulfilled.

With so able a scientist as Dr. J. T. Edwards in charge of the Imperial Institute of Veterinary Research at Mukteswar it is not surprising that army veterinary problems were ultimately referred to that establishment during most of the period under review. At that time it did not seem, and was not in fact, necessary to have a separate military veterinary laboratory. This state of affairs continued very happily until the mid-thirties when it was decided, owing to the increasing amount of investigational work, and the advisability in case of war of having a separate laboratory service, to set up a military veterinary laboratory. This was sanctioned by the Government of India with effect from 1st April 1936, with an establishment of two British officers, one Viceroy's Commissioned officer, one clerk and three laboratory assistants. This institution commenced work in October 1936 with Major W. P. S. Edwards as Officer-in-Charge: he remained as such until fairly well on in the war of 1939–1945.

The Military Veterinary Laboratory, Lahore, worked in close collaboration with the Imperial Institute of Veterinary Research. The official objects for which the Laboratory was instituted were:

1. Examination of morbid specimens from army animals.

2. The field and laboratory investigation of diseases and any special investigation as ordered by General Headquarters from time to time.
3. The investigation in horse-breeding areas of:
   I. Strangles
   II. Sterility
   III. Surra
   IV. Contagious Abortion
   V. Nutritional Diseases
4. The examination of specimens for poisons.

Preparations made in the laboratory included mercuric chloride solution for the surra test in camels, spleen extract and various kinds of vaccines.

The formation of the Military Veterinary Laboratory was indeed more important than the authorities realized at the time. At last, in the long history of the Army Veterinary Service in India a centre had been established for the collection and dissemination of items of scientific progress reported from all over the world to the army itself. Up-to-date methods of treatment and control of disease could be for the first time collated and quickly circulated to those who really mattered, namely, the veterinary officer doing the work. Above all its formation produced a general feeling of completeness and cohesion, of keeping things within the family.

Throughout the war the Military Veterinary Laboratory continued to do sterling work mainly of a routine diagnostic nature. Close collaboration was maintained with Mukteswar. In addition to its statutory work an increasing amount of research was carried out for the Military Farms. Major P. W. Priestley took over as Officer-in-Charge from Major W. P. S. Edwards at the end of 1943 and remained in command until after the war. Many investigations into the diseases of buffaloes took place during this period. These included:

(a) mastitis: after the examination of thousands of samples of milk from buffaloes it was concluded that the average incidence of infection was probably higher than the generally accepted figure of 16 per cent.

(b) contagious abortion: it was contended that probably throughout India at least 50 per cent. of abnormal births occur as a direct result of infection with *Br. abortus* and that the *bovis* type of organism was to be regarded as the primary cause of outbreaks. Experimental vaccination of adult buffaloes with strain 19 vaccine and also with strain 45/20 was undertaken. Calf vaccination was not carried out.

(c) scours in buffalo calves: caused great mortality and was discovered to be caused by *Salmonella typhi-murium*.

Much work was also carried out on pleuro-pneumonia in sheep and goats, rinderpest, foot-and-mouth disease, and equine abortion.

An Indian Field Veterinary Laboratory was formed in 1944-1945 and carried out valuable work in connection with epizootic lymphangitis. Two other field laboratories were established soon after the end of hostilities. In addition mobile anti-surra units carried out routine testing and treatment of horses and mules suffering from equine trypanosomiasis.

Both types of unit did sterling service in Burma where surra and epizootic lymphangitis were of operational importance amongst formations utilising large numbers of mules and horses.

Small diagnostic laboratories were set up attached to veterinary hospitals in Palestine (Ramle) and in Italy. Some work on epizootic lymphangitis was carried out in Italy during the latter part of the war.

After World War II things seemed rather gloomy as far as the ultimate future of the R.A.V.C. was concerned. The horse, after some two thousand years as the devoted companion and help-mate of the fighting soldier, had at last been released from a duty for which he was temperamently unsuited. The mounted arm had passed into history for ever. Research into equine problems in the future would have very much less military significance and could not expect enthusiastic official approval. Be that as it may, it was not long before the Corps seized the opportunity offered it of becoming indispensable experts in the care, management, training and operational use of "war-dogs". This aspect of the research contributed by the R.A.V.C. is given on another page. Most of it emanated from units.

Research work then at the R.A.V.C. Laboratory after the war was severely restricted. Nevertheless, work on equine problems was tackled as it arose. For example, in 1952 a polo pony belonging to General Sir Brian Robertson, then C-in-C Middle East Land Forces, gave a positive reaction to the mallein test in Egypt! This was the starting point of a neat piece of investigational research into melioidosis of the horse (MacLennan 1953). Again, the problem of the debilitated mature horse is ever with us. This was the subject of a new nutritional approach by feeding penicillin and vitamin B12 with successful results (Clifford, Henderson and Wilkins 1956).

Between 1949 and 1952 pregnancy diagnosis, using the Galli-Maini toad test and the Ascheim-Zondek test, was carried out for the Army Medical Services on an experimental basis. Small laboratory animal breeding became a major commitment between the years 1955 and 1959. The School became the official suppliers of these experimental animals for the Medical Services of the Army, Royal Navy and Royal Air Force. Some 20,000 mice per annum with proportionally smaller numbers of guinea-pigs, rabbits and rats were regularly supplied during these years.

The introduction of the use of intra-articular injections of hydrocortisone in the treatment of incipient navicular disease in horses at Aldershot aroused interest in horse circles (Wilkins 1957).

At the end of 1954 the R.A.V.C. Laboratory and the Army Veterinary Stores at Aldershot were amalgamated under the name of the R.A.V.C. School and Stores. Once again the functions of the establishment were widened and it took on instructional duties. Courses in animal management for officers and N.C.O.s were inaugurated and new-commissioned R.A.V.C. officers began once more to come on short indoctrination courses from the R.A.V.C. Depot at Melton Mowbray. Since 1949 the Laboratory interested itself in the effects of nuclear, bacteriological and chemical warfare on animals and for a few years subsequently was one of the only establishments of its kind to do so in the country. It was fitting therefore that the Commandant, Major J. H. Wilkins, should have been invited to become the first chairman of the Atomic Energy Sub-Committee of the British Veterinary Association in 1958. The subject of radiology, for which perhaps the School will always be famous, continues still to be studied vigorously (Bishop 1960).

The Military Veterinary Laboratory, Lahore, continued to render invaluable service after the war. Major A. A. Wilson took over charge when Major F. W. Priestley left India in March 1946. The three field laboratories and two anti-surra units continued to carry out their investigational duties right up to the British withdrawal from India in 1947.

A very important activity carried on at the School since 1929 has been the publication of the R.A.V.C. Journal. The founding of this Journal was a direct contribution to veterinary science in Great Britain and it is considered important enough to warrant separate mention.

In 1882 Veterinary Surgeons J. H. Steel and F. Smith founded and edited *The Quarterly Journal of Veterinary Science in India and Army Animal Management*. This was a literary medium in which the experiences and observations of army veterinary officers could be recorded. The Journal ceased publication in 1890 when Steel died.

The Journal of the Royal Army Veterinary Corps was founded in 1929 and may to all intents and purposes be regarded as a long-delayed revival of the old Journal of Steel and Smith. The chief founder and the first Editor of the R.A.V.C. Journal was Major A. A. Pryer. Under his careful nursing it grew out of its infancy and he handed over a flourishing child to Major G. E. Oxspring, in 1933. Through the devoted guidance of Oxspring the Journal went from strength to strength until Pryer once again became its Editor in 1936. He once more nurtured it and handed over in 1937 a vigorous and admired youth to Major Grahame Williamson who remained as Editor for not more than eighteen months but maintained the high standard established by Majors Pryer and Oxspring. However, there were signs of a creeping apathy appearing in the body corporate, viz. army veterinary officers in general, and a shortage of material for publication often caused some anxiety. This was overcome by many excellent articles being contributed by writers outside the R.A.V.C. During this difficult period it was indubitably the whole-hearted efforts of the next Editor, Lieutenant-Colonel R. H. Knowles, that enabled the Journal to survive. He was in office for five years, 1938-1943, and maintained the high standard of literary achievement and professional interest which had been associated with the name of the Journal since its inception. He was succeeded in 1943 by Major A. V. Franklin who had been brought home from active service in the Middle East to take charge of the Laboratory at Aldershot. He was immediately required to contend with problems resulting from the severe restrictions on allocation of paper which necessitated considerable reduction in size of print and the number of pages in the Journal. Due to his zeal the quality, lay-out and standard were maintained during these difficult years. To him belongs the distinction of being the first and only Territorial Army Editor. Major A. G. Ralston succeeded Franklin as Editor in 1945 and during those irritating years immediately after World War II managed to keep the flag flying with his own untiring efforts. He handed over the Editorship to Brigadier E. S. W. Peatt in 1948 for a brief period of a few months who in turn was succeeded by Major J. H. Wilkins in 1949. A "new look" policy was now adopted and in addition to the usual professional article more stress was laid on Corps and Garrison notes: this was a desperate effort to stimulate interest in a Journal which appeared to be dying. It achieved its aim and passed it, reaching a standard as high as at any time in its history. Major I. S. MacLennan became Editor in 1953 and maintained the standard until 1955 when Wilkins took over again in 1955 until succeeded by Major H. W. Bishop in 1959.

Army veterinary officers as a class do not contribute to scientific literature as prolific-ally as their opposite numbers in civilian life. The reason for this is not easy to understand when one tries to estimate their prodigious practical contributions. It would have been even less if they had not had such a fine regimental journal as *The Journal of the Royal Army Veterinary Corps* in which to publish their important and often original observa-tions and experiences. In the Journal will be found, if one only took the trouble to look the really vast amount of valuable contributions that the Army Veterinary Service have made to veterinary medicine and science during the past thirty years.

It is not essential, although often necessary, to work in a laboratory to help the advance of scientific knowledge. Original observations properly recorded wherever made should constitute "research". Unfortunately, officialdom and public opinion are very suspicious of advances other than in the recognized technologies. For too long a period of time these technologies have been, and still are, confined to the morbid side of veterinary or human medicine. More and more in recent years the prevention aspects of disease has been given greater recognition and vested with more research respect-ability. Preventive veterinary medicine is nothing more nor less than animal manage-ment. Army veterinary surgeons have always enjoyed unique opportunities, especially overseas, of tackling problems in this field. In the realm of the more conventional aspects of research, advances for which the Army Veterinary Service are mainly responsible were stumbled upon as a result of military necessity and/or the application of previous scientific finding to a new problem.

In its long existence, ranging from the Peninsular War and Waterloo to World War II and the recent incident in Cyprus, the Army Veterinary Service can boast of having as former officers some of the most illustrious names and brains in the history of the veterinary profession in this country. Names such as Percivall, Wilkinson, Fleming, Evans, Smith and a host of others stand out as landmarks.

The "father of modern veterinary research" is indubitably Dr. Griffith Evans, the first discoverer (1880) of a pathogenic mammalian trypanosome, *Trypanosoma evansi*, which is the cause of the disease known as surra in equine animals and camels. No importance was at first attached to this momentous discovery by the medical authorities in India. This was obviously due to ignorance, apathy or envy. Evans' work was not appreciated for very many years, not indeed until long after he had left the Army Veterinary Service. He also had another distinction: during his tour of duty in Canada in the 1860s he was one of the very few British Army officers to have an interview with President Abraham Lincoln and be allowed to tour the Front of the American Civil War then raging. (Montgomerie 1935).

Tribute must also be paid to George Fleming, who joined the Army Veterinary Service in 1855 and retired in 1890. He contributed much, perhaps too much, to veterinary research. As Sir Frederick Smith writes "from the first article he wrote in the Crimea in 1857 down to a lecture he gave in 1892 on the 'Shoeing of Army Horses' his pen was never idle." He was greatly in advance of the veterinary thought of his day. The *Veterinary Journal*, now the *British Veterinary Journal*, was founded by him. It is perhaps as well for us to remember that for nearly threequarters of a century (1828 to 1894) the veterinary profession in this country relied on the Army Veterinary Service for its literature. One of the most brilliant of historical army veterinary figures was J. H. Steel. He conceived the idea of the British Veterinary Congress amongst a host of other things. He it was who confirmed in Burma the previous observations of Griffith Evans concerning surra. Steel died at an early age in 1890 but he had already made a niche for himself in the veterinary medical hall of fame by his literary and scientific activities. Major-General Sir Frederick Smith's own contributions to veterinary research in this country are too well known to need much reiteration here. These researches covered pathology, physiology, hygiene, and chemistry; in addition, his penetrating studies of the history of veterinary medicine and science, both civil and military, have indeed benefited the whole profession.

The contributions of the Army Veterinary Service to veterinary medicine, science and research cover a wide range of subjects: radiology, protozoology, mycology, bacteriology, parasitology, surgery, medicine and zootechny.

The first announcement of the introduction of X-rays into the world of science in Great Britain appeared in a newspaper (The Standard) on 6th January 1896. The first X-ray photograph ever taken in this country was on the next day, 7th January 1896. The exposure time was for a period of twenty minutes!

The Army Veterinary Service was extemely quick off the mark in making use of this fascinating new aid to diagnosis. In 1904, a small radiographic outfit was sent out to our troops in South Africa for use, amongst other things, on animals. This set was subsequently sent to the Army Veterinary School at Aldershot where unfortunately it did not prove too successful.

In 1909, an up-to-date apparatus was installed at the School and was used with limited success up to the commencement of World War I. Major A. C. Newsom, A.V.C., was Commandant of the School from 1909 until 1912 and must be regarded as the true pioneer of equine radiology in this country. In the Statistical and General Report of the Army Veterinary Services 1909-1910 two very interesting statements concerning X-rays and radium appear:

"The diagnosis of lameness is being assisted by X-rays. A modern apparatus has recently been installed at Aldershot . . .

"The employment of Radium in the treatment of disease has been practically tested."

Major Newsom had in fact tried radium therapy on navicular disease and certain tumours in horses with quite spectacular results.

At the outbreak of World War I in 1914, the X-ray set at Aldershot was returned to the Research Department, Royal Arsenal, Woolwich. It was not used at all during the war.

After the war Lieutenant-Colonel Watkins-Pitchford, the Commandant, approached the War Office about the apparatus which had been returned to Woolwich in 1914. The Royal Arsenal responded by providing a brand new set.

In 1922, the set was thoroughly overhauled and much new equipment added. An elaborate operating table was erected over a concrete pit, in which was placed the actual X-ray apparatus. The table top was made to slide upon its framework and tilt into the vertical position as necessary. There was an aperture in the table and the X-ray tube could be raised or lowered or traversed so as to correspond to any position of the aperture. If the horse had to be cast, which was exceptional, it was roped to the table top when it was in the vertical position and then rapidly tilted into the horizontal position. (Watkins-Pitchford 1923.) After two horses had broken their legs while having radiographs taken in the cast position the apparatus was dismantled. As a consequence the engineer of the Research Department at Woolwich, Dr. Hunt Sarsfield, was called in to design and construct a special stand on which the X-ray tube was mounted. By means of two long cables from the power-point in the concrete pit it was possible to move the tube outside the X-ray room. Henceforth, horses were X-rayed while standing on a specially constructed concrete floor adjacent to the X-ray room. As this was in the open it obviated the difficulty of leading fractious animals into a room and facilitated the procedure considerably. X-ray examinations were made to diagnose cases of obscure lameness which did not respond to the ordinary methods of the clinician. In all such cases the value of the apparatus as an eliminating process was manifestly demonstrated even when a positive diagnosis could not be made. During this period a large number of exposures were made for experimental purposes. In 1924, certain alterations were carried out to the set to increase its adaptability and usefulness, chiefly to enable antero-posterior views of the limbs to be taken at normal distances from the tube. Experimental work during the following year 1925 was directed mainly towards obtaining clearer definition of the navicular bone in radiographs of the foot. Not very much progress however was made but it was hoped that by using a grid more detail could be attained.

In 1927, Major A. A. Pryer came as Senior Instructor to the Royal Army Veterinary School and immediately interested himself in radiology. His industry and ability enabled him, no matter what he took up, invariably to produce outstanding results. So it was with radiology. So it was with the Journal, which he conceived, founded and edited brilliantly for many years. It is therefore not very surprising that he quickly became the recognised authority in the specialized field of veterinary radiology in this country. He carried out extensive original research in X-raying the horse's foot. He was always in demand at professional meetings to talk on his special subject: one of his best papers was given before the Royal Society of Medicine in 1930 (Pryer 1931). Considerable attention was devoted by him to an attempt to design an apparatus which met most of the requirements for dealing with equine patients. A new Mobilix (Watson) X-ray set was installed at Aldershot in 1930 and the old procedure of taking radiographs outside the X-ray room as explained above was abandoned. Henceforth horses were once again taken inside the X-ray room: Pryer could cope with the most fractious animal by his confident kindliness which was always an inspiration to his helpers. He was ably assisted in these pioneering days by Mr. J. D. G. Crisp, the Senior Laboratory Assistant. It was during this period that after much experimentation a hoof paste was perfected. The paste was used to fill in the clefts of the frog and eliminated the appearance of confusing shadows on the radiograph (Pryer 1931). Pryer continued his work on navicular disease after leaving the School (Pryer 1934).

In January 1932, the School was fortunate to have another enthusiast posted in as Senior Instructor in place of Pryer. This was Major G. E. Oxspring who, during his four years tenure of the appointment, added greatly to our knowledge of equine radiology. He continued the work of Pryer especially into the radiological aspects of navicular disease (Oxspring 1934, 1936). A classical paper of his appeared in the November issue of the *Veterinary Record* in 1935 on this subject for which he was awarded his Fellowship. This contribution remains to this day as the outstanding and most authoritative work on the subject. Oxspring, by his skilled and painstaking investigations based on previous preliminary work of Pryer, proved to a sceptical profession that the presence of navicular disease even in its early stages could be satisfactorily and confidently diagnosed by an experienced veterinary radiologist. Success in veterinary radiology, he clearly showed, depended on a sound knowledge of anatomy, pathology, X-ray physics and long experience in the interpretation of X-ray films. He quickly became an acknowledged expert in this specialized field in this country. During these mid-thirties years, which was no doubt the zenith of achievement of the X-ray department of the Royal Army Veterinary School, the names of Oxspring and Pryer were renowned in professional circles.

In 1936, after careful consideration, and on the advice of the Research Department, Woolwich, a new set was installed to take the place of the old composite X-ray outfit which had been rendered unserviceable by the change in the electrical supply in the Aldershot Command. This set continued to be used until the outbreak of World War II in 1939. When the Depot of the R.A.V.C. moved from Aldershot to Doncaster in 1939 the X-ray apparatus was transferred as well. It finished up at Melton Mowbray after the war when the Veterinary and Remount Centre was established there.

Between the years 1939 and 1943 no radiological work was undertaken at Aldershot. A captured German "Coolinaxis" set was installed in 1943-1944 and functioned very satisfactorily until about 1947 when it was removed for overhaul by R.E.M.E. Unfortunately, it was accidentally damaged in the workshops and with help from Ordnance, a new Mobilix-Watson set was issued from Woolwich. In 1950-1951 special modifications were carried out to the apparatus, which is still in use at Aldershot. An MX2 set with all extras was acquired in 1950 for use on small animals.

Protozoa generally are free living and are found in soil and stagnant water. Most of them are harmless and play an important part in the organization of nature. There are, however, a few which are harmful parasites of the higher animals and are the cause of the most widespread diseases of both man and animals. These include malaria, sleeping sickness, red-water, east coast fever and surra. This subject has become more important in recent years to veterinary than to medical workers. The protozoal diseases of animals are of far greater importance in tropical than in temperate climates. This is mainly because the mode of transmission, unlike most of the bacterial and virus diseases, is mostly by or through an intermediate host which is either a tick or a biting fly. The distribution of these diseases is therefore mainly restricted to the parts of the world where these vectors can survive and multiply. It is not surprising that the Army Veterinary Service in India has contributed so much, directly or indirectly, to our knowledge on these diseases.

Surra occurs in camels, cattle, horses, mules, dogs and elephants. Camels and equine animals are particularly susceptible. The disease is caused by *Trypanosoma evansi*, named after its discoverer Griffith Evans who was an officer of the Army Veterinary Service.

A measure of the research work done by our officers in cameline surra is the fact that so many gained their Fellowships for original work in this field, for example, Olver (1909), Davenport (1923) and Glyn Lloyd (1925).

For many years there was no remedy known for the treatment of surra. In 1911, tartar emetic and a preparation of arsenic were tried intravenously with promising results. Captain H. E. Cross, who became Camel Specialist to the Punjab Government was the pioneer in the use of a prolonged course of intravenous injections of tartar emetic in the treatment of surra in camels. The results achieved by him were so satisfactory that it was decided almost immediately after the first world war in 1919-1920 to make the "Cross Method" of treatment a routine procedure for all surra-infected camels in the army. The next step forward was the work done by Dr. J. T. Edwards at Mukteswar in 1925 on the use of naganol in the treatment of surra in horses and camels. This work was done in close collaboration with the Army Veterinary Service. Running parallel with this research into treatment was the extensive efforts made in the late twenties and early thirties into the field diagnosis of the disease. The formol-gel test was carefully studied in the Sudan by Knowles (1924, 1925) and in 1928-1929 the D.A.D.V.S., Lahore District in India, Major G. F. Steevenson, was one of the first to carry out observations on the use of the mercuric chloride test, which had been discovered by Bennett (1928) that very same year. Both these tests depend upon the presence of non-specific increase of the globulin in the serum of chronically infected animals: in the formol-gel test a positive result is indicated by clotting of the fresh serum after adding one drop of formol to 1 c.c. of suspected serum; in the mercuric chloride test by turbidity after adding one drop of suspected serum to 1 c.c. of a 1:25,000 solution of mercuric chloride.

In India the practical application of the mercuric chloride test was worked out entirely by the Army Veterinary Service. It quickly became the routine test for all camels. The diagnosis of surra in camels by means of this test and the immediate treatment with a single intravenous injection of naganol ("Bayer 205"), as advocated by Major R. H. Knowles in a comprehensive paper published by him in the *Veterinary Journal* in 1927, was adopted as a routine method of dealing with cameline surra, which as a result virtually disappeared in army camels.

Surra in horses is nearly always fatal, death occurring in a week to six months. The condition was first described in India in 1880 by Griffith Evans who discovered in the Punjab the flagellate protozoan parasite, now known as *Trypanosoma evansi*, in the blood of horses and camels. The diagnosis of surra by detection of these trypanosomes in wet blood films or stained blood smears has been easy ever since. However, no treatment in the field was really successfully worthwhile until the "Mukteswar Method" was introduced by Edwards in 1925. Briefly, it consisted of intravenous and intrathecal injections of naganol. Brigadier A. J. Williams, when he became Director of Army Veterinary Services in India in 1928 encouraged his officers to use this treatment to such good effect that very quickly this method of treatment was adopted as routine for equine surra.

During the military operations in Burma in 1931 naganol was successfully used in treatment and also as a preventative for the first time. In previous campaigns in Burma losses from surra were always very heavy. Horses and mules located in districts which were known to be surra infected received one gramme of naganol intravenously at intervals of a month during the surra season. Not one case occurred among 511 animals so treated. In addition, by omitting the intrathecal injection a simpler technique, which was less dangerous, was successfully evolved by the Army Veterinary Service.

In the Burma Campaign in World War II surra became the most serious veterinary problem. Control was dependent on early diagnosis followed by treatment and removal of infected animals before they could become a source of danger to others. Millions of blood smears were examined by the Army Veterinary Service from 1942 onwards necessitating the formation, in 1944, of special Anti-Surra Units, I.A.V.C.

Antrypol, a drug chemically and pharmacologically identical with naganol, which was a German preparation and therefore unobtainable, was used during this campaign for both preventive and curative treatment. It was found that if adequate and exact dosage was employed early over 90 per cent. of horses and mules infected with surra could be cured. Too small a dose was dangerous as the trypanosomes became tolerant to the antrypol, and thereby converting the animal into a reservoir of infection. The problem of weight estimation so that the exact dose could be given, and many other local problems, were solved by Lieutenant-Colonel G. Pfaff. The method of antrypol administration adopted was very elaborate. It was continued for thirty days alternating with calcium lactate which reduced the toxicity of the antrypol but did not affect the trypanocidal action of the drug.

There are two species of piroplasm (babesia) which affect equines.

(i) *Babesia caballi*, the larger parasite, occurs in the red blood corpuscles in characteristic pairs causing fever, haemoglobinuria, and anaemia. Trypan blue is a specific in treatment.

(ii) *Babesia (Nuttalia) equi*, causes biliary fever. This has been very successfully treated for over fifty years by the intravenous injection of quinine acid hydrobromide. Many officers of the Army Veterinary Service helped considerably in the elaboration of this treatment. The chief of these was Brigadier A. J. Williams whose early researches resulted in the inclusion of a special intravenous outfit with all units in the field in World War I. This proved to be especially valuable in Mesopotamia, where the disease was very prevalent. Briefly, the "Biliary Fever Outfit" consisted of an apparatus for the intravenous injection of one dram of quinine acid hydrobromide dissolved in an ounce of water. This treatment was a specific when used in the early stages of the disease. More recently the aromatic diamidines, acridine and quinolyl preparations have largely replaced trypan blue and quinine hydrobromide.

The permanent institution of effective anti-fly measures and careful attention to sanitation carried out by R.A.V.C. officers in military camps in various parts of the East, especially in India, proved the value of these procedures when the incidence of the disease amongst civil and military animals were compared. This was indeed a tangible and valuable contribution of the Army Veterinary Service as a whole in the field of veterinary preventive medicine and animal management.

Diagnosis of biliary fever is established by microscopical examination of blood smears and the demonstration of the piroplasms. However, Major G. F. Steevenson elaborated a simple "graduated tube test" (1924) which has proved a valuable aid to diagnosis. This test is based on the fact that in piroplasomosis there is haemolysis and destruction of red blood cells causing a fall below the normal number depending on the severity of the disease. The red blood cells may fall from a normal 7-8 million cells per cubic millimetre to even 2-3 millions! Application of the test is simple and takes merely a matter of minutes and the results are very reliable. (Davenport 1933.)

Epizootic lymphangitis is a historical military veterinary disease. The three major outbreaks of epizootic lymphangitis during the twentieth century have all been associated with the massing of large numbers of horses due to military operations. These outbreaks were in England after the Boer War, in Europe during World War I, and in Italy, Burma and India during World War II. In spite of the enormous amount of research work which has been done on this disease for very many years, how it originates and spreads is still unknown. The Army Veterinary Service can pride itself in having taken a leading part in research on epizootic lymphangitis for over fifty years.

The disease is a chronic infection of horses and other equidae which results in a "cording" of the subcutaneous lymphatic vessels, especially of the limbs and neck. For many years it was confused with that other hoary army friend, glanders, as the cutaneous lesions of both diseases resemble each other closely. The confusion was resolved in 1873 when the cause was discovered by Rivolta to be a fungus which was given the name of *Cryptococcus farciminosus*. Granulating abscesses develop along the lymphatics of limbs and neck; these later discharge blood-stained pus from characteristic ulcers which contain the yeast-like pathogen.

Some of the earliest reports made in English on epizootic lymphangitis were recorded by Colonel (later Major-General Sir John) Moore in the *Veterinary Record* (1896).

Colonel W. A. Pallin published a book on the subject in 1904 which achieved a measure of success (1904 Pallin).

The British Army was comparatively free from outbreaks of epizootic lymphangitis during World War I as compared with the other allied armies. This was due to the keen clinical outlook for the disease which was kept by all our officers. This in turn was the outcome of their experiences of the outbreaks which followed the South African War, which was still fresh in the minds of most officers. All ulcers on equines were treated with suspicion. The system of control depended on early diagnosis and the immediate destruction of affected animals. The remarkable immunity of the British Army from epizootic lymphangitis as compared with those of the Allies has been put down to the rigid routine wound treatment practised by us.

In World War II the disease was seen extensively in Italy and Burma. Captain J. J. Bullen did some splendid work whilst he was in command of No. 1 Indian Field Veterinary Laboratory, I.A.V.C. in Burma during the latter part of the campaign in that country. He developed cryptococcin, a protein precipitate from sterilized broth cultures of the organism, which caused a marked and persistent allergic reaction when injected subcutaneously into infected animals in doses of 1 c.c. (Bullen 1949-1950-1951).

The clinical picture was well described by Brigadier J. J. Plunkett in 1948 in a paper he presented to the IVth International Congress on Tropical Medicine at Washington (D.C.) (Plunkett 1949). No completely satisfactory treatment is known. According to Plunkett (1949) early cases may be cured by local surgery followed by the intravenous injection of up to 50 c.c.s of a 1:1,000 mercuric chloride solution.

Epizootic lymphangitis was eradicated from the United Kingdom after its introduction after the South African War by a vigorous slaughter policy (Pallin 1904). It is still notifiable under the Diseases of Animals Acts, however.

It is an invidious task to try to record the items of importance in which the Army Veterinary Service have contributed anything of a true research aspect in the field of bacteriology, virology and immunology. For, truly, this formidable trio of labels covers almost the entire range of the recognized research technologies in veterinary science. As it is not possible to deal fully with the subject in the compass of a few pages, an endeavour has been made to present those aspects which are considered of most importance and interest.

In the field of immunology the production of mallein for the diagnosis of glanders and cryptococcin for detecting epizootic lymphangitis have been of peculiar interest to the Army Veterinary Service. The contributions by our officers have not been inconsiderable and are dealt with briefly on other pages. In addition, the production and use of protective substances such as vaccines and sera have always been a major function of army veterinary laboratories. These have included autogenous and stock vaccines for strangles, pustular dermatitis and catarrh in horses, spleen extract and wound vaccines. During World War II, and for some time thereafter, the R.A.V.C. and the Wellcome Research Laboratories collaborated in the production of vaccines and sera; this subject is dealt with in Chapter IX.

Laboratory work was done almost entirely at Aldershot or at the Military Veterinary Laboratory at Lahore after its formation in 1936. Prior to this in India the closest collaboration was maintained with the Imperial Institute of Veterinary Research, Mukteswar, which supervised the research efforts of individual army veterinary officers and co-ordinated their results in conjunction with the Army Veterinary Directorate at General Headquarters. The researches conducted were of an essentially practical and military-economic, rather than of an academic, character. The army veterinary research worker is essentially a clinical scientist, whose interests must lie in the processes of actual disease. His immediate goal is successful therapy and his aim is to appreciate scientifically those phenomena which together help in diagnosis and treatment of disease.

The Army Veterinary Services in India have always had to contend with rinderpest occurring in the cattle of the Military Farms Department and in sheep and goats. For very many years the Imperial Institute of Veterinary Research existed primarily as a vaccine and serum unit concerned with its eradication: army veterinary officers collaborated fully in this function. It was Dr. J. T. Edwards of this Institute who helped to produce the "fixed goat virus", which was a much attenuated form of the virus, free from the risk of conveying piroplasms when injected into cattle as a prophylactic. For many years the highly advocated "serum-simultaneous" method has been used for the conferring of an active and lasting immunity to susceptible cattle.

It was the work of Major J. F. Stirling, however, in using the goat-adapted virus *alone* under field conditions which helped to simplify the technique of operation and to reduce the actual cost involved (Stirling 1932).

The use of vaccines in the fight against rinderpest was never considered seriously by the army veterinary authorities because the administration of those vaccines which produced a strong immunity was attended by some risk of a certain number of animals so treated developing a fatal infection whereas the "safe" vaccines were quite unreliable, conferring little or no immunity. Again, the "serum-alone" method, which was at one time a popular method of prophylaxis, soon went out of fashion. The system of control adopted by the Army Veterinary Service was by conferring an active and lasting immunity by using the "virus alone" or the "serum-simultaneous" method to raise the natural resistance of susceptible animals. A large volume of evidence was collected by army veterinary officers in determining the quality of the immunity produced. Its application was effected to such good purpose that it was very rare for a case of rinderpest to occur among bovines on the Military Dairy Farms. As a result of experimental work carried out by Major G. Barnett (1934-1935) the method of anti-rinderpest inoculations were considerably modified. He concluded that the doses of serum recommended by the Imperial Institute of Veterinary Research were quite unnecessarily heavy and caused blocking out reactions. A great deal of time, money and freightage was thereby saved by not using any serum at all or only in very reduced doses. It is interesting to note from the historical point of view that it was two R.A.V.C. officers serving in Italy in 1918 who first confirmed the spread of rinderpest virus through meat and meat products. (Bull. Off. Internat. des Epizoot. 1957, vol. 48, pp. 148-157 and Veter. Ital. vol. 9, 1958.)

Glanders is a highly contagious disease of the lymphatic system, caused by a bacterium named *Pfeifferella* or *Malleomyces mallei*. It is a disease primarily of solipeds (equidae) but also affects man and members of the cat family which have fed on infected meat. It has always been the scourge of army horses ever since ancient times. Wars have invariably caused the disease to flourish and the post-war distribution of army animals has always served to spread it far and wide. When the disease occurs in the respiratory passages it is called "Glanders", whereas if the lymphatics of the skin are affected the name "Farcy" is given to it.

Perhaps no page in the whole history of the Army Veterinary Service, from the point of view of disease control, is more satisfactory than the record against glanders. The disease was still rife at the beginning of the century but the efforts of the profession in the British Isles were hampered by somewhat defective legislation. Slow progress in control had been made under the old ineffective Order of 1894 but there had not been much enthusiastic encouragement of the efforts of the profession by the authorities. It was the Order of 1907, brought about by the untiring persistence of William Hunting, which really made the eradication of the disease seem possible. Within fifteen years of the promulgation of this Order the dread disease was virtually extinguished! This success was undoubtedly due to the conscientious and careful application of the "mallein test". In the van of this prodigious effort was the Army Veterinary Service. If proof was needed it was indeed shown after World War I when for the first time in the history of the world demobilization of millions of horses was accomplished without any increase in the incidence of glanders in civilian animals.

In glanders, as in tuberculosis, the tissues become hypersensitive to the toxins of the bacillus. This is made use of for diagnostic purposes and the procedure is called the "mallein" test because the toxins dissolved in cultures of the glanders bacillus in a glycerin-containing fluid medium has been given the name of "mallein". Mallein, for normal animals, is an inert substance. Characteristic reactions, however, are manifested by those affected with glanders. It is used in three ways: (a) subcutaneous test, which gives rise to a transient fever in glandered animals. (b) ophthalmic test, producing a pus-forming inflammation of the eye when the concentrated mallein is instilled into the eye of a diseased horse; and (c) the intradermo-palpebral test, which gives rise to a local swelling and pus formation when a small amount of concentrated mallein is injected into the skin of the lower eyelid of a horse suffering from the disease.

The intradermo-palpebral mallein test for glanders was originally suggested by Professor Lanfanchi of Bologna Veterinary School. It was warmly adopted by the French Army almost immediately in 1915. Major (later Sir Frederick) Hobday, after being initiated into the mysteries of the test, was sent to give lectures and demonstrations upon its use to all army veterinary officers along the Western Front in France. It became at once the authorized method of testing. Millions of doses were used and by its employment glanders, the most harassing agent of all armies of previous wars, was at last put under control. Through this herculanean effort, it may rightly be inferred, the disease was eradicated from the British Isles itself shortly after the war.

In 1915, owing to the enormous demand for mallein, sanction was obtained for an establishment of one captain, with one civilian laboratory assistant, and two female packers to carry out the work of mallein production in a laboratory of the Army Veterinary School at Aldershot. The School, of course, had been closed down since the outbreak of war and it was very gratifying indeed to re-open it again although it was only part of the establishment. Captain F. C. Minett was placed in charge of the new enterprise and by the end of 1915 the output from this laboratory exceeded 50,000 doses a month!

It is interesting to observe that the authorities seriously suspected artificial glanders infection of horses by enemy agency in the United Kingdom when an extensive outbreak occurred among mules in a remount depot near Taunton in 1915. A similar allegation was made about extensive outbreaks in South and South-West Africa. Thus amongst so many other things, glanders has the dubious distinction of being perhaps one of the earliest bacteriological warfare agents.

The subsequent interest of the Army Veterinary Service in glanders, from 1919 to the present date, has been vigorously maintained. In the field, by conscientious mallein testing of all equines in every military theatre of the world; at home, by producing mallein and aiding the Ministry of Agriculture in preventing the reintroduction of the disease into this country. As far as is known, the R.A.V.C. School is the only institute in the United Kingdom which still produces mallein. The name of Mr. J. D. G. Crisp, who was employed first as a soldier and later as a civilian laboratory assistant at the School, will always be associated with this aspect of the work at Aldershot. He helped Captain F. C. Minett at the beginning and continued under a long list of officers to produce a high-quality mallein until his retirement in 1960.

Anthrax is a rapidly fatal disease caused by the *Bacillus anthracis*, which is unique in that it is the only aerobic sporulating pathogenic bacterium. The herbivorous animals, especially cattle and sheep are particularly susceptible. Other animals, including man, can be infected but are not so susceptible.

Throughout the years the Army Veterinary Service, especially in India, has had to contend with this dangerous disease amongst cattle on military farms and sheep and goats. Its officers devised effective methods of prophylactic vaccinations and even treatment in many cases, particularly towards the end of an outbreak. They kept records of all anthrax-infected districts and lands, and informed mounted units of their existence so that the grass from these lands was not used. Grounds that were used for burial and post-mortems in previous days were carefully mapped out: all these procedures helped agricultural India where virulent enzootic outbreaks of anthrax were not uncommon.

The army veterinary officer in India helped to try out every known method of immunity production under exacting field conditions. Anti-serum was always available from the Imperial Institute of Veterinary Research and spore vaccines were obtained from the Insein Laboratory, Rangoon and from Mukteswar.

In 1944 and 1945, up to 11,000 sheep and goats were exported monthly by the Army from India to Ceylon. The incidence of anthrax was initially very high as the disease is endemic in Southern India. However, as soon as the Army Veterinary Service was allowed to carry out a policy of adequate supervision and to establish a number of inland reception centres for collection and holding purposes, a spectacular decrease in anthrax incidence resulted.

Major G. E. Oxspring whilst serving in the Military Dairy Farm in Jubbulpore in India did extensive work on bovine nasal granuloma (Oxspring 1931). In the early stages the lesions appear as small hard nodules localized on the nasal mucous membrane, especially on the septum nasi. As the disease progressed, the growths gave the appearance of masses of granulation tissue, which often attained the size of a hen's egg and obliterated the nasal fossae. A fairly satisfactory method of treatment was developed: intravenous injections of tartar emetic at intervals of three to four days.

Knowles (1927) worked on immunization problems in bovine pleuro-pneumonia. He found that a reliable immunity response could be achieved from a vaccine produced by the virus being cultivated in 2 per cent. peptone and 10 per cent. horse serum. Avirulent strains could confer a strong immunity with a dose of 2 c.c. of culture virus given subcutaneously.

Contagious pleuro-pneumonia in goats and sheep was without doubt the most serious disease encountered in the movement of these animals to our troops in the forward areas in India and Burma. For example, out of 18,714 cases admitted sick in 1944-1945, 15,511 (83 per cent.) died. More than one type of infection was involved. Ear tip vaccination with pleural exudate and lung mash was tried out. Various methods of curative treatment was resorted to, the most effective of which was the intravenous injection of 0.5 per cent. iodine solution in doses of up to 5 c.c.s

The incidence slowly subsided at the end of the war but, although the Army Veterinary Service had gained valuable experience, it may be said that this disease was more than a headache and baffled everyone including Mukteswar.

Investigations were undertaken into the control of caprine pleuro-pneumonia at the Military Veterinary Laboratory, Lahore in 1945. The objects of the work were:

(a) to find the earliest point at which immunity becomes apparent;
(b) to discover a satisfactory means of immunization;
(c) to see whether strains from different localities were antigenically identical.

Five vaccines were tested: 49th and 85th generation culture virus gave the best results, some immunity developing twelve to fourteen days after inoculation.

The problem of bovine abortion in military farms in India never assumed the same significance as it does in the more intensive stock farming and high milk-producing areas in Great Britain. However, over a period of years some work was directed towards an assessment of the degree and types of the disease. Various strains of the *Brucella abortus* were isolated. An interesting indirect connection was an epidemic of undulant fever which occurred in troops in the Punjab in the thirties which drew attention to the prevalence of *Brucella melitensis* infection in goats.

Work done at the Military Veterinary Laboratory showed that the incidence of abortion amongst buffaloes throughout India caused by *B. abortus* was relatively high. It was estimated that at least 50 per cent. of abnormal births was due to this cause. The value of strains 19 and 45/20 were assessed in fairly large scale experiments carried out in 1945-1946.

Equine abortion was always related to that of sterility in the various remount depots in India. *Salmonella abortus equi* was invariably isolated but investigations into the added effects of nutritional deficiencies, especially vitamins, were studied through many years.

The use of a vaccine produced at the Military Veterinary Laboratory was attended by some success.

Major W. P. S. Edwards carried out work at this laboratory on the treatment of sterility in the mare using a Fallopian tube insufflator (Edwards 1942) with little success. Kingston (1934) and Ralston (1934, 1936) made valuable contributions to our knowledge of sterility in the mare, in treatment and prophylaxis, whilst serving in remount breeding areas in India.

It is a significant fact that throughout the years respiratory diseases accounted for much of the horse "wastage" in the army. Many of the Statistical and General Reports of the Army Veterinary Service of former years confirms this statement. Coughing, catarrh, laryngitis, influenza and pneumonia formed (and form) the "acute" group and roaring, grunting and broken wind were the stalwarts of the "chronic" group. It is not surprising that there is a very considerable volume of published observations by army veterinary officers on these equine respiratory conditions. It is difficult to do justice to all this work in a few pages: only the salient facts are recorded.

One of the first of officially-sponsored subjects of army veterinary research was pneumonia. The authorities actually agreed to make a grant of money for this purpose, "provided that the investigation should be limited to a certain definite time". This epitomises succinctly the bureaucratic attitude towards research.

This happened in 1915, but warrants a mention in our tale. During the first twelve months of World War I there were heavy and continuous losses among remount horses from pneumonia. There was a lot of confusion concerning the cause of the disease and this persuaded the authorities to appoint Lieutenant-Colonel Watkins-Pitchford to carry out some research work on the disease. He made an admirable job of it (Watkins-Pitchford 1917) and as a consequence of his recommendations mortality dropped to insignificant proportions. In the past, the bugbear diseases of all armies was glanders, mange and to a lesser extent epizootic lymphangitis. One of the greatest potential dangers to military animals remaining to this day is influenza with the often concomitant catarrh, coughing and laryngitis. We still have no cut-and-dried method of dealing with the condition. Army veterinary officers in all parts of the world have had to cope with this insidious syndrome and have contributed considerably to our knowledge. Mention has already been made of Watkins-Pitchford (1917) who in 1915 had found a *Bacillus subtilis* organism, similar to that reported by Koneff in 1909, present in the blood of horses suffering from catarrh and pneumonia. Colonel Olver had demonstrated the bacillus in similar circumstances in North America in 1918. The vaccine produced by Watkins-Pitchford and Olver to counter the outbreaks in remounts in U.K. and North America respectively was very successfully used. Subsequently, Olver employed a similar vaccine in Egypt with equal success but when it was tried in India (Todd and Soutar 1938) it proved unsatisfactory.

Severe outbreaks of equine influenza occurred in India in 1930-1931 and much field research work was carried out by R.A.V.C. officers. Lieutenant-Colonel V. C. Leckie and Major G. F. Steevenson ascertained in prolonged and painstaking work that the average period of immunity after an attack was four years. In addition, it was demonstrated that horses and mules which had recently suffered from catarrh or strangles showed a strong immunity towards influenza. In 1935, another severe outbreak in India was very successfully controlled by quite original veterinary police and hygienic measures introduced by Lieutenant-Colonel G. W. Godwin (Todd and Soutar, 1938). In most cases the usual symptoms were exhibited and the sequelae varied to include roaring, laminitis and debility. The prevention of complications was considered the main objects of treatment; fresh air and gentle movement being better than housing in stables.

Like human influenza this disease, which is caused by a virus identical with that causing equine virus abortion, has a history of great panzootics in the past when the horse-drawn traffic in many of the large cities was virtually stopped. There are no specific means of controlling it even today although the introduction of antibiotics can mitigate the outcome by attacking the secondary bacterial organisms. Means of immunization are not yet really available and control still depends on isolation, quarantine and veterinary hygienic measures. The experience therefore of the Army Veterinary Service in dealing with the disease and its sequelae in large groups of horses in the past is still worth noting.

Strangles is an acute infective disease of horses which in typical cases runs a febrile course and is characterised by inflammation of the nasal and pharyngeal mucosa, with suppuration of the regional lymph glands. The cause is considered to be a virus plus the *Streptococcus equi*. Its incidence varies in different countries. It is "rare" in Ireland, rather mild in form in England, frequently assumes economic importance on the continent of Europe and in India, as will be endorsed by generations of army veterinary officers, it is a universal disease of young horses. It will be the meticulous and painstaking work of the Army Veterinary Service in India to which the following remarks will mainly apply.

In all the Army Remount Depots in India strangles was a nuisance: it assumed a virulence and incidence of such a degree as to cause many a headache at General Headquarters to say nothing of the serious economic loss, which was due not only to the heavy mortality but the invariably protracted debility of the sufferers.

Perhaps no R.A.V.C. officers knew more about strangles than Major T. F. Arnold (1931, 1933) and Major F. J. Andrews, who with the laboratory help of the Imperial Institute of Veterinary Research did some magnificent pioneering work on the disease. Research was mainly directed to the control of strangles by means of antisera, vaccines and chemotherapeutic agents. Valuable negative results were obtained. Simple medicines and measures combined with good nursing often gave as good results. Arnold did find however that, although neither age nor previous attacks confer absolute immunity, successive attacks were of a milder nature.

Other experiments carried out by Andrews, who became the field investigation officer, included attempts to transmit the disease with prepared cultures, the influence of external temperature on the incidence of the disease and the comparison of grazing with stall feeding on the disease. He found that the incidence was higher in stall-fed animals and that cured horses if mixed with non-infected ones transmitted the disease up to 100 per cent. In addition, it was discovered that the infectivity of the disease before (closed) and after (open) the abscess was opened showed:

(1) percentage of in-contacts infected from a closed case ranged from 45 per cent. to 50 per cent.

(2) percentage of in-contacts infected from an open case ranged from 64 per cent. to 77 per cent.

To some extent the Military Veterinary Laboratory at Lahore owed its establishment to the researches into strangles, for Major F. J. Andrews, who investigated the disease in collaboration with Mukteswar from 1933 to 1936, was withdrawn in 1936 in which year the Laboratory came into existence.

Some work (Mosley, Heane and Shirlaw 1934) was carried out on equine encephalo-myelitis in India where it was first recorded in 1933 in an outbreak in an Indian Cavalry regiment when seventy-one cases occurred of which twenty-four (33.8 per cent.) proved fatal.

The disease is commonly called kumri, muttra paralysis or simply paraplegia. At least four immunologically distinct viruses have been isolated from horses suffering from encephalomyelitis: in Germany (Borna disease), in North and South America and in the Far East. All are destructive and naturally occur in other species of animals and all but Borna disease have been found as the cause of serious diseases in man.

As regards work in parasitology mention has already been made earlier in this chapter of the work done on strongylosis in horses by Knowles and Franklin (1940), Knowles and Blount (1941) and Blount (1941). Bennison (1943) carried out interesting investiga-tions into demodicosis of horses. Throughout the years both before and after World War II army veterinary officers have helped to try out every new anthelmintic drug brought out on the market, not only in horses but also in dogs. Perhaps one of the most enthusiastic officers was Colonel J. R. Hodgkins in this connection. As far back as 1921 and for many years afterwards he did much work on "habronemiasis" in horses.

The story of the army evolution of the treatment of mange is not without interest. In World War I there were widespread outbreaks of mange in horses in all theatres of operations. At first, the system of treatment was to dress continuously with a mixture of paraffin or sulphur and a fixed oil. As a rule the results were unsatisfactory as there was blistering of the skin and loss of condition. It was ultimately established that horse fat was the only safe vehicle for the sulphur (Holmes, 1920). It was not until the very end of the war that the ideal method of using oily dressings was discovered: this was the use at short intervals of horse fat and sulphur dressing combined with hot water and steam baths. The most practicable means of dealing with mange on a large scale was however by using dips containing the polysulphides of sulphur in aqueous solution. The pioneer of all dipping procedures in the treatment of mange, and for the elimination of ectoparasites in animals was indubitably Lieutenant-Colonel Watkins-Pitchford who introduced the method in South Africa at the beginning of the century.

The Army Veterinary Service, for the first time in veterinary history, thus evolved by the end of the war an effective routine for the control of mange. This consisted of:

    (i) regular and frequent inspections;

    (ii) segregation of affected and doubtful cases;

    (iii) isolation;

    (iv) disinfection;

    (v) dipping in calcium sulphide baths.

Sulphurous acid vapour baths was also pioneered by the R.A.V.C. as was the use of sodium hyposulphite and hydrochloric acid. The latter method was tried out for the first time in this country in 1933 and was said to be superior to oily dressings, ointments, dips and vapour baths.

The outstanding practical research worker in the field of wound treatment during the latter part of, and just after, World War I was Captain E. S. W. Peatt. He carried out extensive experiments in adapting Carrel's tube treatment to veterinary surgery (Peatt, Fellowship Thesis 1918). When Dr. Morrison called attention in the *British Medical Journal* (1917) to the value of B.I.P.P. in the treatment of infected wounds, Peatt immediately took it up and became the pioneer in its use in the veterinary field. He tried it out with good results in the Salonika Expeditionary Force (Peatt, 1919). Between the wars he continued to try out every new drug which was reported as having any wound-healing properties.

Army veterinary officers in general added their quota to the literature on field trials on the chemotherapeutic and antibiotic agents.

The condition known as "roaring" is peculiar to the equine race. In man, however, disease of the nervous system sometimes produces a similar syndrome. The subject therefore has always been of some interest to biologists and medical men. Many army veterinary officers have added considerably to the sum knowledge on this subject. Four names spring immediately from the past: Hobday, Townsend, Argyle and Glyn Lloyd. The first two—especially Hobday, of course—are associated with the well-known surgical operation, known colloquially as 'hobdaying'', in which the ventricles of the diseased larynx are removed or stripped. The other two officers contributed valuable data to the aetiology of the condition (Argyle 1933) and to the use of nerve sutures as a possible surgical procedure (Glyn Lloyd 1936). Townsend in addition to becoming expert in the hobday operation, made popular by his superb technique the "standing operation". He followed up the histories of fifty-seven horses on which he had operated for roaring and found that, amongst a host of other things, the operation caused grunting in forty-five cases but had no effect on the heart (Townsend 1937).

Townsend (1927) also introduced into this country a surgical operation for the cure of wind-sucking and crib-biting in horses.

After the operations in Burma in the first Wingate expedition of 1943, it was reported that the neighing of ponies and the braying of mules were frequently responsible for giving our positions away to the enemy. The D.D.V.S. Central Command in India (Colonel C. M. Stewart) was asked to solve this tricky problem. Ponies and mules should be de-voiced before proceeding on operations and it was a moot point whether a surgical operation could be devised to effect this satisfactorily. Numerous experimental operations were carried out and eventually a technique was perfected which included the total excision of the vocal cords (Stewart 1946) under a general anaesthetic.

The value of this work, of course, is quite incalculable; it will never be possible to assess the number of human lives that were saved as a direct result of the operation preventing betrayal of the positions of our forward troops nor will it be possible to calculate its imponderable effect on the fighting morale of our soldiers.

In the early stages of the campaign in Burma in World War II saddle galls were on a fairly large scale. A plastic operation of the "Cherry" type was devised for application to animals with considerable scar tissue. Results of the operation were extremely good (1944) and in this way in a very short period 250 equines otherwise useless were rendered serviceable. For all practical purposes, the animal was provided with a new back! (Edwards 1946.)

Stewart (1938) made careful observations on non-sweating (or dry-coat) affecting racehorses in India. This stimulated Lieutenant-Colonel D. F. G. Smith and Sir Charles Lovatt Evans in 1956 to carry out very important fundamental physiological investigations into this interesting condition (Smith et al. 1957).

Stewart (1942) also investigated a similar condition in cattle in India.

Short (1940) did some interesting work on the eye of the horse with special reference to the fundus.

Everyone who has anything to do with horses strives to possess a copy of that universally admired War Office publication *Animal Management*. We all realize that this book has formed the background skeleton of so many other books written by ex-cavalry officers, horse-masters and other enthusiasts: but few of us know that it was originally prepared in the Army Veterinary Department mainly from original observations of army veterinary officers. One of its chief "architects" was Butler, later Major-General E. R. C. Butler. The book is a permanent memorial and reminder of the prodigious contributions to horse management and to veterinary science in general that the Army Veterinary Service has made throughout the years.

Mention can be made of only two fields, and that very briefly, in which much work was accomplished by army veterinary officers: shoeing and feeding.

It was in 1907 that Blenkinsop, when serving in South Africa, introduced a special shoe to counter slippery road surfaces. It was a thin broad-webbed shoe, with half the width of the web at the toe bent up at an angle of twenty-two degrees. Several different tools were devised subsequently at the School of Farriery at Aldershot under Captain Budd to make the "Blenkinsop" shoe accurately as we know it today. This shoe has always given gratifying results when used: this is due to the fact that it is physiologically sound and reduces concussion. It was at the Army Veterinary School at Aldershot that Captain R. F. Linton (later the well known professor of hygiene and animal husbandry at the Royal (Dick) Veterinary School in Edinburgh) did much fundamental work on animal foods and nutrition.

The knowledge of animal management under all conditions and in all climates has always been a prerequisite of the army veterinary officer. It is not easy, and a trifle invidious, to instance distinct advances in this field due entirely to the efforts of members of the Army Veterinary Service. It is usually possible to find someone in the recent or remote past who often had the same or a similar idea. The value of the army contribution has really often been in popularising a good but forgotten technique or, because they happened to be a disciplined scientific body dealing in large numbers of animals, and so able to push forward a potentially bright idea which suited military exigencies. One has in mind such things as the stomach tube and its uses during the thirties, the development of various kinds of equine mouth gag and the methods of coping with large numbers of diseased or susceptible animals. All this knowledge has accumulated throughout the years so that today in our mechanized age, it has become the virtual monopoly (in the British Army) of the Veterinary Services. Valuable contributions have also been made in the transportation of animals by road, rail, sea and air. The usefulness of a modern field veterinary unit is very limited without mechanical transport for the movement of animals, and this was found to be the case especially in Italy during World War II. The ordinary 3-ton lorries which were normally available were quite unable to cope with the large numbers of horses and mules to be moved and a very serviceable utility trailer was improvised by the R.A.V.C. These trailers became an essential part of the equipment of all veterinary and remount units.

The use of naval and inland water transport craft for transhipping animals was first used successfully in the Arakan Operations, 1944-1945 (Nair 1947) under the aegis of the Army Veterinary Services. After the war and mainly in the Middle East many improvements were suggested and carried out by the R.A.V.C. in this method of transportation of animals (Ward 1957, Gale 1958). Much experience has now been acquired by the R.A.V.C. in the transportation of equine animals by air, dropping of mules by parachute (Barlow 1946), and lowering of war dogs from helicopters by means of a winch. (Wilkins 1953.)

Through the years, in peace or in war, the R.A.V.C. have devised all kinds of gadgets and temporary expedients to meet local problems of animal management. A lot of these have become accepted practice but their origin has often been forgotten: only a few were ever recorded. Such mundane things as the loading of an awkward horse or mule, prevention of tail-rubbing, slinging of horses and mules in the open, or the making of a manger using the ubiquitous oil-drum and a thousand other items, which taken together, constitute "zootechny" or the proper and humane care and management of animals.

It was not until 1941 that war dogs were re-introduced into the British Army; they had been employed to some extent in World War I but did not survive into the peace establishments of the army between the wars. A War Dog Training School was formed in 1941 and the R.A.V.C. soon began to take an interest in this novel commitment. After the war it was quickly appreciated that dogs had come to stay in the army and would in future become an integral part of the military organization. It was soon realized that the only Corps in the modern army which was exclusively qualified to cope with the supply, care, training and veterinary requirements of war dogs was the R.A.V.C. (Wilkins 1957).

In the same way as the War Office publication *Animal Management* has become the last word in the care of large animals, especially equines, so the official booklet *Training of War Dogs* is the *vade mecum* as far as war dogs in the army is concerned; Major G. D. Young, R.A.V.C. (1952) was the chief author.

Research into canine diseases began as soon as war dogs were introduced into the army (Danby 1944) mainly with emphasis on the haemolytic streptococci. Since those days, however, much work has been carried out on distemper (Singleton and Hunter 1956), leptospirosis (Wilkins 1950), filariasis (Clabby 1956-1957) and many other conditions. Experiments in breeding (Clabby and Laing, 1957) of a suitable type of war dog were studied in Singapore and, over a period of years, the War Dog Training School at Melton Mowbray collaborated with Sir Solly Zuckerman and his staff at Birmingham University in researches into the dog's "sixth sense" viz. his ability after training to detect buried non-metallic mines.

On the night of 12/13th July 1917 the Germans used mustard gas for the first time at Ypres on the Western Front in France. Research and development of war gases, their effects on army animals and especially protection, has been carried on at the Chemical Defence Experimental Station at Porton ever since those days. Naturally, the R.A.V.C. helped in projects specifically affecting army animals and, to this end, had a specially-selected officer on the establishment of the Station. It is therefore no surprise that in the years immediately preceding World War II the veterinary profession in this country looked to the Army Veterinary Service to guide them in providing adequate technical advice. Nor did they look in vain (Williamson, 1937). Major R. M. Bamford toured the country lecturing and demonstrating on the subject to various divisions of the National Veterinary Medical Association (now the British Veterinary Association) before and during the war as did Major W. P. Blount during the latter part of the war

(Blount, 1944). Gas respirators for various types of animals and pigeons were developed by the scientists of the Ministry of Supply with R.A.V.C. collaboration (Wilkins, 1947). The effects of "smoke" containing zinc chloride formed the subject of a long research project (Wilkins, 1948).

Although courses on the veterinary aspects of nuclear warfare have been held at the R.A.V.C. School for many years and although a fair amount has been published (Wilkins 1949, 1955-1958) from the theoretical angle, the R.A.V.C. has not up to now engaged in research on the biological effects of radiation. However, a R.A.V.C. officer was attached to the Medical Research Council Radiobiological Unit at Harwell in November 1960 and this may point the way to future developments in the evolution of the Royal Army Veterinary Corps.

APPENDIX I

Directors of the Army Veterinary Services 1796–1961

PRINCIPAL VETERINARY SURGEONS

1796   Professor Edward Coleman, F.R.S.

1839   Mr. Frederick C. Cherry

1854   Mr. John Wilkinson

1876   Mr. James Collins

1883   Dr. George Fleming, C.B., LL.D.

DIRECTOR-GENERALS

1890   Veterinary Colonel James D. Lambert, C.B.

1897   Veterinary Colonel Sir Francis Duck, K.C.B.

1902   Major-General Henry Thomson, C.B.

1907   Major-General Sir Frederick Smith, K.C.M.G., C.B.

1910   Major-General Sir Robert Pringle, K.C.M.G., C.B., D.S.O.

1917   Major-General Sir Layton J. Blenkinsop, K.C.B., D.S.O.

1921   Major-General W. Dunlop Smith, C.B., C.M.G., D.S.O.

1925   Major-General Henry T. Sawyer, C.B., D.S.O.

1929   Major-General William S. Anthony, C.B., C.M.G.

1933   Major-General J. J. B. Tapley, C.B., D.S.O.

DIRECTOR

1937   Brigadier C. A. Murray, C.B.E.

DIRECTORS ARMY VETERINARY AND REMOUNT SERVICES

1941   Brigadier C. A. Murray, C.B.E.

1943   Brigadier G. A. Kelly, C.B.

1947   Brigadier J. J. Plunkett, C.B.E.

1951   Brigadier A. G. Heveningham, C.B.E.

1955   Brigadier A. G. Ralston

1959   Brigadier J. Clabby, O.B.E.

APPENDIX II

Directors of Veterinary Services, India, 1866-1947

PRINCIPAL VETERINARY SURGEONS IN INDIA

1866   Mr. R. J. G. Hurford

1871   Mr. J. Siddall

1876   Mr. F. F. Collins

1889   Lieutenant-Colonel W. A. Russel

PRINCIPAL VETERINARY OFFICERS IN INDIA

1894   Colonel F. Duck

1897   Colonel H. Thomson

1902   Lieutenant-Colonel B. L. Glover, C.B.

1903   Colonel J. Matthews, C.B.

1906   Colonel J. A. Nunn, C.B., C.I.E., D.S.O.

1908   Colonel C. Rutherford, C.M.G.

1913   Colonel E. H. Hazelton

1916   Colonel L. J. Blenkinsop, D.S.O.

DIRECTORS

1918   Brigadier-General C. E. Nuthall, C.B., C.M.G.

1919   Major-General Sir John Moore, K.C.M.G., C.B.

1921   Colonel on the Staff H. T. Sawyer, C.B., D.S.O.

1925   Brigadier F. W. Hunt, C.B., C.M.G., C.B.E.

1928   Brigadier A. J. Williams, D.S.O.

1932   Brigadier H. S. Mosley, D.S.O.

1936   Brigadier H. C. Dibben, C.I.E.

1940   Brigadier J. J. M. Soutar, C.B.E.

1944   Brigadier E. S. W. Peatt, O.B.E.

DIRECTOR OF REMOUNT AND VETERINARY SERVICES

1946   Brigadier E. S. W. Peatt, O.B.E.

APPENDIX III

Commandants of the Army Veterinary School 1880-1961

1880   Veterinary Surgeon 1st Class J. D. Lambert
1881   Veterinary Surgeon 1st Class W. B. Walters
1883   Veterinary Surgeon 1st Class E. T. Cheeseman
1887   Veterinary Captain F. Smith
1892   Veterinary Major S. L. Longhurst
1897   Veterinary Major R. Moore
1902   Major E. R. C. Butler
1905   Major E. Taylor
1909   Major A. C. Newsom
1912   Major A. G. Todd
1914-1917   E. E. Martin

CENTRAL VETERINARY RESEARCH INSTITUTE

1918   Lieutenant-Colonel H. Watkins-Pitchford, C.M.G.

ROYAL ARMY VETERINARY SCHOOL

1921   Lieutenant-Colonel H. Watkins-Pitchford, C.M.G.
1923   Lieutenant-Colonel A. J. Williams, D.S.O.
1924   Colonel A. G. Todd, C.B.E., D.S.O.
1925   Lieutenant-Colonel J. J. Aitken, C.M.G., D.S.O., O.B.E.
1928   Lieutenant-Colonel H. S. Mosley, D.S.O.
1929   Lieutenant-Colonel E. P. Argyle, D.S.O.
1930   Lieutenant-Colonel H. J. Holness, D.S.O.
1932   Lieutenant-Colonel H. C. Dibben
1934   Lieutenant-Colonel J. R. Hodgkins, D.S.O.
1935   Lieutenant-Colonel J. O. Andrews, D.S.O.

R.A.V.C. LABORATORY

1938   Major R. H. Knowles
1943   Major A. V. Franklin
1945   Major A. G. Ralston
1947   Major L. W. Coulden
1949   Major J. H. Wilkins
1952   Major I. S. MacLennan

R.A.V.C. SCHOOL AND STORES

1955   Major J. H. Wilkins
1959   Major H. W. Bishop

APPENDIX IV
Roll of R.A.V.C. Officers who served in World War II.
(The ranks and decorations shown do not take into account changes since early 1945).

Major	J. B. Abbott	Capt.	J. G. S. Boyle	Capt.	J. W. Corrie
Capt.	A. D. Adams	Major	G. C. Brander	Major	L. W. Coulden
Capt.	F. Alexander	Major	H. W. Brekke	Capt.	R. H. M. Coulton
Capt.	F. C. Alexander	Major	M. Bridgeman, T.D.	Capt.	P. V. Coveney
Major	G. G. Alton	Capt.	R. C. Broad	Capt.	R. L. Cox
Major	F. J. Andrews	Lieut.	F. B. Brocklehurst	Capt.	G. E. Crabtree
Major	T. F. Arnold	Major	J. G. Brotherston	Major	J. Craig
Major	W. F. Aston, T.D.	Capt.	J. Brown	Major(QM)	T. B. Crawford
Capt.	B. G. Aylward	Capt.	R. A. Brown	Capt.	W. Crerar
Major	A. M. Bain	Capt.	J. F. Brownlie	Lt.-Col.	R. C. Crowhurst,
Capt.(QM)	P. Baines	Capt.	W. Bruce		O.B.E.
Lieut.(QM)	E. B. Ball	Major	D. A. D. Brydon	Lt.-Col.	F. L. Cundell
Major	W. B. Bamber	Capt.	W. G. Buchanan	Lt.-Col.	J. D. Daly
Col.	R. M. Bamford,	Capt.	J. J. Bullen	Major	J. L. Dalzell
	O.B.E.	Major	J. A. Bunker	Capt.	K. Dalzell
Capt.	C. C. Bannatyne	Major	D. Burgess	Major	D. C. E. Danby
Capt.	G. R. Bargh	Capt.	N. F. S. Burke	Lieut.	F. L. Davidson
Lt.-Col.	K. I. Barlow, M.B.E.	Major	N. McG. Burns	Capt.	J. Davie
Col.	G. Barnett,	Capt.	C. A. Butler	Major	R. H. K. Davis
	O.B.E., M.C.	Major	K. E. Cabban	Major	P. W. Dean
Major	W. Barr, T.D.	Major	D. W. Caldwell	Capt.	R. de Bruyn
Lieut.	J. C. Barrowman	Capt.	W. D. Caldwell	Capt.	H. D. Dewar
Major	W. E. Barry	Major	R. H. B. Callum	Brig.	H. C. Dibben, C.I.E.
Lt.-Col.	V. A. Bartrum,	Capt.	D. Cameron	Lieut.(QM)	T. Dingley
	O.B.E.	Capt.	J. A. Cameron	Major	R. J. H. Dixon
Major	C. S. Bassett	Capt.	J. M. Cameron	Capt.	J. G. Donald
Lt.-Col.	G. L. Beaumont	Major	J. D. Campbell	Capt.	J. F. Donnelly
Capt.	B. Bee	Capt.	M. A. Carmichael	Capt.	G. F. P. Doran
Major	H. Begg	Lieut.(QM)	T. Carson	Capt.	L. Dougal
Lt.-Col.	J. Bell	Lieut.(QM)	A. Carter	Lieut.	G. P. Doughill
Lt.-Col.	J. C. Bennison	Capt.	T. A. M. Chambers	Capt.	J. Dougill
Major	R. F. Bett	Capt.	F. A. Chapman	Capt.	J. F. Douglas
Lieut.	K. J. Biddis	Capt.	C. N. Chappel	Lt.-Col.	R. A. Douglas
Capt.	N. McG. Black	Major	G. J. Christie	Lieut.	J. C. Drake
Major	T. M. Black	Major	J. Clabby, M.B.E.	Capt.	K. W. G. Drury
Capt.	P. R. Blair-Fish	Major	A. J. Clarke	Capt.	R. S. Dugdill
Capt.	R. V. Blamire	Major	H. A. Clay	Capt.	F. M. B. Duncan
Major	P. H. Blampied	Lieut.(QM)	W. H. Cliff	Major	L. J. P. Duncan
Major(QM)	W. C. Blane	Major	J. N. Cloke	Capt.	T. H. Duncan
Major	W. Blanshard	Capt.	D. J. Clow	Capt.	L. Dyer
Capt.(QM)	W. Bleasdale	Major	J. J. Clune	Capt.	W. H. Dymock
Major	W. P. Blount, T.D.	Lt.-Col.	W. S. Codrington	Major	F. J. Eardley, T.D.
Capt.	M. H. Blunt	Capt.(QM)	W. E. Collyer	Capt.	J. Edgar
Major	T. Boundy	Capt.	K. G. Comrie	Lt.-Col.	B. C. M. Edmonds
Capt.	E. B. Bowditch	Capt.	G. F. Connolly	Capt.	A. M. Edwards
Capt.	D. I. Bowen	Lieut.	L. Constance	Lieut.(QM)	F. J. Edwards
Capt.	P. D. G. Bowen	Major	C. D. Cooke	Major	J. B. Edwards

Lt.-Col.	W. P. S. Edwards	Major	W. A. Greig	Capt.	F. T. W. Jones
Major	R. P. Evans	Major	J. R. Grey	Col.	J. Judge
Major	J. Facer, T.D.	Major	R. B. Griffiths	Col.	J. J. Kane, O.B.E.
Lieut.	G. B. Fairweather	Lieut.(QM)	R. S. Groombridge	Col.	J. S. Keane, O.B.E.
Major	C. G. Farmer	Capt.	T. W. Groves	Lt.-Col.	A. J. Kelly
Capt.	V. D. C. Farrant	Lieut.	J. G. Hall	Brig.	G. A. Kelly, C.B.
Capt.	G. S. Ferguson	Capt.	P. K. J. Hall-Patch	Lt.-Col.	R. K. Kent
Lt.-Col.	C. P. Fisher	Capt.	F. B. Halpin	Lieut.	J. E. Kenyon
Capt.	F. K. Fletcher	Major	D. G. Hanbury	Capt.	P. A. Kerr
Capt.	D. A. Forbes	Major	B. S. Hanson	Major	G. F. Kershaw
Major	A. E. C. Foster	Lieut.(QM)	W. Harris	Major	M. J. Killelea
Capt.	A. H. Foster	Lt.-Col.	J. F. Hart, O.B.E.	Lieut.(QM)	L. B. C. Killestein
Capt.	J. L. Foster	Major	R. W. Hartley	Lt.-Col.	J. S. Kingston, M.B.E
Capt.	H. J. Fox	Capt.	D. Harvey	Lieut.	M. Kirk
Major	A. V. Franklin, T.D.	Capt.	J. D. Hawkins	Major	A. K. Kirkwood
Major	A. C. Fraser	Lt.-Col.	F. B. Hayes, O.B.E.	Lieut.	J. R. Knowles
Capt.	J. Fraser	Lieut.(QM)	L. F. Hayes	Lt.-Col.	R. H. Knowles
Capt.	H. H. Frost	Capt.	A. H. S. Hayward	Capt.	A. H. Laing
Capt.	F. C. Fry	Col.	C. W. Heane	Capt.	D. P. W. Lake
Capt.	A. McD. Fyfe	Capt.	D. Heatley	Lieut.	H. T. C. Laker
Capt.	K. R. Gabb	Lt.-Col.	J. P. Hegarty, M.C.	Capt.	A. A. Lamont
Capt.	K. C. Gammack	Capt.	J. Helme	Lieut.	J. Lang
Capt.	J. F. Garden	Major	D. C. Henderson	Capt.	W. Lang
Capt.	J. C. A. Gardner	Major	A. G. Heveningham	Lt.-Col.	J. A. Langley
Capt.	I. G. George	Lt.-Col.	J. Hickman	Capt.	F. G. C. Lawfield
Capt.	W. A. Gibbs	Capt.	D. Hill	Capt.	T. M. Leach
Capt.	G. McC. Gibson	Capt.	J. N. M. Hills	Capt.(QM)	D. Leatherdale
Capt.	A. E. Gillespie	Capt.	J. J. R. Hindle	Major	J. Leigh
Lt.-Col.	D. A. Gillmor	Lt.-Col.	V. G. Hinds, T.D.	Capt.	J. M. F. Leitch
Major	H. Gillmor	Major	P. H. Hobbs, M.B.E.	Lieut.	J. Letham
Lieut.	K. C. Gledhill	Lieut.	G. Holford	Major	H. D. Lewis
Major	R. C. Glover	Col.	C. Holland, M.C.	Major	E. H. Lewis-Bowen
Lt.-Col.	G. W. Godwin	Major	C. D. Hopkins	Major	A. G. Limont
Major	J. Going	Capt.	R. B. Hornby	Lieut.(QM)	A. G. Ling
Major	G. V. Golding	Capt.	G. G. B. Howat	Capt.	T. Lithgow
Major	F. W. Goodall	Lt.-Col.	W. B. Howe	Col.	G. Lloyd, D.S.O.
Lt.-Col.	R. A. Gooderidge,	Lt.-Col.	H. J. Hughes, M.B.E.	Capt.	H. G. Lloyd
	O.B.E.	Lieut.	J. R. Humphreys	Lieut.	R. F. A. L. Longley
Capt.	W. A. M. Gordon	Capt.	R. Hunnam	Lt.-Col.	W. S. Lornie,
Major	J. F. Gracey	Lieut.(QM)	R. H. Hunt		M.C., T.D.
Capt.	R. W. Graham	Lieut.	R. I. C. Hyam	Capt.	S. Loughridge
Lt.-Col.	T. Grahame, T.D.	Major	J. H. A. Garvis	Major	H. B. Luxmore
Lieut.	D. L. Grant	Capt.	D. G. Jarvis-Evans	Major	W. St. J. F.
Lieut.	G. S. Grater	Capt.	A. R. Jennings		Macartney
Capt.	W. Van O Gray	Lt.-Col.	H. Jerrom	Lieut.	C. McB. McCance
Capt.	A. R. Green	Lieut.	R. Jobling	Capt.	J. McCorkindale
Lt.-Col.	D. A. Green	Lieut.	H. M. John	Capt.	M. R. McCrea
Major	E. D. Greenway	Capt.	W. G. Johnston	Major	R. McCrea, M.B.E.
Capt.	G. E. Greenwell	Major	D. W. Jolly	Lt.-Col.	A. P. MacDonald,
Capt.	F. G. Greer	Major	C. N. Jones		O.B.E.
Capt.	D. H. Greeves	Lieut.	J. Jones	Major	J. Macdonald
Lieut.	A. Gregor	Lieut.	O. G. Jones	Capt.	D. W. Macdonald

Capt.	J. B. McDougall	Major	J. M. Morrison	Major	F. W. Priestly
Capt.	G. McElligott	Capt.	D. T. Mortimer	Major	L. E. Pritchard,
Lieut.	D. L. MacFarlane	Major	W. P. Moss, M.C.,		O.B.E.
Lieut.	I. M. Macfarlane		T.D.	Lt.-Col.	A. A. Pryer, D.S.O.
Lt.-Col.	J. H. McGhee	Lieut.	T. H. Muir	Capt.	J. S. Pybus
Capt.	A. Mackay	Lieut.(QM)	J. J. Murphy	Major	A. G. Ralston
Lieut.	J. C. MacKellar	Lt.-Col.	M. A. Murphy	Lieut.	L. F. Rees
Capt.	H. H. H. S.	Brig.	C. A. Murray,	Lt.-Col.	P. A. Reeves
	Mackenzie		C.B.E.	Lieut.	D. T. Reid
Capt.	M. McE.	Lieut.	H. P. J. Murray	Major	J. D. Rennie
	Mackinnon	Capt.	A. Mutch	Capt.	C. C. Renwick
Major	W. Mackinnon	Major	J. C. Newhook	Capt.	E. P. Rice
Capt.	G. K. Maclachlan	Capt.	C. M. Newsholme	Lieut.	D. A. Richardson
Lt.-Col.	I. McLaren	Major	B. J. W. Nicolas	Capt.	P. Richmond
Capt.	I. S. McLaren	Lieut.	D. I. Nisbet	Capt.	J. E. M. Ridge
Capt.	B. Mclean	Major	D. L. O'Brien	Lieut.	B. Rimmer
Lieut.	I. S. Maclennan	Col.	S. O'Donel, M.C.	Major	J. Ritchie
Lieut.	K. J. R. MacLennan	Major	E. O'Kelly	Lt.-Col.	J. C. Rix
Capt.	A. MacI. MacLeod	Major	J. A. O'Neil	Capt.	A. I. Robertson
Capt.	A. W. MacLeod	Major	M. J. O'Reilly	Lt.-Col.	R. H. Robertson,
Capt.	D. MacLeod	Capt.	F. H. Orr		O.B.E.
Capt.	F. H. McMillen	Major	D. W. Owen	Capt.	J. H. Robins
Capt.	C. McNulty	Capt.	R. C. Park	Capt.	P. Robinson
Lt.-Col.	I. D. Macrae	Major	G. B. Parker	Lt.-Col.	J. McL. Ross, M.B.E.
Major	R. I. Macrae	Capt.	I. V. G. Parker	Lt.-Col.	W. M. Rouse
Capt.	R. G. Mares	Lieut.(QM)	R. Parkin-Ashton	Lieut.	E. F. Rowell
Major	S. W. Marriot,	Capt.	J. D. Parkinson	Lieut.	N. Salisbury
	O.B.E.	Major	J. H. Parsons	Capt.	C. N. Saunders
Capt.	W. B. Martin	Lieut.	R. G. Pearson	Capt.	D. J. P. Scott
Capt.	G. Mason	Capt.	R. W. H. Pearson	Lieut.	H. M. Scott
Major	G. S. Mason	Brig.	E. S. W. Peatt,	Capt.	K. E. Scott
Lieut.	A. Matheson		O.B.E.	Capt.	G. W. Serth
Capt.	O. Y. Mayor	Capt.	H. G. Pembrey	Lt.-Col.	A. D. Seton
Major	D. R. Melrose	Capt.	K. C. Peters	Lieut.	G. A. M. Sharman
Major	A. O. Merry	Capt.	A. W. Peyton	Capt.	D. B. Shaw
Capt.	W. B. Milburn	Col.	G. Pfaff, M.B.E.	Major	T. L. Shea
Capt.	A. M. Millar	Lieut.	L. S. Pfob	Lt.-Col.	G. V. Short, M.B.E.
Lieut.	P. G. Miller	Major	J. Phillips	Capt.	D. R. Shorter
Capt.	W. Miller	Capt.	R. N. Phillips	Capt.	A. C. Shuttleworth
Col.	J. J. Mills	Capt.	E. Pierson	Lieut.	D. Sillars
Major	F. J. Milne	Capt.	E. G. Pilgrim	Lieut.	L. S. Sim
Capt.	W. M. Milne	Capt.	H. Platt	Capt.	R. F. Simon
Lieut.	K. I. Miscampbell	Lieut.	W. Plowright	Capt.	C. A. C. Simpson
Capt.	P. J. Mitchell	Col.	J. J. Plunkett, O.B.E.	Major	K. S. Simpson
Capt.	F. C. Moody	Major	L. H. B. Poer, M.C.	Capt.	W. B. V. Sinclair
Capt.	J. B. D. Morgan	Capt.	A. Pollock	Lt.-Col.	W. L. Sinton, M.B.E.
Capt.	K. U. Morgan	Lieut.	A. M. Pomphrey	Lt.-Col.	S. L. Slocock, M.C.
Capt.	T. J. Morgan	Capt.	H. L. Pook	Capt.	A. H. Smith
Capt.	C. A. B. Moring	Lieut.	A. J. Porteous	Major	B. Smith
Capt.(QM)	B. Morris	Lt.-Col.	C. U. K. Porter	Lt.-Col.	D. F. G. Smith
Major	A. M. Morrison	Lieut.	J. P. A. Potts	Capt.	I. M. Smith
Major	J. G. Morrison	Capt.	J. H. Power	Capt.	H. E. Snalam

Lieut.	J. S. Snowdon	Lieut.	R. C. Taylor	Capt.	A. H. Watson
Brig.	J. J. M. Soutar, O.B.E.	Lieut.	R. R. Temple	Major	L. A. Watson
		Lt.-Col.	D. I. C. Tennant	Major	W. J. B. Watson
Lt.-Col.	J. Southell	Major	J. V. Tevlin	Capt.	A. G. Welch
Lt.-Col.	P. S. Sparling	Capt.	E. V. Thomas	Lieut.	J. Wellington
Capt.	L. H. Sparrow	Lieut.	P. D. I. Thomas	Lieut.	G. J. White
Capt.	A. B. O. Stabler	Major	W. H. Thomas	Capt.	J. T. Wickens
Lt.-Col.	R. H. Stalker	Capt.	S. H. Thompson	Major	F. J. Wier
Capt.	H. B. Steele	Col.	C. H. S. Townsend, C.B.E., M.C.	Major	J. H. Wilkins
Capt.	R. L. Steele			Lt.-Col.	H. B. Williams, O.B.E.
Col.	G. F. Steevenson, O.B.E.	Lt.-Col.	S. L. Trevor	Major	G. T. Williamson
		Lt.-Col.	E. G. Turner, D.S.O.	Major	J. P. Wilmot Smith
Major	H. Stephenson, M.C.			Lieut.	A. Wilson
Brig.	C. M. Stewart	Capt.(QM)	W. E. Turton	Capt.	A. A. Wilson
Capt.	D. MacK. Stewart	Capt.	E. A. Tutton	Lieut.	J. C. Wilson
Lieut.	J. Stewart	Lieut.	D. B. Underwood	Lieut.	J. P. Wilson
Major	J. R. Stewart	Lieut.	F. J. Usher	Capt.	P. Wilson
Capt.	T. Stewart	Major	P. H. Wait	Capt.	R. M. Wilson
Lieut.	J. Stirling	Capt.	J. Walker	Major	D. H. Witherington
Lt.-Col.	E. V. H. Studdy	Lieut.(QM)	R. C. Walker	Capt.	J. C. Wood
Capt.	J. F. C. Swan	Lieut.	R. J. C. Walker	Capt.(QM)	J. E. Wood
Major	L. R. Swifte	Capt.	R. O. W. Walpole	Lieut.	J. G. P. Wood
Capt.	P. E. Sykes	Capt.	V. C. Ward	Lt.-Col.	P. F. Woodland
Capt.	A. Taylor	Capt.	A. G. Wardrop	Major	W. H. Wortley
Major	G. B. Taylor	Lieut.(QM)	G. J. Warren	Capt.	R. A. Wright
Capt.	J. C. Taylor	Lieut.(QM)	J. W. Warrer	Major	G. D. Young
Lt.-Col.	J. F. L. Taylor	Major	G. F. Watkins		

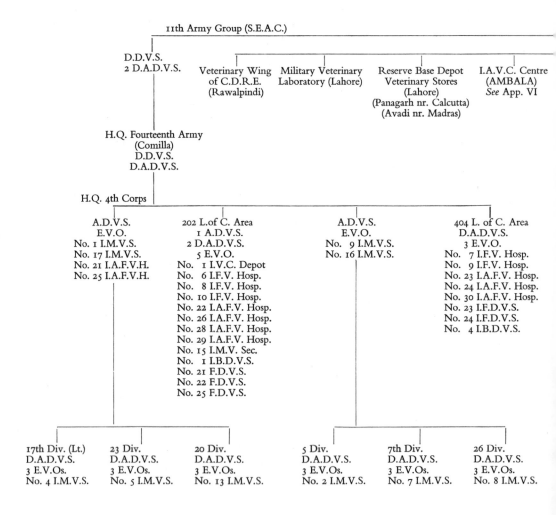

11th Army Group (S.E.A.C.)

D.D.V.S.
2 D.A.D.V.S.

Veterinary Wing | Military Veterinary | Reserve Base Depot | I.A.V.C. Centre
of C.D.R.E. | Laboratory (Lahore) | Veterinary Stores | (AMBALA)
(Rawalpindi) | | (Lahore) | See App. VI
| | (Panagarh nr. Calcutta)
| | (Avadi nr. Madras)

H.Q. Fourteenth Army
(Comilla)
D.D.V.S.
D.A.D.V.S.

H.Q. 4th Corps

A.D.V.S. | 202 L. of C. Area | A.D.V.S. | 404 L. of C. Area
E.V.O. | 1 A.D.V.S. | E.V.O. | D.A.D.V.S.
No. 1 I.M.V.S. | 2 D.A.D.V.S. | No. 9 I.M.V.S. | 3 E.V.O.
No. 17 I.M.V.S. | 5 E.V.O. | No. 16 I.M.V.S. | No. 7 I.F.V. Hosp.
No. 21 I.A.F.V.H. | No. 1 I.V.C. Depot | | No. 9 I.F.V. Hosp.
No. 25 I.A.F.V.H. | No. 6 I.F.V. Hosp. | | No. 23 I.A.F.V. Hosp.
| No. 8 I.F.V. Hosp. | | No. 24 I.A.F.V. Hosp.
| No. 10 I.F.V. Hosp. | | No. 30 I.A.F.V. Hosp.
| No. 22 I.A.F.V. Hosp. | | No. 23 I.F.D.V.S.
| No. 26 I.A.F.V. Hosp. | | No. 24 I.F.D.V.S.
| No. 28 I.A.F.V. Hosp. | | No. 4 I.B.D.V.S.
| No. 29 I.A.F.V. Hosp. |
| No. 15 I.M.V. Sec. |
| No. 1 I.B.D.V.S. |
| No. 21 F.D.V.S. |
| No. 22 F.D.V.S. |
| No. 25 F.D.V.S. |

17th Div. (Lt.) | 23 Div. | 20 Div. | 5 Div. | 7th Div. | 26 Div.
D.A.D.V.S. | D.A.D.V.S. | D.A.D.V.S. | D.A.D.V.S. | D.A.D.V.S. | D.A.D.V.S.
3 E.V.Os. | 3 E.V.Os. | 3 E.V.Os. | 3 E.V.Os. | 3 E.V.Os. | 3 E.V.Os.
No. 4 I.M.V.S. | No. 5 I.M.V.S. | No. 13 I.M.V.S. | No. 2 I.M.V.S. | No. 7 I.M.V.S. | No. 8 I.M.V.S.

UNITS

Peace units	Total No.	Mobilized units
Ind. Mil. Vet. Hosp. Cl. I	13	Ind. Vet. Hosp. (Field or Exp.▮
Ind. Mil. Vet. Hosp. Cl. II	14	Ind. Adv. Fd. Vet. Hosp.
Ind. Branch Vet. Hosp.	23	Ind. Mob. Vet. Sections
I.A.V.C. Centre (including		Ind. Vet. Reception Hospitals
A.V. School and Officers		Ind. Vet. Con. Depots
Training School)	1	Ind. Bde. Vet. Sections
Ind. Mil. Vet. Laboratory	1	Ind. Vet. Dets.
C.D.R.E. (Vet. Wing)	1	Ind. Res. Base Depot Vet. Sto▮
		Ind. Fd. Depot Vet. Stores
		Ind. Base Depot Vet. Stores
		Ind. Fd. Vet. Laboratories
		Ind. Anti-Surra Units

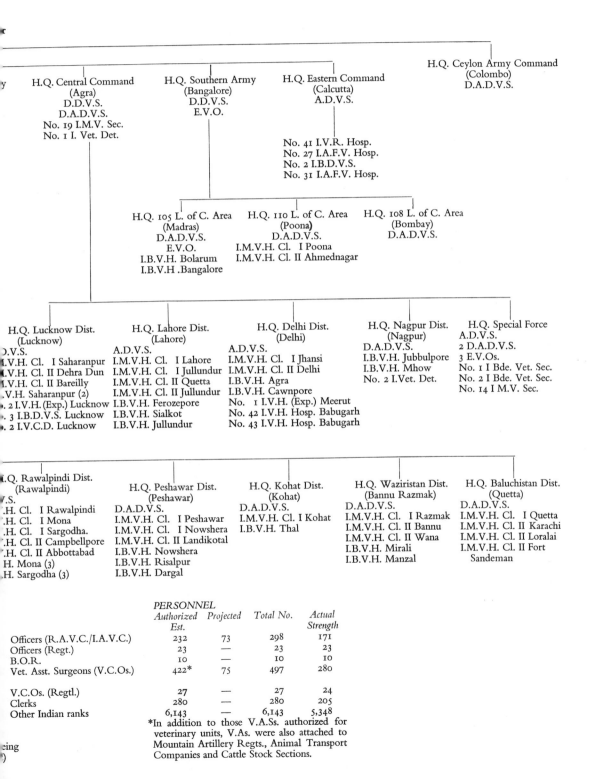

y   H.Q. Central Command   H.Q. Southern Army   H.Q. Eastern Command   H.Q. Ceylon Army Command
         (Agra)   (Bangalore)   (Calcutta)   (Colombo)
         D.D.V.S.   D.D.V.S.   A.D.V.S.   D.A.D.V.S.
         D.A.D.V.S.   E.V.O.
         No. 19 I.M.V. Sec.
         No. 1 I. Vet. Det.

                                                              No. 41 I.V.R. Hosp.
                                                              No. 27 I.A.F.V. Hosp.
                                                              No. 2 I.B.D.V.S.
                                                              No. 31 I.A.F.V. Hosp.

                      H.Q. 105 L. of C. Area   H.Q. 110 L. of C. Area   H.Q. 108 L. of C. Area
                           (Madras)   (Poona)   (Bombay)
                           D.A.D.V.S.   D.A.D.V.S.   D.A.D.V.S.
                           E.V.O.   I.M.V.H. Cl. I Poona
                           I.B.V.H. Bolarum   I.M.V.H. Cl. II Ahmednagar
                           I.B.V.H .Bangalore

H.Q. Lucknow Dist.   H.Q. Lahore Dist.   H.Q. Delhi Dist.   H.Q. Nagpur Dist.   H.Q. Special Force
    (Lucknow)   (Lahore)   (Delhi)   (Nagpur)   A.D.V.S.
D.V.S.   A.D.V.S.   A.D.V.S.   D.A.D.V.S.   2 D.A.D.V.S.
I.V.H. Cl. I Saharanpur I.M.V.H. Cl. I Lahore   I.M.V.H. Cl. I Jhansi   I.B.V.H. Jubbulpore   3 E.V.Os.
I.V.H. Cl. II Dehra Dun   I.M.V.H. Cl. I Jullundur I.M.V.H. Cl. II Delhi   I.B.V.H. Mhow   No. 1 I Bde. Vet. Sec.
I.V.H. Cl. II Bareilly   I.M.V.H. Cl. II Quetta   I.B.V.H. Agra   No. 2 I.Vet. Det.   No. 2 I Bde. Vet. Sec.
.V.H. Saharanpur (2)   I.M.V.H. Cl. II Jullundur I.B.V.H. Cawnpore   No. 14 I M.V. Sec.
. 2 I.V.H. (Exp.) Lucknow I.B.V.H. Ferozepore   No. 1 I.V.H. (Exp.) Meerut
. 3 I.B.D.V.S. Lucknow   I.B.V.H. Sialkot   No. 42 I.V.H. Hosp. Babugarh
. 2 I.V.C.D. Lucknow   I.B.V.H. Jullundur   No. 43 I.V.H. Hosp. Babugarh

.Q. Rawalpindi Dist.
    (Rawalpindi)   H.Q. Peshawar Dist.   H.Q. Kohat Dist.   H.Q. Waziristan Dist.   H.Q. Baluchistan Dist.
.S.   (Peshawar)   (Kohat)   (Bannu Razmak)   (Quetta)
.H. Cl. I Rawalpindi   D.A.D.V.S.   D.A.D.V.S.   D.A.D.V.S.   D.A.D.V.S.
.H. Cl. I Mona   I.M.V.H. Cl. I Peshawar   I.M.V.H. Cl. I Kohat   I.M.V.H. Cl. I Razmak I.M.V.H. Cl. I Quetta
.H. Cl. I Sargodha.   I.M.V.H. Cl. I Nowshera   I.B.V.H. Thal   I.M.V.H. Cl. II Bannu   I.M.V.H. Cl. II Karachi
.H. Cl. II Campbellpore   I.M.V.H. Cl. II Landikotal   I.M.V.H. Cl. II Wana   I.M.V.H. Cl. II Loralai
.H. Cl. II Abbottabad   I.B.V.H. Nowshera   I.B.V.H. Mirali   I.M.V.H. Cl. II Fort
H. Mona (3)   I.B.V.H. Risalpur   I.B.V.H. Manzal   Sandeman
.H. Sargodha (3)   I.B.V.H. Dargal

PERSONNEL

	Authorized Est.	Projected	Total No.	Actual Strength
Officers (R.A.V.C./I.A.V.C.)	232	73	298	171
Officers (Regt.)	23	—	23	23
B.O.R.	10	—	10	10
Vet. Asst. Surgeons (V.C.Os.)	422*	75	497	280
V.C.Os. (Regtl.)	27	—	27	24
Clerks	280	—	280	205
Other Indian ranks	6,143	—	6,143	5,348

*In addition to those V.A.Ss. authorized for
veterinary units, V.As. were also attached to
Mountain Artillery Regts., Animal Transport
Companies and Cattle Stock Sections.

eing
)

APPENDIX VI

ORGANIZATION OF I.A.V.C. CENTRE, AMBALA—(EARLY 1944)

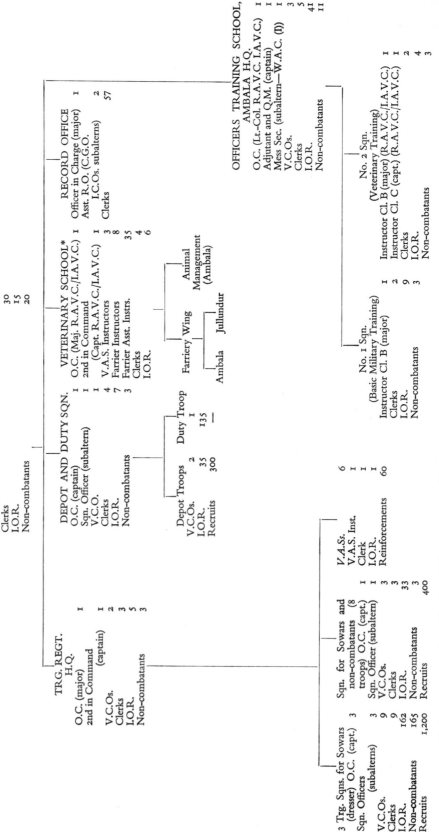

Centre H.Q.

Officer Commanding (colonel, R.A.V.C.)	1
2nd in Command (lieut-colonel)	1
Adjutant (captain)	1
Quartermaster (Spl. List Q.M.)	1
Administrative Officer (major or captain)	1
Asst. Accounts Officer (C.G.O./I.C.O.—subaltern)	1
V.C.Os.	6
Clerks	30
I.O.R.	15
Non-combatants	20

RECORD OFFICE

Officer in Charge (major)	1
Asst. R.O. (C.G.O.)	1
I.C.Os. subalterns	2
Clerks	57

VETERINARY SCHOOL*

O.C. (Maj. R.A.V.C./I.A.V.C.)	1
2nd in Command (Capt. R.A.V.C./I.A.V.C.)	1
V.A.S. Instructors	3
Farrier Instructors	8
Farrier Asst. Instrs.	35
Clerks	4
I.O.R.	6

Farriery Wing — Animal Management (Ambala)

Ambala — Jullundur

DEPOT AND DUTY SQN.

O.C. (captain)	1
Sqn. Officer (subaltern)	1
V.C.O.	4
Clerks	7
I.O.R.	3
Non-combatants	

	Depot Troops	Duty Troop
V.C.Os.	2	1
I.O.R.	35	135
Recruits	300	—

OFFICERS TRAINING SCHOOL, AMBALA H.Q.

O.C. (Lt.-Col. R.A.V.C. I.A.V.C.)	1
Adjutant and Q.M. (captain)	1
Mess Sec. (subaltern—W.A.C. (I))	1
V.C.Os.	3
Clerks	5
I.O.R.	41
Non-combatants	11

No. 1 Sqn. (Basic Military Training)

Instructor Cl. B (major)	1
Clerks	2
I.O.R.	9
Non-combatants	3

No. 2 Sqn. (Veterinary Training)

Instructor Cl. B (major) (R.A.V.C./I.A.V.C.)	1
Instructor Cl. C (capt.) (R.A.V.C./I.A.V.C.)	1
Clerks	2
I.O.R.	4
Non-combatants	3

TRG. REGT. H.Q.

O.C. (major)	1
2nd in Command (captain)	1
V.C.Os.	2
Clerks	3
I.O.R.	5
Non-combatants	3

Sqn. for Sowars and non-combatants (8 troops)

O.C. (capt.)	1
Sqn. Officer (subaltern)	1
V.C.Os.	3
Clerks	3
I.O.R.	33
Non-combatants	3
Recruits	400

3 Trg. Sqns. for Sowars (dresser)

O.C. (capt.)	3
Sqn. Officers (subalterns)	3
V.C.Os.	9
Clerks	3
I.O.R.	162
Non-combatants	165
Recruits	1,200

V.A.Ss.	6
V.A.S. Inst.	1
Clerk	1
I.O.R.	1
Reinforcements	60

* In August 1944 the Army Veterinary School was separated from the I.A.V.C. Centre and continued to function as a separate instructional institution.

APPENDIX VII

Organization of the Army Veterinary and Remount Services, early 1945.

(Excluding India and Burma)

War Office

D.A.V.R.S

A.D.A.V.S., A.D.R., D.A.A.V.R.S

Home Forces	21st Army Group	Middle East Forces	Central Mediterranean Forces	Paiforce	East Africa	U.S.A.	Control Commissions and Civil Affairs V. & R. Staff for:
D.A.D.V.R.S. Northern Command	A.D.V.R.S.	D.D.V.R.S., GHQ. A.D.V.R.S. Palestine	D.D.V.R.S, A.F.H.Q.	A.D.V.R.S.	D.A.D.V.R.S.	Remount Purchasing Commission	Germany
D.A.D.V.R.S. Scottish Command	D.A.D.V.R.S.	A.D.V.R.S., Syria	A.D.V.R.S., A.F.H.Q.	Remount Purchasing Commission			Austria
D.A.D.V.R.S. Eastern Command	No. 5 Vet. Hosp.		A.D.V.R.S, 15th Army Group	No. 3 Indian M.V.S.			Greece
D.A.D.V.R.S. Southern and Western Comds.	No. 6 V.R.C.S.	D.A.D.V.R.S. Egypt (B.T.E.)	A.D.V.R.S., 8th Army	No. 12 Mobile Vet. Detachment			Eritrea
No. 1 Reserve Vet. Hosp.	No. 2 Field Remount Depot	Nos. 1 & 2 Vet. Hospitals	A.D.V.R.S. H.Q. 1 Dist.	No. 1 Advanced Depot Vet. Stores			Cyrenaica
R.A.V.C. Records Office		Nos. 3 & 4 Base Remount Depots	Nos. 4, 6 & 7 Vet. Hosp. Italian Vet. Hosps. (2)				Tripolitania
R.A.V.C. Laboratory			No. 812 Base Remount Depot				Dodecanese
Army Veterinary Stores		Remount Purchasing Commission, Cyprus	No. 1 Field Remount Depot				
No. 2 Base Vet. Depot Stores		Nos. 1, 2 & 3 Livestock Depots Army Pig Farms	Remount Purchasing Commissions—North Africa, Sicily and Italy				
No. 2 Advanced Depot Veterinary Stores		Meat Inspection Pool of V.Os.	Nos. 1, 2, 3 & 804 V.R.C.S.				
Remount Depot, Melton Mowbray		V. & R. Detachm't B.T.E.	Nos. 1, 4, 6, 803 & 817 C.M.V.S.				
Remount Purchasing Commission U.K.		Base Depot of Vet. Stores	No. 2 Vet. Laboratory				
No. 5 Field Remount Depot			School of Farriery				
Veterinary Pharmacy, Scottish Command			R.A.V.C. Port Detachment Bari				
R.A.V.C. Detachment C.D.E.E.			No. 3 Base Depot Vet. Stores				

APPENDIX VIII

R.A.V.C. with C.M.F.
Strength on 1st May, 1944

UNITS AND HQ'S	DESIG. OF UNITS	OFFICERS	O.RS
A.F.H.Q.	D.D.V. & R.S. D.A.D.V. & R.S. S/Capt.	3	4
HQ. A.A.I.	A.D.V. & R.S.	1	3
HQ 5th Army (Br. Inc.)	A.D.V. & R.S.	1	1
HQ 8th Army	A.D.V. & R.S.	1	2
One Field Remount Depot.	No. 1 Field Remount Depot.	6	100
One Base Remount Depot.	812 Base Remount Depot.	6	67
Two Veterinary Hospitals	4 & "X" Veterinary Hospitals	4	118
One Remount Purchasing Commission	No. 3 Remount Purchasing Commission	2	3
Four Veterinary & Remount Conducting Sections.	Nos. 1, 2, 3 & 804 Veterinary and Remount Conducting Sections	4	136
Four Cavalry Mobile Veterinary Sections.	Nos. 1, 4, 6 & 803 Cavalry Mobile Veterinary Section.	4	76
Three Corps Detachments R.A.V.C.	Nos. 1, 2 & 3 Corps. Detachments R.A.V.C.	3	18
One V. & R. Pool of Officers	V. & R. Pool of Officers	7	
One Base Depot of Veterinary Stores.	No. 3 Base Depot Veterinary Stores.	1	7
Five Cypriot Pack Transport Coys.	Nos. 618, 619, 620, 621 & 622 Cypriot. Pack Transport Coys.	5	15
Four Pack Transport Coys. R.A.S.C.	Nos. 573, 574, 359 & 786 Pack Transport Coys. R.A.S.C.	4	12
Two Group HQ. Indian Pack Transport Coys.	"A" and "B" Group HQs. Indian Pack Transport Coys.	2	
Five British Cadres for Italian Pack Transport Coys.	Nos. 3, 4, 7, 8 & 14 (Group Cav.) Italian Pack Transport Coys.	5	5
Two Mountain Regts. R.A.	Nos. 7 & 85 Mountain Regt. R.A.	2	10
One CMP Dog Training Establishment	"A" CMP Dog T.E.		2
One CMP Dog Section	51 CMP Dog Section		2
Authorised Rfts.		2	3
	TOTAL ..	63	584

NOTE: 1. All base V & R Units and V & RCSs operated with increments of Italian soldiers or civilians, and CMVS also in certain stages of the operations when holdings were large.

NOTE: 2. Figure 584 includes 61 Farriers, 37 Clerks, 15 Saddlers

NOTE: 3. These figures increased later

Organization of the Army Veterinary and Remount Services in C.M.F. on 1st May, 1945

D.D.V. & R.S., A.F.H.Q.

A.D.V. & R.S., A.F.H.Q.

A.D.V. & R.S., 15 Army Group

A.D.V. & R.S. Eighth Army Field Units.

1 Gp. HQ. Cyp. Pk. Tp. Coys.
618 Cypriot P.. Tp. Coy.
619 Cypriot Pk. Tp. Coy.
620 Cypriot Pk. Tp. Coy.
621 Cypriot Pk. Tp. Coy.
622 Cypriot Pk. Tp. Coy.
623 Cypriot Pk. Tp. Coy.
686 Cypriot Pk. Tp. Coy.
85 Mountain Regt.
252 It. Pk. Tp. Gp. HQ.
266 It. Pk. Tp. Coy.
267 It. Pk. Tp. Coy.
268 It. Pk. Tp. Coy.
269 It. Pk. Tp. Coy.

V. & R. Units
803 C.M.V.S.
1 V. & R.C.S.
804 V. & R.C.S.
6 C.M.V.S.
817 C.M.V.S.

A.D.V. & R.S. Fifth Army (Br. Inc.) Field Units

A Gp. HQ. Ind. Pk. Coys.
6 Ind. Pk. Tp. Coy.
13 Ind. Pk. Tp. Coy.
34 Ind. Pk. Tp. Coy.
B Gp. HQ. Ind. Pk. Coys.
2 Ind. Pk. Tp. Coy.
12 Ind. Pk. Tp. Coy.
17 Ind. Pk. Tp. Coy.
26 Ind. Pk. Tp. Coy.
21 Gp. HQ. Ital. Pk. Coy.
3 Italian Pk. Coy.
4 Italian Pk. Coy.
7 Italian Pk. Coy.
14 Italian Pk. Coy.
250 Italian Pk. Coy.
359 Pk. Tp. Coy. R.A.S.C.
786 Pk. Tp. Coy. R.A.S.C.
573 Pk. Tp. Coy. R.A.S.C.
574 Pk. Tp. Coy. R.A.S.C.
4 Gp. HQ. Pk. Tp. Coys.
253 It. Pk. Tp. Coy.
270 It. Pk. Tp. Coy.
271 It. Pk. Tp. Coy.
272 It. Pk. Tp. Coy.
273 It. Pk. Tp. Coy.

V. & R. Units
1 C.M.V.S.
4 C.M.V.S.
2 V. & R.C.S.
3 V. & R.C.S.

D.A.D.V. & R.S. 3 Dist. Field Units.

SO (MED)
Sheep Pur. Centre
C.M.P. Dog Section
33 Ind. Catt. Stk. Sect.
2 Dog Sections
Sect. Dog Trg. Centre

V. & R. Units
1 Corps Det. R.A.V.C.
2 Corps Det. R.A.V.C.
3 Corps Det. R.A.V.C.
5 Remount Purchas. Comm.
601 Ital. Vet. Hosp.
7 V. & R.C.S.
8 C.M.V.S.
812 Base Remt. Depot.
125 Ital. Vet. Hosp.
7 Vet. Hosp.
4 Vet. Hosp.
1 Field Remt. Depot
3 B.D.V.S.
1 Sch. of Farriery
2 Vet. Lab.
Pool of Officers

SICILY
3 Remount Pur. Comm.
8 V. & R.C.S.

---

1 District

6 Vet. Hosp.
2 Ind. Catt. Stk. Sect.

MALTA

L. D. Animals

NORTH AFRICA

6 Remount Pur. Comm.

HQ. L.F. & M.L.

Senior Vet. Officer
Staff Capt.

Abbreviations: SO (MED)—Special Ops (Mediterranean) HQ, LF & ML—Land Forces Greece and Military Liaison.

APPENDIX X

Animal Statistics – Central Mediterranean Force
Period: 1 January – 31 December, 1944

(a) Remounts

	Horses	Mules
Number of animals issued to Field Units from C.M.V.S. & V. & R.C.S.	590	9,954
Number issued to U.S. Forces from Remount Depots	—	2,512
,, ,, L.F.A. from Remount Depots	—	141
,, ,, Partisans Jugoslavia from Remount Depots	43	884
,, ,, M.E.F. (Light Draught) from Remount Depots	388	21
,, ,, Italian Army from Remount Depots	10	85
	1,031	13,597

(b) Animal Provision

	Horses	Mules
Requisitioned and Purchased in Sicily	153	4,038
,, ,, ,, Italy	40	2,568
Shipped from Middle East	50	5,346
Received from Italian Army	610	1,069
	853	13,021

(c) Evacuations

	Horses	Mules
Number of sick and wounded animals evacuated to veterinary hospitals from Field Units	216	4,342
Number of sick evacuated to veterinary hospitals by Remount Depots	513	1,819
Total sick evacuated	729	6,161
Plus total number of sick held on 1 January, 1944	6	83
TOTAL	735	6,244
Total died, destroyed or cast in Veterinary hospitals	157	685
	578	5,559
Less number discharged to Remount Depots	339	4,187
Number of sick held on 31 December, 1944	239	1,372
Percentage of hospitalised animals discharged from veterinary hospitals to duty during the year	46%	68%

(d) Casualty State in Field Units

Period	Evacuated Sick and Wounded		Killed and Died inclusive Gunshot Wounds		Destroyed inclusive Gunshot		Totals	Average Field Strength	Average Monthly Wastage
	H	M	H	M	H	M			
Jan. Mar.	42	670	9	388	3	52	1,160	4,300	8.9%
Apr. June.	56	930	6	237	1	66	1,296	8,700	5.3%
July Sept.	55	1,292	14	395	9	108	1,873	8,500	7.3%
Oct. Dec.	63	1,450	11	754	8	128	2,414	8,400	9,6%
Totals	216	4,342	40	1,774	21	354	6,743	7,475	7.8%

(e) Castings

	Horses	Mules
Number of animals cast in Veterinary Hospitals	68	340
,, ,, ,, Remount Depots	134	367
TOTAL	202	707

APPENDIX XI

Casualty and Remount State in V. & R. Advanced Units – January – March, 1945
Central Mediterranean Force

	Sick Received		Sick Evacuated		Remounts Received		Remounts Issued		Average Holdings	
	Horses	Mules	Horses	Mules	Horses	Mules	Horses	Mules	Horses	Mules
1 V. & R.C.S.	23	212	26	203	25	265	27	252	20	202
2 V. & R.C.S.	22	679	5	280	21	500	37	793	18	478
3 V. & R.C.S.	14	349	4	234	—	485	7	452	13	329
804 V. & R.C.S.	28	192	12	204	31	57	21	259	17	193
7 V. & R.C.S.	—	2	12	101	96	1,253	87	1,199	50	666
8 V. & R.C.S.	—	—	—	—	4	428	4	299	13	654
1 C.M.V.S.	13	345	14	358	16	406	16	408	1	29
4 C.M.V.S.	18	182	15	180	14	243	16	258	2	24
6 C.M.V.S.	—	59	—	29	1	153	2	188	2	22
803 C.M.V.S.	15	132	15	130	15	135	16	142	5	26
817 C.M.V.S.	13	58	12	234	27	1,051	59	1,618	24	324

GENERAL INDEX

INDEX OF NAMES